CANADA

L. Superior

MINNESOTA

WISCONSIN

MICHIGAN

L. Michigan

L. Huron

L. Erie

L. Ontario

IOWA

ILLINOIS

INDIANA

OHIO

Missouri R.

WITHDRAWN

Ohio R.

MISSOURI

KENTUCKY

WEST VIRGINIA

VIRGINIA

Ozark Mts.

TENNESSEE

Mt Mitchell

Appalachian

Blue Ridge

NORTH CAROLINA

ARKANSAS

SOUTH CAROLINA

Red R.

Mississippi

MISSISSIPPI

ALABAMA

GEORGIA

LOUISIANA

FLORIDA

Everglades

NEW YORK

Adirondack Mts.

Green Mts.

VERMONT

NEW HAMPSHIRE

MAINE

Mt Washington
White Mts

MASSACHUSETTS

Mountain

Catskill Mts.

CONNECTICUT

RHODE ISLAND

Long Island

PENNSYLVANIA

NEW JERSEY

DELAWARE

MARYLAND

UNITED STATES

ATLANTIC OCEAN

GULF OF MEXICO

Wild Flowers of The United States

Volume One   *Part One of Two Parts*

Wild Flowers of

General Editor WILLIAM C. STEERE
Director, The New York Botanical Garden

COLLABORATORS

Rogers McVaugh	Reed C. Rollins
Robert B. Mohlenbrock	John W. Thomson
Gerald B. Ownbey	Robert E. Woodson

Publication of THE NEW YORK BOTANICAL GARDEN

Harold William Rickett

The New York Botanical Garden

The United States

Volume One *Part One of Two Parts*

THE NORTHEASTERN STATES

FROM THE ATLANTIC TO MINNESOTA AND MISSOURI
AND FROM THE CANADIAN BORDER TO
VIRGINIA AND MISSOURI

McGRAW-HILL BOOK COMPANY · NEW YORK

To DAVID and PEGGY ROCKEFELLER,
without whose enthusiasm and generosity
these books could not have been written,
illustrated or published

Illustrations printed in England by
W. S. COWELL LTD, BUTTER MARKET, IPSWICH

Text printed in the United States of America by
HINKHOUSE INC., NEW YORK, NEW YORK

Bound in the United States of America by
RUSSELL-RUTTER COMPANY, INC., NEW YORK, NEW YORK

Library of Congress Catalog Card Number 66–17920
First Edition 52614

FOREWORD

BEHIND THIS VOLUME lies a story; the chain of events leading from the original idea to its realization deserves recording. Nearly ten years ago, before Hawaii and Alaska achieved statehood, Diarmuid C. Russell had the perspicacity to realize that not only were most popular books on American wild flowers incomplete and undependable, but also that they left great geographical areas untouched. Determined that something must be done to relieve a situation so frustrating to wild-flower enthusiasts, Mr. Russell convinced his friends, Mr. and Mrs. David Rockefeller, also interested in plants, of the crying need for a series of definitive new books. As a member of the Board of Managers of The New York Botanical Garden, Mrs. Rockefeller very naturally brought the idea to the Garden, where it was greeted with enthusiasm. The preparation of a series of comprehensive books covering all the wild flowers of the United States in scientifically accurate yet non-technical language and with each species beautifully illustrated in color is an especially appropriate activity for The New York Botanical Garden to undertake because of its able staff with long experience in floristic work, supported by a magnificent library and outstanding herbarium. Moreover, because the wild flowers of the United States are now well known to systematic botanists, the time seemed ripe to embark upon the enormous task of making this information available, in an interesting and attractive manner, to the intelligent public as well as to other scientists who must know the names of plants, yet who are not taxonomists.

With the help of Mrs. Roxana S. Ferris of Stanford University, the Garden set about making an estimate of how many volumes would be needed, how many kinds of plants were to be described and illustrated in each one, and, most important, what total cost might then be anticipated. The estimate of funds to prepare the text, to obtain the best possible photographs, and to manufacture the plates reached a total of over one million dollars. In spite of the magnitude of this estimate, the National Committee for the Wildflowers of the United States was established, with Mrs. David Rockefeller as chairman and Mr. Russell as secretary, to raise the necessary funds. When the Committee had obtained somewhat more than half of the total amount, it made the optimistic and positive decision that work on the books should begin, and Dr. Rickett was appointed as Senior Botanist for the program on April 1, 1963.

Many individuals and several organizations, among them the Reader's Digest Foundation, the James Foundation of New York, Inc., the Richfield Oil Corporation, The Aaron E. Norman Fund, Inc., the Harriett Pullman Schermerhorn Charitable Trust, the Silver Spring Foundation, the Jeroboam Foundation, Inc., and the Rockefeller Brothers Fund, contributed to the Wild Flowers of the United States Fund of The New York Botanical Garden. A grant was made by the National Geographic Society especially to further the research and the compilation of existing research involved in the preparation of the text. Some of the personal gifts, even though small, undoubtedly strained the resources of the donor; such gifts have been especially welcome because of the spirit in which they were made, through the recognition of a worthy cause. Other personal gifts have been large. We are grateful indeed to all those whose generosity has made possible the appearance of this first volume, as well as substantial progress on those to be published later.

The New York Botanical Garden takes great pride in sponsoring this publication. Our primary hopes are that this and succeeding books will serve to interest many more people in plants and teach them about plants; after all, dissemination of information is a central responsibility of botanical gardens, which deserve much wider recognition as the educational institutions they are. This book is a natural evolutionary development of the activities of the Garden, whose staff members have produced, during the past 65 years, more handbooks for the identification of plants than any other institution in this hemisphere. Nathaniel L. Britton, founder and first director of the Garden, prepared many manuals for the identification of plants of various areas of North America, among them *An illustrated flora of the northern United States* (three editions, in joint authorship with Addison Brown), a one-volume work, *Manual of the flora of the northern United States and Canada* (two editions), *North American trees* (with J. A. Shafer), *Flora of Bermuda*, *The Bahama flora*, and *Botany of Porto Rico and the Virgin Islands*. Among other important handbooks by staff members are *Flora of the southeastern United States* and *Manual of the southeastern flora* by John K. Small, *Flora of the Rocky Mountains and adjacent plains*, *Flora of the prairies and plains of central North America*,

June 1965

and many local and state floras by Per A. Rydberg, and *Plants of the vicinity of New York* and *The new Britton and Brown illustrated flora* by Henry A. Gleason. Arthur Cronquist has recently produced a one-volume *Manual of vascular plants of northeastern United States and adjacent Canada*, and has contributed to several volumes of *Flora of the Pacific Northwest*. Otto Degener has issued many volumes of his continuing illustrated series, *Flora hawaiiensis*, and David D. Keck collaborated with Philip A. Munz on *A California flora*. It is unusually appropriate that Harold William Rickett, staff member of the Garden, and author of *Wild Flowers of America*, *The new field book of North American wild flowers*, and *The Odyssey book of American wildflowers*, should bring about the transmutation of technical manuals and floras into well-illustrated books that are comprehensible to students, amateurs, and the lay public.

It should be emphasized that much new information on plants appears in this book as the result of the extensive original research during its preparation carried on by Dr. Rickett, his staff, and the panel of distinguished botanists who collaborated. This fact points up the additional strength and reliability given this book and its successors in the series by their provenance in a research-oriented institution.

To all those who have contributed time, energy, funds, skills, knowledge, enthusiasm, and interest to the creation of this book, we express our appreciation.

WILLIAM CAMPBELL STEERE

CONTENTS

PREFACE

THE idea of this book was to present *all the wild flowers* of the northeastern United States in color photographs and non-technical descriptions, so that for the first time the layman might be able to identify any he might find.

Color photographs, valuable as they are, cannot differentiate *all* these species, numbering several thousands; but the present collection will approach that ideal more closely than any previous one. One of the most rewarding aspects of my work was the discovery of the astonishing number of competent and enthusiastic amateurs of botany and photography. Nearly a hundred persons submitted color photographs; some only a dozen or so, while others sent hundreds. Forty-nine of these persons are represented in the book by the illustrations; their names are listed below and beneath the illustrations themselves. While all deserve our grateful recognition, two must be specially mentioned here. Charles Johnson was commissioned by The New York Botanical Garden for the purpose, and covered many thousands of miles in search of the species to be included. Samuel Gottscho, in the later years of a notable career in commercial photography, turned to wild flowers and has attained a remarkable proficiency in naming and portraying them.

Besides all the original photographs never before published, Nelson Doubleday Inc. has kindly permitted the use of many others made by Johnson which appeared in their publication *Wild Flowers of North America* by Lemmon and Johnson.

Mrs. Anne Ophelia Dowden, well-known for her exquisite paintings of flowers, added the trailing arbutus that decorates the title-page.

The terminology of systematic botany has a peculiar fascination – for the botanist, who prefers "infundibuliform" to "funnel-shaped" and apparently believes that all our own hearts are upside-down, "obcordate." For the layman these words derived from Latin and Greek are generally horrific. It is fortunately possible to describe plants quite completely and precisely without most of them. A few technical terms are necessary and certainly accessible to anyone who does not insist on being spoon-fed.

However, it is necessary to reaffirm that most wild flowers have no names in ordinary English, and that those names in English that do exist are often confusing. The use of botanical names is prerequisite to any intelligent understanding of wild flowers. They are not really difficult; it is only fear that makes so many laymen afraid of them.

To my botanical colleagues it is necessary to point out that current taxonomic opinion must sometimes be sacrificed to clarity for the lay reader. The harebells and lobelias undoubtedly belong in one family; but keeping them distinct makes it easier for the amateur to find them in a book and learn their names. The arrangement of families in purely artificial groups is again a concession to ease of recognition; this being based on such easily seen characteristics as number and symmetry of petals rather than the more recondite criteria of the botanist. Phylogeny, the supposed evolutionary relation of families, is not germane to our present purpose.

The collaborators named on the title-page have given freely of their time and knowledge, both in providing valid taxonomic criticism and in guiding the photographer to plants to be photographed. One of them, having contributed advice and encouragement, was tragically and prematurely taken from us: Robert Everard Woodson is mourned as a skilled botanist and as a cultured and sympathetic colleague.

William Campbell Steere, as general editor of the entire project, has furnished valuable suggestions and pulled me out of many a hole.

Finally, appreciation is due to those who have worked with me day by day in the production of the manuscript. Rachel Speiser made the drawings, combining fine aesthetic feeling with artistic technique and a remarkably perceptive eye. Dorothy Langguth managed a voluminous correspondence, organized the enormous number of photographs submitted, and typed the entire manuscript. Without the loyal devotion of these helpers the book could not have been produced.

June 1965

HAROLD WILLIAM RICKETT

LIST OF PHOTOGRAPHERS

Robert G. Aborn, Millington, New Jersey
Mrs. Ruth McVaugh Allen, Riverton, New Jersey
George G. Becker, Chatham, New Jersey
R. O. Brodeen, Elizabeth, New Jersey
Harry E. Cain, Fairmont, West Virginia
Robert B. Clark, Ithaca, New York
Robert Clewell, Tallahassee, Florida
Earl L. Core, Morgantown, West Virginia
Mrs. A. Gerard DeVoe, Pelham Manor, New York
Raymond J. Dobbs, Miami, Florida
Julian P. Donahue, East Lansing, Michigan
Virginie F. and George A. Elbert, New York, New York
Richard B. Fischer, Ithaca, New York
John Fogelson, New York, New York
John H. Gerard, Alton, Illinois
William T. Gillis, East Lansing, Michigan
Samuel H. Gottscho, Gottscho-Schleisner, Inc., New York, New York
Donald B. Gray, Kennett Square, Pennsylvania
Carmen and Bernard Horne, Jackson, Michigan
Roland M. Houseknecht, Monroeton, Pennsylvania
Charles C. Johnson, New York, New York
William S. Justice, Asheville, North Carolina
Robert E. Lee, West Salem, Wisconsin
William M. Leeson, LaVale, Maryland
W. R. Lenhart, Morgantown, West Virginia

Vicki Love, Madison, Wisconsin
Henry M. Mayer, Cleveland, Ohio
L. C. McDowell, Charleston, West Virginia
John Merkle, Flint, Michigan
Evan J. Miller, Harrisburg, Pennsylvania
Allan Murray, New York, New York
Mrs. Henry D. Phelps, Middletown, Rhode Island
Norman Pollock, Middletown, New York
William L. Rhein, Harrisburg, Pennsylvania
Vinton Richard, Orient, New York
Dorothy M. Richards, Dayton, Ohio
Harold W. Rickett, New York, New York
André Robyns, St. Louis, Missouri
John P. Roche, Caldwell, New Jersey
Reed Rollins, Cambridge, Massachusetts
Oren S. Ryker, Riverhead, New York
A. Clayton Scribner, Rowayton, Connecticut
Jay Shuler, Greenville, South Carolina
John J. Smith, New York, New York
Nancy Stees, West Chester, Pennsylvania
Robert B. Taylor, Narberth, Pennsylvania
Leonard J. Uttal, Madison Height, Virginia
Edward G. Voss, Ann Arbor, Michigan
Dorcas A. Ward, Kennett Square, Pennsylvania
Willam C. White, Barneveld, New York
Mrs. Virginia Williamson, Lyndhurst, New Jersey

INTRODUCTION

How many Wild Flowers?

THERE ARE more wild flowers in any part of the country than most persons who live there realize. Some five thousand kinds – species – of flowering plants grow in the northeastern United States. This formidable figure, to be sure, includes trees and shrubs, grasses and sedges and rushes, as well as the herbaceous flowering plants that are "wild flowers" to most of us. But even if we subtract the woody, grassy, and sedgy flowering plants, we are still faced with some three thousand different wild flowers in this one part of the country.

No book intended for the layman, the amateur naturalist, has ever treated all these plants. One deservedly famous book, first published seventy years ago and many times reprinted, describes some five hundred. Another well-known and much used guide treats about eight hundred. Some of the most modern books run to about a thousand. But in scarcely any of such books is there any statement that their coverage is thus limited. The unfortunate consequence is that one who seeks to identify a wild flower has no assurance that the flower is in the book.

Another aspect of our flora of which the layman is usually unaware is the existence in some groups of many closely related species which even the professional may have difficulty in distinguishing. We all recognize violets. But different species of violets interbreed, forming groups of plants with characteristics intermediate between those of the parents – which themselves differ only slightly. Everyone knows the goldenrods. But in the northeastern United States there are some seventy-five species, many of which are extremely variable especially in such easily seen characteristics as the shape or hairiness or toothing of the leaves – the very characteristics by which the untrained person seeks to recognize them. These species too interbreed. Consequently, such species seem to overlap; one must study the minute botanical characteristics to be sure of what one has – and even then one may not get an answer.

From these facts it is evident that any work that describes only an unspecified fraction of our native flora, and describes that fraction in nontechnical language, is likely to lead to frustration. Of course many wild flowers are easily recognized and present no special difficulties; bloodroot, columbine, lady's-slippers, the various wild lilies, and many others. But a host of more difficult kinds remains – the very kinds that one looks for in a book. In this volume we have tried to include all the wild flowers that properly belong to the area covered, excluding trees and shrubs, grasses, sedges, and rushes, and a number of unattractive weeds with small greenish flowers which are not likely to excite the interest of the amateur. (The amateur must realize, however, that even in this long-settled part of North America new studies by botanists are constantly revising our ideas of the species found growing wild. No book can ever be final.) Wild flowers that properly belong to other parts of the country but that enter our area along its margins – southern species, western species, far-northern species – are mentioned but not described (they are more adequately treated in other volumes of this series). In all, we include some seventeen hundred species. We have kept the technical language of the botanist to a minimum; a certain few technical

1

terms are absolutely necessary to any sort of precision, but those that are here used are so few and so frequently used that they need present no difficulty to any intelligent and interested reader. An illustrated glossary of these terms follows this introduction on pages 16 to 21.

The Names of Wild Flowers

To identify something is to match it with other somethings to which a name has been given; when we have identified it, it has a name.

All the individual plants that look alike make up what the botanist calls a *species*. All the bloodroots of the world make up a species; all the wood lilies another; and so on. The word has several times been used in the preceding pages; it is the fundamental word in the dictionary of botany (and of all biology). The name of a plant is the name of the species to which it belongs.*

Many species closely resemble other species. The wood lilies resemble, in many respects, the field lilies, turk's-cap lilies, madonna lilies, and other lilies. Such a group of similar species forms a *genus* (plural genera). If a species has no close likeness with another species, then it is a genus by itself, a genus as well as a species. Bloodroot is such a species.

As everyone knows, the botanist names species in Latin. Why not in English? One reason is obvious: English is not understood all over the world. *We* should resent it if plants had only French names, since few of us understand French. But couldn't we use English among ourselves, for the wild flowers that grow in this country or in England? We could indeed; but the result, unfortunately, would be endless confusion. English names have not been given by scientists; they have grown up among country folk. A name is often given to one plant in one part of the country and to another plant in another part of the country. Mayflower means one thing in Connecticut and something quite different in Wisconsin. Second, many names are misleading, suggesting relationships that do not exist and confusing different plants under similar names. Blue-eyed-grass and grass-of-Parnassus are not grasses, nor are they closely related to each other. Virginia-cowslip, also called Virginia-bluebells, is unre-

lated to the cowslips and bluebells of English literature. The name bluebells, indeed, is applied to a number of species in different families. Lily-of-the-valley is not a lily, and water-lilies are not even in the lily family. Third, many species have more than one common name, some being local, others more general. Columbines are known in one part of the country as rock-bells. Some of the bluets are known also as Quaker-ladies, innocence, baby-blue-eyes, and various other things. In England, with its longer history, matters are even worse. According to Geoffrey Grigson, the common self-heal is also known, in various parts of England, as all-heal, blackman's-flower, blue-curls, bumblebees, carpenter's-grass, carpenter's-herb, fly-flowers, heart-o'-the-earth, heart's-ease, herb-bennet, hoodweed, pickpocket, prince's-feather, proud-carpenter, touch-and-heal, and wood-sage. And finally, many – indeed most – wild flowers have no English names, or no distinctive names. Most of the species of *Viola* are just called violets.

Some botanists have manufactured English names for plants that had none. But common names have to grow from daily familiarity and use, not from a knowledge of botany. "Linear-leaved smooth aster" is scarcely a "common name"; it is scarcely English; and it has scarcely ever been used. Some attempts have been made to standardize the spelling and hyphening or compounding of English names; yielding such horrific results as "Eschscholtz' falsehellebore." To repeat: common names are those given by people; they cannot be dictated from centers of botanical or horticultural learning.

Latin names were not given arbitrarily by botanists just to end confusion. At the time when botany was beginning to be a science, shortly after the invention of printing in Europe, learned men were still talking and writing to each other in Latin; it was a common European language. It was natural, therefore, that when they spoke of a

---

*The species of the botanist is what many persons call a "variety." This term, however, has another meaning in botany.

plant they should use its Latin name. And these names, which became known to all botanists, have been maintained since then (with some changes in the interest of simplicity). The plant known in England by so many names is now known all over the world, by botanists of every nationality and language, as *Prunella vulgaris*. The advantages of such a name are obvious.

Many persons are afraid of Latin names, regarding them as something only very learned men can use. They forget – or do not realize – that botanists use Latin names as the *only practical means* of dealing with the vast and varied world of plants. Botanical names are really very simple. Every genus of plants is named by a single word, often a Latin word, almost always a word in the form of Latin. All the species of lilies form the genus *Lilium*; all the violets the genus *Viola*; all the goldenrods the genus *Solidago*; bloodroot is the genus *Sanguinaria*.* Many of these names are in frequent use by gardeners: delphinium, geranium, dianthus, petunia; they are common names as well as botanical names.

Every species of plants is named by two words.§ The first is the name of the genus to which it belongs. The second is a qualifying word, frequently a Latin adjective. The wood lilies form the species *Lilium philadelphicum*.† One species of violet is *Viola palmata*. Such names record the place of origin of the plant first so named by a botanist, or some characteristic of the plant itself (as a "palmate" or "hand-shaped" leaf). Or a plant may be named for its discoverer or to commemorate some botanist, by turning

his name into Latin and putting a special ending on it: *Aster shortii* was named for Charles Wilkens Short, a Kentucky physician who was very active in the collection of wild flowers in the first half of the nineteenth century. But whatever the form and meaning of the words, this cardinal principle of the nomenclature of plants is clear: a species is named by two words, the first of which is the name of the genus. This is true even when the genus is composed of only one species. The genus *Sanguinaria* contains only the species *Sanguinaria canadensis*.

The pronunciation of botanical names may seem to offer some difficulties. The general rule is not to affect a classical style but to pronounce them as if they were English words. We already do this with such Latin words as geranium, chrysanthemum, verbena, hibiscus, which double as common names. The same rule applies to the second part of a species name: *ovata* like ovate (which rhymes with state), not "ovahta." The diphthong "ch" is generally pronounced as in "architect," not as in "church." (Of course, if one goes to France, Italy, or Germany, one will find people pronouncing such words in *their* language.) Place the accent where it is easiest: Sanguinária, Maiánthemum, Smilacína. Pronounce every syllable: *vulgare* rhymes with "carry" not with "care." It is unfortunate that there are no rules for the pronunciation of English that are not "more honored in the breach than in the observance"; but happily there are few real problems in the pronunciation of English names of wild flowers.

The Identification of Wild Flowers

When we see a flower whose name we do not know, what should we notice in it? Which of its characteristics will help us to identify and name it? Color? Size? Shape of leaves? Number of petals? Chromosomes?

The last, of course, is absurd; the very word

is unfamiliar to most persons. Yet chromosomes are used by scientists in classifying plants. How scientific must we be? The answer is – moderately.

Many books on wild flowers have simply evaded the problem; their readers must simply turn pages until they see a picture that resembles their unknown plant. This is not a bad method, providing a large enough number of plants are illustrated; the present volume may be used in this way. However, the number of possibilities is so large that such a method of identification takes

*Note that botanical names are customarily printed in italic. The name of the genus begins with a capital letter.

§ Or sometimes by more than two; but then some are joined by hyphens so that the name appears in two parts: *Aster novae-angliae.*

† The second word is now usually written with a small initial letter. The first word, the name of the genus, may be abbreviated to its initial letter: *L. philadelphicum.*

much time. And plants vary so much that even photographs may not correspond in color or form with a given unknown specimen. Moreover, final identification often depends on characteristics not evident in any photograph. Some way of arranging and classifying flowers by selected characteristics is desirable.

The most common arrangement in popular books is by color. This is the most obvious characteristic of a flower, and classification by color would seem an obvious solution to the problem. But there are not enough colors! When one is dealing with almost two thousand species, *nearly a third of which have white flowers*, we still have the problem. And this does not reckon with the numerous colored species that have white-flowered forms (wild geranium, blue-eyed-grass, pink lady's-slipper, etc.); nor with the white-flowered species that sometimes have pink flowers (Indian pipe, pipsissewa, wild carrot, yarrow, etc.); all these must be shown in two places. Moreover, it is often difficult to know just *how white* a flower must be to be called white; many are greenish, almost white. Similar remarks apply to the other colors. Some flowers change color as they age (vervain, Virginia-bluebells, etc.). And then there are all the flowers that sport more than one color. . . .

If not color, then what about size? Obviously a plant changes its size as it grows, and its eventual or maximum size depends too much on the environment (there are trees at timberline in the mountains whose trunks, after a hundred years,

may be two feet thick at the base but only five feet tall).

Size, however, is useful in comparing species, in gaining an approximate idea of what to look for, and sometimes in distinguishing related species. The dimensions indicated in the descriptions in this book represent either a range of size at maturity or the largest size ordinarily attained by the species in question. The measurements are made in feet and inches, since these are the units most familiar to the lay reader; the metric system of the scientist might be confusing. For small parts, such as the petals, it is unfortunately necessary to state sizes in fractions of an inch – thirds, fifths, etc. Below is a rule with inches divided in such fractions; it may be traced on thin paper which can then be pasted on an ordinary ruler for actual use with the flower parts.

It has not been practical to indicate on all the photographs the exact scale. Some show entire plants, some details, even single flowers, often greatly magnified. Most of the photographs were submitted without data on the actual size of the plant represented. The reader must consult the text to learn on what scale a plant is shown in the illustrations. The drawings, however, are all approximately one-half natural size, except where another scale is indicated; "× 2" means "twice natural size."

So we fall back on such characteristics as shape of leaves, teeth at the margins of leaves, hairiness or smoothness, number of petals and of other parts of the flowers, position and grouping

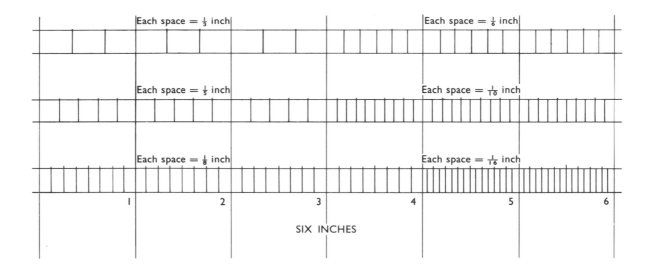

Each space = $\frac{1}{3}$ inch   Each space = $\frac{1}{6}$ inch

Each space = $\frac{1}{5}$ inch   Each space = $\frac{1}{10}$ inch

Each space = $\frac{1}{8}$ inch   Each space = $\frac{1}{16}$ inch

1   2   3   4   5   6

SIX INCHES

of flowers: and these are the characteristics actually used by botanists. They are, in general, easy to see; but a hand magnifier is necessary for some very small plants (such as whitlow-grass) and for the very small flowers of some large plants (in the mint and daisy families, for instance). And if we use the botanists' own means of identification, it is convenient to arrange the genera and species in a botanical classification.

The genera of plants are grouped in what the botanist calls *families*. Lilies, for instance, share certain peculiarities with hyacinths, tulips, day-lilies, and even onions; all these, which are in different genera, are included in the lily family. Roses, apples, cherries, strawberries, blackberries, five-fingers, avens, and many others make up the rose family; it is evident from this list that the features that unite such different species are not always obvious. Like genera and species, families have botanical names. These are very simply constructed by adding the termination -aceae to the essential part of the name of one of the genera: *Liliaceae* from *Lilium*, *Rosaceae* from *Rosa*, and so on.* Again the English names, though not so confusing as the names of species, are inadequate. The daisy family is also known as the sunflower family; the bean family is in many books called the pulse family – though few of their readers will know what pulse is.

In using a botanical system of classification, one thing is important: we use not one characteristic alone, but a combination of characteristics. Many different plants have divided leaves; but when we find such leaves attached singly on the stem, with a pair of appendages at the base of each, and flowers with numerous stamens and several pistils, we are led to the rose family.

On pages 12–14 the reader will find the fourteen groups in which all the plant families that are represented in this book are arranged. The arrangement is by characteristics that are easily seen. If he turns to the page indicated for any group, he will there find the families of that group distinguished by a few additional characteristics. Within the family the genera are similarly separated; and within each genus its various species are briefly characterized. Naturally we use more and more detail as we arrive at the smaller units. In deciding between several related and similar species, the times of flowering, the kinds of situations in which they grow, and the range of country in which they are found are often valuable. A plant said to inhabit tidal marshes along the coast would probably not be found on dry slopes farther inland.

The period of flowering is indicated by such phrases as "March to May" or "May to September." This does not generally mean that a particular plant, or the plants of a particular place, will bloom throughout that period; but rather that within that period plants of that species will be found in bloom *somewhere*. Those that grow in southern states will, of course, bloom earlier, and probably cease from blooming earlier, than plants of the same species farther north. Plants at sea level will flower before plants of the same species in the mountains.

The range of a species is indicated in this book by a sort of abbreviated formula. Names of states are given so as to roughly outline the area in which the species is found. For ease of reference, the state farthest to the northeast is named first; from there we go to the state farthest to the northwest; and then to the southern corners. "From Quebec to Minnesota and southward to Maryland, Ohio, Illinois, and Kansas" outlines an area enclosing most of the range of this volume and a little beyond. The information is gained largely by examining specimens preserved in herbaria. Since it was not possible for the author to look at and identify all the specimens of every species in all the herbaria of the country, he has had to rely on the published records of other botanists and on their identification of the specimens. This introduces a chance of error; even botanists make mistakes. The necessarily brief form of statement also may lead to error; the species may not occupy *all* the country enclosed. Plants often migrate along valleys and watercourses; mountains may offer barriers to some; some will not grow at high altitudes, others not at sea level. The reader must therefore look upon the stated range as an approximation.

Note on the use of a hand magnifier: Such an instrument, a miniature microscope, may be obtained in a variety of sizes and shapes and for a variety of

*There are a few well-known exceptions to this scheme, sanctioned by long usage: *Cruciferae, Umbelliferae, Labiatae, Compositae.*

prices. For botanical work the best magnification is "10×", which means that it magnifies the diameter of what is seen ten times. The higher-priced ones give a wider and flatter field of view. Such magnifiers should be held *close to the eye* and the object to be viewed brought up until it is in focus, usually at about an inch from the lens; one must stand so that as much light as possible falls on the object.

What is a Flower?

A flower, apart from being often a delight to our senses, is the reproductive part of the plant that bears it. Besides the more or less showy and obvious parts for which we cultivate flowering plants in our gardens, it consists of certain less decorative, often concealed parts, sometimes called the essential parts because of their functions in reproduction. Ambrose Bierce (in his *Devil's Dictionary*) wrote that flowers "are commonly badly designed, inartistic in color, and ill-smelling"; and many flowers indeed merit such disparaging description. They are limited to the essentials.

The Parts of Flowers: To describe a flower in such a way that one can distinguish it from other flowers makes necessary a certain technical vocabulary, fortunately neither large nor complex. Stamens, pistil, petals and corolla, sepals and calyx, perianth – these are the words used throughout this volume for the elements that make up a flower. Some are scarcely technical and will be already familiar to the reader. Everyone knows that flowers have *petals*; together they constitute the "crown" of the flower, the *corolla*. The *sepals* are the exterior parts, commonly green and shaped like small leaves, which enclose all other parts in the bud; together they compose the "covering", the *calyx*. The useful term *perianth* ("around the flower"; i.e. around the essential parts) means both calyx and corolla, if both are present, or the calyx only if a corolla is lacking.

Within the perianth stand the *stamens*, the male, pollen-forming parts; and in the center of the flower one or several *pistils*, the female, seed-forming organs. These last, stamens and pistils, are the essential reproductive parts.

All the above words may be found, defined and illustrated, in the glossary which follows this introduction. The drawings on this page show how the different parts are situated in two common types of flower.

One further term is useful. With most flowers certain special leaves are associated that differ from the ordinary foliage of the plant. These are often smaller but sometimes larger, and they may differ in shape from the foliage; they may be variously colored, sometimes simulating petals. These

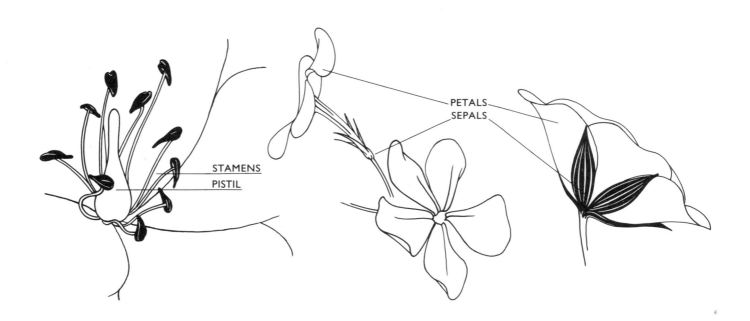

STAMENS
PISTIL
PETALS
SEPALS

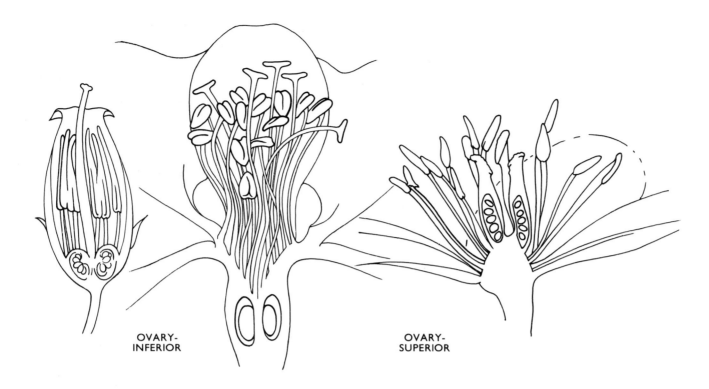

OVARY-INFERIOR   OVARY-SUPERIOR

are *bracts*. The red or white leaves of poinsettia are bracts; the bright-colored parts of Indian paintbrush are bracts; the small scales on the flowerstalks of ladies'-tresses and bog-pink are bracts. See diagrams of flower-arrangement on page 8.

The Diversity of Flowers: If this were the whole story, understanding flowers would be easier. Unfortunately for the would-be botanist – though fortunately for all who enjoy nature – flowers are of an immense variety. Some have no petals (but the sepals may be colored like petals; see the drawing and photograph of marsh-marigold). Some have no perianth at all (cypress spurge). In many species there are two kinds of flowers, male or *staminate* and female or *pistillate* (see devil's-bit, arrowhead), on the same plant or on different plants. There may be an indefinite multitude of stamens (marsh-marigold) or a definite small number (wild geranium). The same is true of pistils. One especially puzzling feature of the pistil is that its lower part, the *ovary* which contains the small bodies that will become seeds, is in many species below the point of attachment of all the other parts of the flower and, as it were, embedded in the flower-stalk (see iris, evening-primrose). This usually shows as a swelling below

the flower; the contained ovary may only be seen by cutting through this swelling, as shown in the drawings of sectioned apple blossom and blueberry flower herewith. Parts of the flower may be joined. In many families the petals are joined to form a tube or cup (turtle-head, phlox); stamens also may be joined together (hibiscus) or even joined to the petals (phlox).

One of the striking characteristics of a flower is expressed in terms of its symmetry. As one looks directly at a lily or wild geranium flower its petals may be seen to be all alike and to radiate from the center like the spokes of a wheel; we say that they are radially symmetric. No matter which way we divide such a flower by a cut passing through its center, the two halves will match. Contrast with this a violet or a lady's-slipper; one petal, the lowest, is strikingly different from the others. In the mint family, the upper "lip" of the corolla (which is composed of joined petals) differs in size and shape from the lower. If such a flower is divided vertically, two matching halves may be obtained; but if we divide the flower in any other way, we get unlike halves. The two sides are symmetric, but not top and bottom. We call this bilateral (two-sided) symmetry.

The arrangement of flowers – the inflorescence – is also useful in distinguishing families and genera. In the pink family and others the central stem ends in a flower, two flowers spring from its stem below it, two flowers spring in the same way from each of *their* stems, and so on; a sort of candelabrum is formed. This is called a *cyme*. The flowers of Canada mayflower, baneberry, mustard, shinleaf, mullein, and other plants are arranged along the sides of a central stalk, in what is called a *raceme* if the flowers are obviously stalked or a *spike* if the stalks are very short. In the primrose and parsley and other families flower-bearing stalks radiate from the tip of a stem, in what is known as an *umbel*. Clovers and milkworts have flowers with very short stalks tightly massed in *heads*. In other plants flowers are borne singly, at the tip of the stem or in the angles (axils) where leaves meet the stem. These arrangements may be useful in placing an unknown plant in its family (as the forget-me-not family), or even in its genus (as in the lily family).

Fruits

A fruit is the product of a flower, and all flowers that – so to speak – play their full part in nature form fruits. The fruit is the developed ovary of the pistil, often with other parts of the flower adhering. To the botanist all bodies with this origin are fruits, regardless of edibility, texture, or other qualities. The pods of beans and peas and lilies are fruits as well as apples and

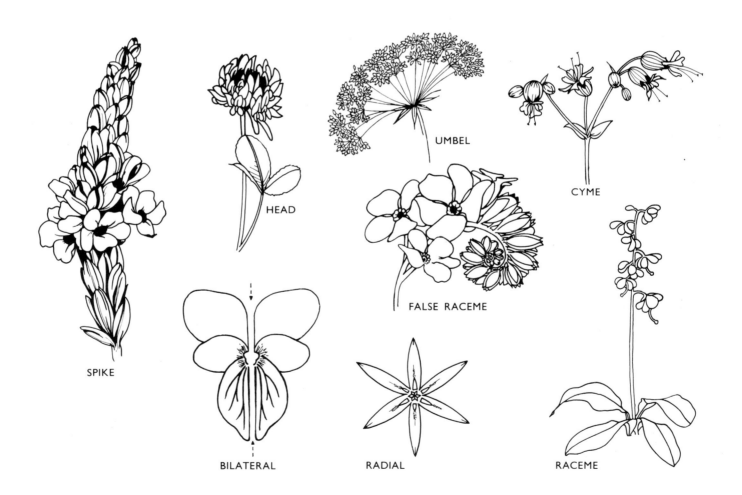

SPIKE

HEAD

UMBEL

CYME

FALSE RACEME

BILATERAL

RADIAL

RACEME

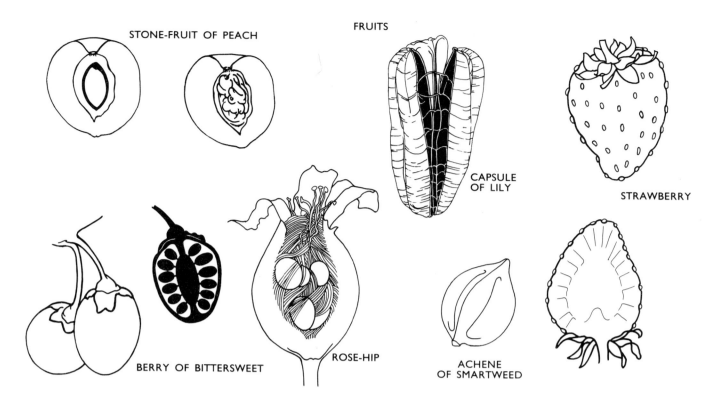

STONE-FRUIT OF PEACH

FRUITS

CAPSULE OF LILY

STRAWBERRY

BERRY OF BITTERSWEET

ROSE-HIP

ACHENE OF SMARTWEED

peaches and blueberries. This may confuse the amateur, for many small, hard fruits are popularly called seeds. Seeds are the product of the minute bodies, *ovules*, inside the ovary of the pistil; seeds (in flowering plants) are inside fruits. The so-called seeds of sunflowers or strawberries are developed from ovaries, and *each contains a seed*. In strawberries, roses, and other plants, many such fruits are seated upon or enclosed in another part of the flower, which becomes succulent and is a "fruit" in the ordinary non-botanical sense.

The botanist has few special technical terms for fruits; he uses ordinary English words, such as "berry" and "nut," but unfortunately uses them somewhat differently. In the description and identification of wild flowers no great difficulty is created by the terms used for fruits. Perhaps the only important new term to be acquired is *achene*, the name for the small, hard, seedlike fruits already mentioned. And one must remember that, to the professional botanist, strawberries are not berries, but tomatoes are!

Leaves

A vast technical vocabulary has grown up in the botanical description of leaves: their arrangement on the stem, their shapes, the presence or absence of teeth at their margins and the shape of such teeth when present, the course of their veins, the texture and thickness of their blades, the down or wool or bristles or other covering on their surfaces – all such characteristics are botanically described by words derived from Latin. Fortunate-

ly, the amateur naturalist need not concern himself with this terminology, unless he must consult the technical manuals. For present purposes, most characteristics of leaves may easily be described in ordinary English: such words as toothed or plain, smooth or woolly, leathery or delicate are sufficiently precise for the description of our species. Shapes, however, are somewhat more difficult to characterize, and two words are here in-

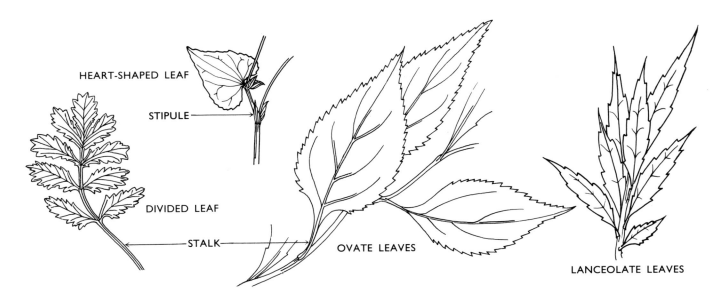

troduced in the interests of precision: *ovate* and *lanceolate* (see drawings and the glossary). The parts of a leaf are commonly *stalk* and *blade*, though either may be lacking; they are mentioned here only to emphasize that the stalk is a part of the leaf and not a *stem*. A distinction essential for precision is that between a true stem and the stalk of a leaf. They differ both internally and exter-nally. This is especially important in the recogni-tion of divided (compound) leaves, which have several distinct segments of the blade, or small blades, on one stalk (see the accompanying draw-ings). At the base of the leaf there is frequently a pair of small appendages called stipules. The angle between the upper side of the leaf-stalk and the stem from which it issues is called the *axil*.

Stems

The only difficulty that may be encountered in the description of the stem of a plant is con-nected with the fact that it may be underground. Such stems are glorified by such terms as *tubers* and *rhizomes*; they are not roots, though they are commonly mistaken for roots. The underground part, containing a red sap, from which the leaf and flower of a bloodroot grow, is not the root but the stem. Many species have such stems, which grow horizontally beneath the surface of the ground. Others grow from *bulbs*, which are composed of a diminutive stem covered by circu-lar and often succulent leaf-bases (these are com-mon in the lily family). The word is often wrongly used for roots, tubers, etc. Underground parts, however, are not generally seen – and should not be seen – by nature-lovers, and need play very little part in the identification of wild flowers.

Picking and Transplanting

The last sentence in the preceding section brings me to a plea for the preservation of natural beauty.

Most amateur naturalists will not purposely despoil nature. In fact, some who know where the lovely *Arethusa* grows refuse to lead others to the spot. Yet damage is often done through lack of information.

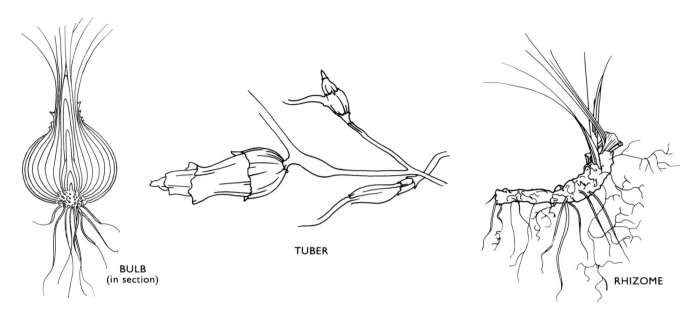

BULB
(in section)

TUBER

RHIZOME

It would be foolish to write "Don't pick the wild flowers." You may fill your arms with goldenrods – and more will grow, next summer, from the same roots. You may pick bouquets of violets and Dutchman's-breeches, so long as you leave most of the leaves and do not disturb the underground parts. The point is that the life of plants depends mainly on their leaves. When goldenrod blooms its growing season is done; the leaves have done their work, and enough surplus food has made its way from them to the subterranean stem and roots – enough to start the next season with. Plants that bloom in the spring – some even before the leaves are fully developed – must retain their leaves *after* flowering for the same reason. As for the annuals, as touch-me-not, the ground is full of their seeds; some will sprout next year.

Pick, then, with understanding.

Transplanting is another matter. Most wild flowers are hard to grow and do not easily take to a new environment. Some can be moved success-fully – by an experienced gardener. Some – and unfortunately many of those most desirable for the wild-flower garden – very rarely survive the operation. It is even of no avail to "give them the same environment as that in which they thrive naturally." Indian paintbrush and false foxglove (and, indeed, many in their family) are parasitic upon the roots of other plants – which you can scarcely cultivate in your garden. The orchids grow in a close and mutually beneficial relationship with fungi in the soil which are exacting in their requirements. Orchids transplanted sometimes live a few years and then disappear. The same is true of trailing arbutus, which in several states is protected by law.

So – unless one has skill and experience above what is usual, and a sufficient area of natural woodland, swamp, or meadow – it is best to leave the wild things to flourish in their own places. That is why I wrote that the underground parts "should not be seen" by nature-lovers.

GUIDE TO THE FAMILIES OF FLOWERING PLANTS

treated in this book

The families of flowering plants represented in this book are here arranged in fourteen groups according to the number of petals and stamens they possess and other easily seen characteristics. Unfortunately they do not all fit easily into such a method of classifi-cation. Genera and species are classified by botanists not by such simple characteristics as those mentioned, but by other, technical features many of which are not easily seen by the amateur. In this way the bota-nist arrives at a "natural" system of classification, that is, one that represents, as far as possible, natural relationships. The families of plants are natural groups of genera. But the number of petals and of stamens may vary in such natural groupings. In the lily family, characterized by three sepals and three petals, the Canada mayflower has only two of each. In the rose family, whose species generally have five petals, burnet has none. The water-lily, St.-John's-wort, and loosestrife families are particularly irritating in this respect.

The fourteen artificial groups here presented are marked, therefore, by numerous exceptions. The justification for their use is simply that they assist in identification. With an unknown plant in his hand the reader may be led to the correct family by answering the following questions and searching among the fourteen groups for one with the corresponding characteristics. The accompanying chart may help in this search. (Some kinds of wild flowers, however, have outstanding characteristics which will lead one straight to the description of the family, side-stepping the groups; or even to the species. Such "shortcuts to identification" are to be found on page 15.)

Is a perianth (petals and sepals, or sepals alone) present?
To answer this question it is sometimes necessary to examine unopened buds, for the perianth may fall as the flower opens.

Moreover there are deceptive families which *pretend* to have petals or sepals but actually have none. If the plant to be identified has milky juice when broken, it may belong to the spurge family, which has tiny flowers which do not look like flowers in a group sometimes surrounded by petal-like bracts or nectaries. Jack-in-the-pulpit has flowers without perianth all enveloped in the large, decorative bract which forms the "pulpit." See also the four-o'clock family (page 98).

Is the perianth in one circle or in two (does it have only sepals or both sepals and petals)? Here again it is best to observe the unopened buds. Many flowers with a perianth in two circles lose their sepals as they open, so that they might mistakenly be taken as having a perianth in one circle only (sepals).

In the parsley family the sepals are very small, often merely a ring at the base of the petals. The same is true of some flowers in the valerian family. In others the sepals may be merely bristles.

How many petals are present? To answer this, a number of flowers should be examined, to determine whether the number of petals is fixed or indefinite. If the petals are joined to form a cup, tube, or funnel, or a two-lipped corolla, their number is the number of lobes at the end.

Are the petals joined or separate? The petals are often deceptive in this, being joined only at the base. One must often pull off one petal to see if the others come with it.

Is the symmetry of the petals radial or bilateral? Radial symmetry is illustrated by a wheel: like parts radiate from the center and no matter how one turns it the right and left halves are similar. Bilateral symmetry may be illustrated by a chair: the right and left halves, as one faces it, are similar, but not the upper and lower halves. To put it differently, any straight line passing in any direction through the center of a wheel divides it into like parts; but only a vertical line does this for a chair. A rose is radially symmetric, an orchid bilaterally symmetric.

Are the stamens numerous and indefinite in number or of a small definite number? If the number is small and definite, the exact number should be noted, and the relation between stamens and petals.

Is a single pistil present with one style, or does it have more than one style? Or are there more than one pistil in the flower, each with its style or styles? If a style is cleft at the top into two or more branches, it is still only one style. Most of the pistils in our wild flowers have a single style; some have three or five; and a number of species have more than one pistil.

Are the leaves borne singly, in pairs, or in circles? This is perhaps the easiest characteristic to determine, but unfortunately it is so variable as to be only sometimes useful.

The Fourteen Groups of Families

1.　The flowers have three sepals and three petals, in many species all alike; the petals are mostly separate and radially symmetric. There are three, six, or more stamens. The leaves lack teeth on their edges and the veins in most species run from base to tip without visible branches.

Exceptions: *Maianthemum* has two sepals and two petals. The leaves of *Trillium* have veins that branch and form a network.

The following may seem to belong here but are placed in other groups: *Tradescantia* (II); *Cabomba* and *Brasenia* (V).

CHART OF GROUPS I TO XIII

(Not all genera and species will fit this scheme; see the descriptions of the groups for the exceptions.)

Start at the left and follow lines until a Roman numeral is reached; this is the number of a group.

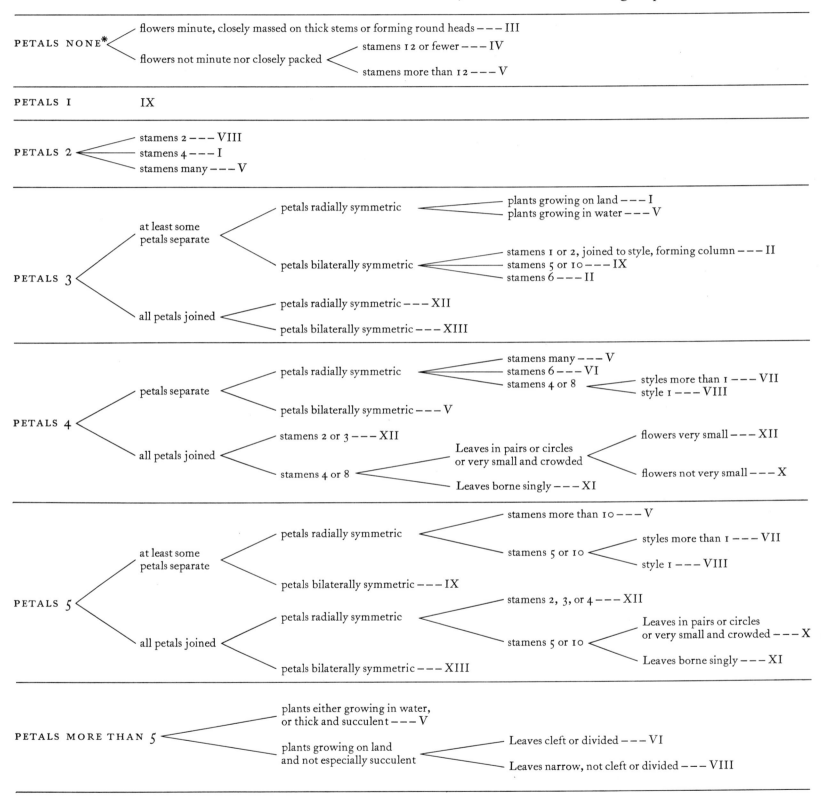

PETALS NONE* — flowers minute, closely massed on thick stems or forming round heads --- III
flowers not minute nor closely packed — stamens 12 or fewer --- IV
stamens more than 12 --- V

PETALS 1   IX

PETALS 2 — stamens 2 --- VIII
stamens 4 --- I
stamens many --- V

PETALS 3 — at least some petals separate — petals radially symmetric — plants growing on land --- I
plants growing in water --- V
petals bilaterally symmetric — stamens 1 or 2, joined to style, forming column --- II
stamens 5 or 10 --- IX
stamens 6 --- II
all petals joined — petals radially symmetric --- XII
petals bilaterally symmetric --- XIII

PETALS 4 — petals separate — petals radially symmetric — stamens many --- V
stamens 6 --- VI
stamens 4 or 8 — styles more than 1 --- VII
style 1 --- VIII
petals bilaterally symmetric --- V
all petals joined — stamens 2 or 3 --- XII
stamens 4 or 8 — Leaves in pairs or circles or very small and crowded — flowers very small --- XII
flowers not very small --- X
Leaves borne singly --- XI

PETALS 5 — at least some petals separate — petals radially symmetric — stamens more than 10 --- V
stamens 5 or 10 — styles more than 1 --- VII
style 1 --- VIII
petals bilaterally symmetric --- IX
all petals joined — petals radially symmetric — stamens 2, 3, or 4 --- XII
stamens 5 or 10 — Leaves in pairs or circles or very small and crowded --- X
Leaves borne singly --- XI
petals bilaterally symmetric --- XIII

PETALS MORE THAN 5 — plants either growing in water, or thick and succulent --- V
plants growing on land and not especially succulent — Leaves cleft or divided --- VI
Leaves narrow, not cleft or divided --- VIII

* See also page 14

II. The flowers have three sepals and three petals; the petals are separate in most species (joined in some) and bilaterally symmetric. There are six stamens in some, but in the largest family, the orchids, the one or two stamens are joined with the style. The leaves lack teeth on their edges, and their veins run from base to tip without visible branches or connections.

Exceptions: some of the orchids seem to have only two sepals; two of the three are joined. *Tradescantia* has radially symmetric petals.

III. The flowers are minute and do not look like flowers. They lack petals and most lack sepals also; a number are packed into a cylindrical or spherical mass. In many species the mass of flowers is enveloped in or associated with a single large bract, petal-like in some. The leaves lack teeth on their edges; their veins are variously branched or not.

IV. The flowers lack petals and those of some families lack sepals also. Sepals when present may have a petal-like appearance. Bracts or nectaries around a cluster of small flowers may simulate a perianth. With few exceptions the leaves lack teeth on their edges; generally several veins branch from the midrib and themselves give off smaller veins.

This is the most puzzling group, in which things are often not what they seem. The difficulty is complicated by the occurrence, in other groups, of flowers with both petals and sepals that shed their sepals as the flower opens — leaving a single circle of parts that may then be mistaken for sepals. Similarly flowers with sepals only may lose them and be classed as having no perianth. The only way to guard against such errors is to examine unopened buds. Moreover, there are in several families characterized by having petals, occasional species with no petals. And in some species the petals are so small and un-petal-like that they may be overlooked.

The following lists contain the most noteworthy of these perplexing plants.

Plants which shed their sepals so that their petals may be mistaken for sepals: The poppy family; *Actaea; Talinum.*

Plants which shed their sepals so that they have apparently no perianth: *Thalictrum; Cimicifuga; Trautvetteria; Hydrastis.*

Genera including species with no petals in families that normally have petals: *Lepidium; Draba; Cardamine; Stellaria; Ludwigia; Chrysosplenium; Astilbe; Saxifraga; Paronychia; Alchemilla; Sanguisorba;* and many species of the buttercup family.

Genera whose petals are easily overlooked: *Myosurus; Trollius; Delphinium; Nuphar.*

V. The flowers have two or more sepals and five or more petals. The petals are separate and radially symmetric. There are many stamens (generally more than twenty).

Exceptions: in the water-lily family *Cabomba* and *Brasenia* have only three or four petals and from three to eighteen stamens. *Delphinium* and *Aconitum* are bilaterally symmetric. Some species of *Hypericum* and *Hudsonia* have fewer than twenty stamens. Many species of the buttercup family lack petals.

The following may seem to belong here but are placed in other groups: *Portulaca* (VIII); *Talinum* (VIII); *Podophyllum* (VI).

VI. The flowers have two, four, or six sepals and four, six, or eight petals. The petals are separate and radially symmetric. The stamens may number six, eight, twelve, or eighteen, but not twice the number of petals.

Exception: *Podophyllum* has twice as many stamens as petals.

VII. The flowers have four or five sepals and four or five petals. The petals are separate and radially symmetric. The stamens equal the petals in number or are twice as many. There is more than one style in a flower (either a pistil with two or more styles, or two or more pistils).

Some species of *Hypericum* (V) may seem to belong here.

VIII. The flowers have two, four, or five sepals and four or five petals. The petals are separate and radially symmetric. The stamens are equal in number to the petals or are twice as many. There is a single style in each flower.

Exceptions: *Portulaca* and *Talinum* may have more numerous stamens. *Schrankia* has petals joined. *Cassia* has slightly unequal petals.

Species with petals only slightly joined or only slightly different may seem to belong here if they are not very carefully examined; there are such species in *Verbascum* (XIII); *Mentha* and *Isanthus* (XIII); and other genera.

IX. The flowers have three or five sepals and three or five petals. At least some of the petals are separate (some but not all may be joined), and they are bilaterally symmetric. There are five or ten stamens.

X. The flowers have two, four, or five sepals and four or five petals. The petals are joined and radially symmetric. The stamens equal the petals in number or are twice as many. The leaves are all at the base or very small and crowded or in pairs or circles. The ovary is superior.

Triosteum may seem to fit here but is placed with its relatives in XII.

XI. The flowers have four or five sepals and four or five petals. The petals are joined and radially symmetric. The stamens equal the petals in number. The leaves are borne singly on the stems and are not very small and crowded.

Exception: *Echium* has bilaterally symmetric flowers.

XII. The flowers have three, four, or five sepals and three, four, or five petals. The petals are joined and radially symmetric. There are two, three, or four stamens, generally fewer than the petals (equaling them in one family with leaves without teeth in pairs or circles and inferior ovary).

Exceptions: the flowers of *Valeriana* and *Triosteum* are very slightly bilateral in symmetry. *Trio-*

steum has five stamens. *Justicia* has bilaterally symmetric petals.

XIII. The flowers have four or five sepals and four or five petals. The petals are all joined and bilaterally symmetric. The stamens number from two to five. The flowers are in various types of inflorescence but not in heads that simulate single flowers.

Exceptions: the flowers of *Mentha, Isanthus, Verbascum, Veronica* are almost radially symmetric.

Justicia (XII) and *Echium* (XI) may seem to fit here.

XIV. The flowers are very small, many massed in a head which may be taken for a single flower. There are four or five petals, joined, radially or bilaterally symmetric. These are the large daisy family and the very small teasel family.

SHORT-CUTS TO IDENTIFICATION

1.   It is well to get acquainted first with the daisy family; the species are numerous and many are very common. The description of the family is on page 426 and many species are illustrated in plates 136 to 176.

2.   Aquatic plants – plants growing in water – occur in many families. The following are the commonest: the water-lily family; the arrowhead family; species of *Ranunculus; Nasturtium;* species of *Polygonum; Chrysosplenium; Elodea; Utricularia; Bidens beckii; Nymphoides; Justicia.*

3.   Plants that are completely lacking in green color occur in the pyrola and broom-rape families.

4.   Plants with milky juice (seen when stem or leaves are broken) occur in the dogbane, milkweed, and spurge families.

5.   Plants with flowers in umbels are found in the parsley and primrose families; umbels of a somewhat

different character (false umbels) occur in the lily and milkweed families.

6.   Plants with flowers in a narrow, coiled inflorescence are characteristic of the forget-me-not, phlox, and waterleaf families.

7.   If a flower has four sepals, four petals, and six stamens, two shorter than the other four, it is in the mustard family.

8.   Flowers with a corolla of joined petals with distinct upper and lower lip are mostly in the mint and snapdragon families. The plants of the mint family have square stems.

9.   Prickly plants with a stem composed of thick joints are in the cactus family.

10. Plants that climb by tendrils may be in the lily, bean, or cucumber family.

Note: It is important to bear in mind that all the guides to families, genera, and species in this book are good only for the species included. If used for plants of other regions they will lead to error.

GLOSSARY

The definitions that follow are intended to apply only to the plants described in this book. The words in parenthesis are corresponding technical terms used by botanists.

ACHENE   a small, dry fruit that does not open at maturity; it contains one seed and is itself often miscalled a seed.

ARROW-SHAPED   of leaves, shaped like an arrow-head with pointed lobes extended away from the tip (*sagittate*).

AXIL   the upper angle between a leaf and the stem to which it is attached.

BERRY   botanically, a fruit formed from one ovary and wholly succulent; this excludes many "berries" of ordinary speech, as strawberries and raspberries, but includes grapes, tomatoes and bananas.

BILATERAL   of the symmetry of a corolla, the two sides being alike but the upper and lower parts different (*irregular* or *zygomorphic*). Compare radial.

BLADE   the more or less flat and thin part of a leaf (*lamina*); contrasted with the stalk (*petiole*), which is also part of the leaf.

BRACT   a more or less leaflike body associated with a flower or inflorescence, differing from the ordinary foliage in size, shape, or color or in any combination of these.

BULB   botanically, a more or less spherical, usually underground body composed of circular, concentric, and generally succulent leaf-bases attached to a small flat or dome-shaped stem. Plantsmen use the word also for various rhizomes, tubers, and corms.

CALYX   the outer circle of the perianth, or the perianth itself in flowers that have only one circle: the sepals taken collectively. These may be distinct or joined to form a cup or tube, and may be of any color. The calyx encloses the other parts of the flower in bud.

CAPSULE   a dry fruit that opens along two or more lines when mature. Compare follicle. The fruit – pod – of the bean family may also open along two lines, but is always called a legume.

CIRCLE   of leaves or other parts, three or more attached at one level (*whorl*).

CLEFT   of the blade of a leaf, the margin indented at least halfway to the middle; more deeply than lobed, not so deeply as divided.

COLUMN   in an orchid flower the central body made up of stamen(s), style, and stigma.

CORM   a short, thick, erect, more or less spherical underground stem; often miscalled a bulb.

COROLLA   the inner circle of the perianth in flowers that have two circles; the petals taken collectively. These may be distinct or united to form a cup or trumpet or tube or a two-lipped body.

CYME   an inflorescence consisting, in its simplest form, of a flower that terminates a stem and two flowers on stems that arise below it. These two lateral flowers may in turn each be accompanied by two flowers, and so on; a cyme may be broad and flat, consisting of hundreds of flowers.

DISK   the central part of a flower-head of the daisy family, bearing many small disk-flowers. Compare ray. Also any flat, circular part of a single flower.

DIVIDED   of leaves, having the blade cut into several distinct segments (*leaflets*) on one stalk or attached to one midrib (*compound*). The segments may be mistaken for small leaves on a common stem; but buds, generally present on stems, are lacking. See palmate and pinnate.

DOWNY   of leaves and stems, bearing very short hairs, easier to feel than to see (*pubescent, puberulent*). Compare hairy, woolly.

16

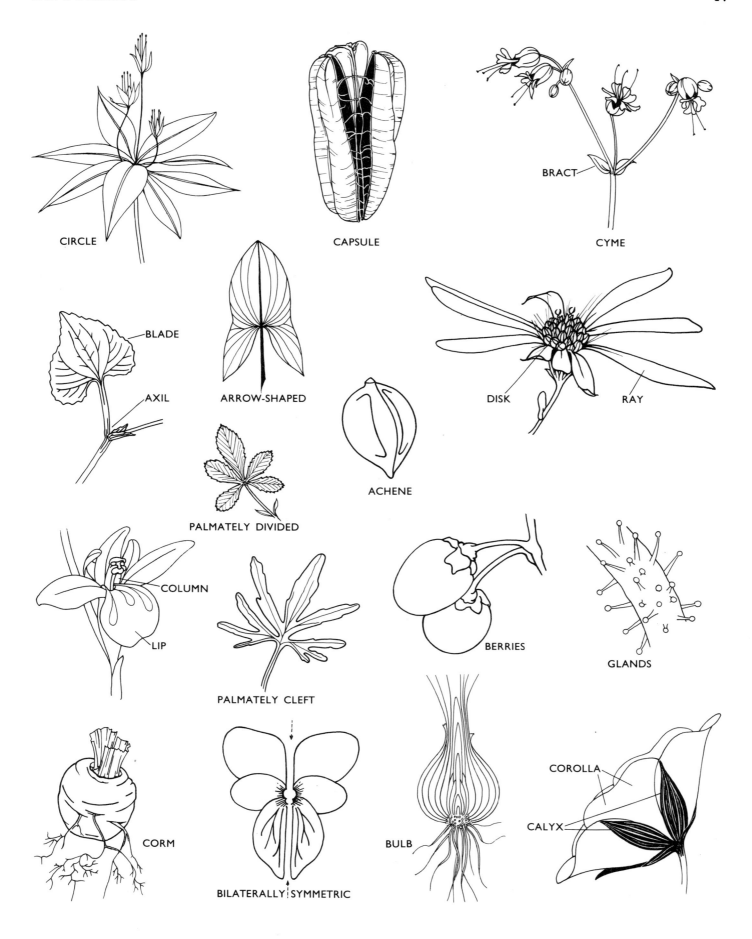

CIRCLE

CAPSULE

BRACT

CYME

BLADE

AXIL

ARROW-SHAPED

DISK   RAY

ACHENE

PALMATELY DIVIDED

COLUMN

LIP

PALMATELY CLEFT

BERRIES

GLANDS

CORM

BILATERALLY SYMMETRIC

BULB

COROLLA

CALYX

ELLIPTIC   of leaves, having the outline of the geometrical ellipse; a curved line such that the sum of the distances between any point on it and two points called foci remains constant.

FALSE RACEME   an inflorescence of flowers attached along a common stem, like those in a raceme, but arranged alternately to right and to left along one side of the stem, which is often coiled at the tip. Bracts, if present, are *opposite* the flowers (*cincinnus*).

FOLLICLE   a dry fruit that opens lengthwise along one line. Compare capsule, legume.

FRUIT   the body that normally contains the seed(s) in flowering plants. It is formed from the ovary or ovaries with or without surrounding parts of the flower.

GLANDS   small bodies that secrete various substances. In flowering plants they are typically on the surface, spherical and generally stalked. They are responsible for the odors of many plants.

HAIRY   of leaves and stems, bearing visible hairs projecting more or less straight from the surface (*hirsute, villous,* etc.). Compare downy, woolly.

HEAD   an inflorescence of flowers on very short stems which arise very close together at the summit of a stem.

HEART-SHAPED   of the blade of a leaf, indented at the base, more or less ovate in general outline, pointed or blunt at the tip (*cordate*).

INFERIOR   of an ovary, having sides united with the surrounding part(s) of the flower so that it cannot be removed entire; embedded in the receptacle. The stamens and perianth may *seem* to arise from its upper surface. Compare superior.

INFLORESCENCE   a group or cluster of flowers unmixed with foliage leaves; bracts may be included.

INVOLUCRE   a circle of bracts; often present in the parsley family and always in the daisy family.

KEEL   the two joined lower petals of a papilionaceous flower of the bean family.

LANCEOLATE   of a leaf-blade, much longer than wide and tapering to a point; the widest part between the base and the middle.

LEGUME   the pod of the bean family; containing one seed, or – more commonly – several seeds in one row attached to the side; often opening along two parallel lines, so that two

halves separate, but in many species not opening; of various textures, thin, papery, woody, or even succulent.

LIP   (1) in an orchid flower, the one petal, usually the lowest, that differs from all other parts of the perianth; (2) in various bilaterally symmetric flowers with joined petals, the upper or lower part of the corolla.

LOBED   of the blade of a leaf, having the margin indented, the indentation not so deep as when the blade is cleft.

MIDRIB   (1) the central vein of an undivided leaf-blade; (2) the part to which the segments of a pinnately divided leaf are attached.

NOTCHED   of the margin of a leaf, marked by shallow, pointed indentations (*emarginate*).

OBLONG   of the blade of a leaf, longer than wide, with more or less parallel sides.

OVARY   the basal part of a pistil, containing the ovule(s).

OVATE   of the blade of a leaf, somewhat longer than wide, the widest part being between the middle and the base; having the general outline of a hen's egg, but the end either round or pointed.

OVULE   rudimentary seed, contained (in flowering plants) in the ovary.

PAIRED   of leaves, two at the same level; usually on opposite sides (*opposite*).

PALMATE   of a leaf-blade, so divided that the segments all radiate from the tip of the stalk; also used of the lobes of a lobed or cleft blade, the lobes spreading out from a central part, somewhat as the fingers of a hand radiate from the palm.

PAPILIONACEOUS   butterfly-like; of the flowers of the bean family (see the introduction to this family).

PAPPUS   in the daisy family, the hairs, bristles, teeth, or scales that take the place of the calyx in individual flowers.

PARASITE   a plant or animal that obtains food directly from another living organism.

PERIANTH   the envelope of a flower, which surrounds stamens and pistil; composed of calyx and corolla, or of calyx only.

PETAL   one of the parts that compose the corolla, the inner of two rings of the perianth; they may be separate or joined, and radially or bilaterally symmetric.

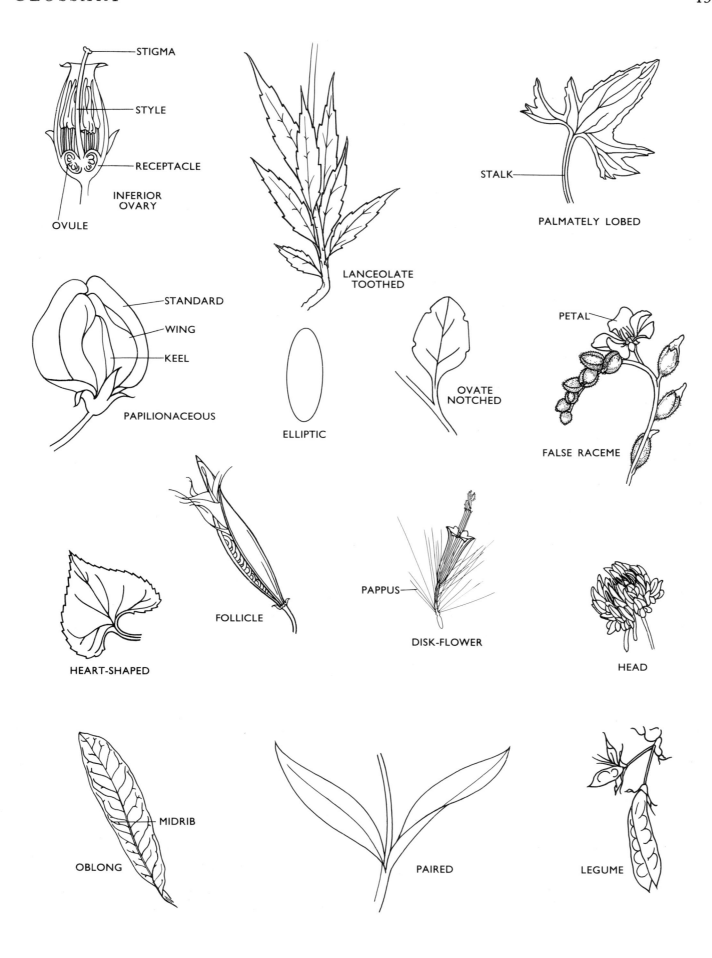

STIGMA

STYLE

RECEPTACLE

INFERIOR
OVARY

OVULE

PALMATELY LOBED

STALK

LANCEOLATE
TOOTHED

STANDARD

WING

KEEL

PAPILIONACEOUS

ELLIPTIC

OVATE
NOTCHED

PETAL

FALSE RACEME

FOLLICLE

PAPPUS

DISK-FLOWER

HEART-SHAPED

HEAD

MIDRIB

OBLONG

PAIRED

LEGUME

PINNATE   of a leaf-blade, so divided that the segments are arranged along two opposite sides of a midrib, like the elements of a feather; also used of the lobes of a cleft or lobed blade, the lobes extending on either side of a central unlobed part.

PISTIL   the part of a flower that receives pollen and contains an ovule or ovules and after fertilization develops into a fruit; one or several pistils stand in the center of the flower.

PLAIN   in this book used of the margin of a leaf-blade that has no teeth or notches or scallops (*entire*).

POD   any dry fruit that is not small and seedlike; see capsule, follicle, legume.

POLLEN   minute grains produced, in flowering plants, in sacs that form part of a stamen, and, when carried to an appropriate stigma, inducing the development of seed and fruit.

RACEME   an inflorescence of flowers arranged along the sides of a central stem; the flowers at each point may be single (*simple raceme*) or in smaller racemes (*compound raceme*). In many racemes flowers continue to develop at the tip while the older flowers below are forming fruit. The flowers are in the axils of bracts if bracts are present. Compare false raceme.

RADIAL   of petals, symmetric in any direction, all alike (*regular*, *actinomorphic*). Compare bilateral.

RAY   in the daisy family one of the petal-like flowers at the margin of the flower-head of many species; also called ray-flower. Compare disk.

RECEPTACLE   the tip of the stem of a flower to which perianth, stamens, and pistil(s) are attached; sometimes joined with the bases of these parts and in many families forming a disk, cup, or tube (*hypanthium*).

RHIZOME   a stem that grows underground and extends more or less parallel to the surface; it usually bears scale-like vestiges of leaves, and roots, and has a bud or buds at one end. Compare corm, tuber, bulb. There is no sharp distinction among these types of stems.

ROOT-TUBER   an enlargement of a root. See tuber.

SCALLOPED   of the margin of a leaf, marked by notches, these separated by round projections rather than sharp teeth (*crenate*).

SEPAL   one of the parts of the calyx, surrounding all other parts of the flower. They are frequently green, like small leaves, but may be of any color and may resemble petals.

SINGLE, SINGLY   of leaves or flowers, only one at any one level (*alternate*).

SPADIX   in the arum family, the thick stem on which the small flowers are borne.

SPATHE   a large bract or pair of bracts, often enclosing a flower or inflorescence; used especially in the arum family, in which the spathe may be petal-like; also in the iris and spiderwort families.

SPIKE   an inflorescence of flowers with very short stems on the sides of a long central stem. There is no sharp distinction between spike and raceme, and in this book some inflorescences are called spikes that others may call racemes.

STALK   of a leaf, the narrow part (*petiole*) that bears the blade (*lamina*); it may be lacking, the blade being attached directly to the stem. The stalk is part of the leaf, the term stem being reserved for the part of the plant that forms the buds from which new leaves and stem and flowers emerge; anatomically leaf-stalk and stem are quite different. The word stalk is, however, often used for the stem that supports a flower.

STAMEN   the part of a flower that forms the pollen.

STANDARD   the upper petal of a papilionaceous flower of the bean family.

STIGMA   the part of the pistil, usually a sticky disk or line, that receives the pollen; it is commonly at or near the tip of the style.

STIPULE   one of a pair of appendages at the base of a leaf in many species. Stipules may be minute and hair-like or scale-like, or stiff and sharp, or like segments of the leaf-blade.

STYLE   the narrow part of the pistil that extends up from the ovary and bears the stigma at or near its tip; it may be lacking, the stigma being then borne directly on the ovary.

SUPERIOR   of an ovary, attached to the receptacle only by its base, its sides free from other parts of the flower. Compare inferior. A pistil with superior ovary may be lifted out of the flower.

TENDRIL   a slender small branch, or part of a leaf, which coils about or adheres to a support.

TOOTHED   of the margin of a leaf-blade, having sharp projections (*serrate*, *dentate*, etc.).

TUBER   a short, thick underground stem. Compare rhizome, bulb, and corm; there is no sharp distinction among these types of stems.

UMBEL   an inflorescence of flowers on stems that radiate from the tip of a main stem; a compound umbel bears smaller umbels at the end of each of the radiating stems.

WING   botanically, (1) a thin but rigid membrane or flange that extends out from the surface of a stem or leaf-stalk or fruit or seed; (2) one of the lateral petals of a papilionaceous flower in the bean family.

WOOLLY   of a stem or leaf, bearing curved soft hairs, which may be tangled (*tomentose*). Compare hairy, downy.

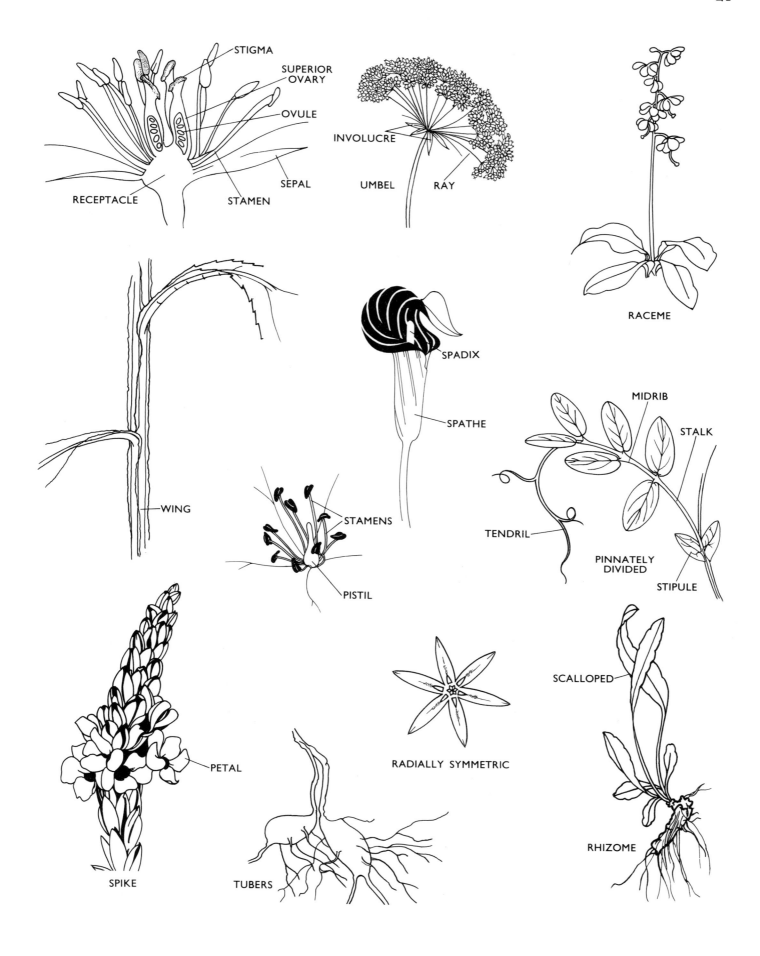

STIGMA

SUPERIOR
OVARY

OVULE

SEPAL

RECEPTACLE

STAMEN

INVOLUCRE

UMBEL

RAY

RACEME

WING

SPADIX

SPATHE

STAMENS

PISTIL

MIDRIB

STALK

TENDRIL

PINNATELY
DIVIDED

STIPULE

SCALLOPED

PETAL

RADIALLY SYMMETRIC

SPIKE

TUBERS

RHIZOME

GROUP I

SEPALS three, petals three; petals mostly separate, radially symmetric. Stamens three, six, or more. Leaves mostly without teeth on their edges; veins running from base to tip usually without visible branches.
Exceptions: *Maianthemum* has two sepals, two petals, four stamens. *Trillium* has leaves with branched veins forming a network.

I. *Plants with superior ovary.*
   A. Land plants with six stamens in a flower: lily family. (*Tradescantia* in the dayflower family, group II, seems to belong here.)
   B. Plants growing in water or in wet places, with three or more stamens in a flower: water-plantain family; eel-grass family. (*Cabomba* and *Brasenia* in the water-lily family, group V, may seem to belong here.)

II. *Plants with inferior ovary.*
   A. Plants with six stamens in a flower: daffodil family.
   B. Plants with three stamens in a flower: iris family.

THE LILY FAMILY (LILIACEAE)

The lily family is a large and familiar one, including many ornaments of our gardens as well as beautiful flowers of field and woodland. Many species are perennial, forming bulbs or rhizomes which live from year to year. In this family we cultivate asparagus, onions, hyacinths, lilies, lily-of-the-valley, and others. The family is known all around the world.

The *Liliaceae* are easily recognized by (1) the perianth of two circles of three parts each (commonly all alike); (2) the six stamens; (3) the leaves, which are undivided, with few exceptions lacking in marginal teeth, and lined with lengthwise, mostly unbranched veins (except *Trillium*); (4) the superior ovary (or mostly superior ovary —the lower part may be joined to surrounding parts of the flower), easily seen in the midst of the stamens. (In one genus, *Maianthemum*, the parts of the flower are in twos and fours instead of threes and sixes, but in other respects it is clearly a member of this family.) The fruit of many species is a pod (capsule) which splits into three parts when ripe; in others it is a berry.

Guide to Genera of the Lily Family

To identify a plant in this family, it is useful to separate the genera into two groups by the arrangement of their leaves, each group being subdivided according to the disposition and color of the flowers.

I. *Stems bearing leaves well above the ground (if they are all at the base or crowded on a short stem near the ground, see group II).*

A. Flowers in umbels, or occasionally single, at the summit of the stem, with or without additional flowers from the axils of the upper leaves: *Lilium* (perianth yellow, orange, or red, more than an inch long); *Medeola* (leaves in one circle); *Disporum* (leaves borne singly; perianth white or yellowish, not more than an inch long).

22

B. Flowers borne singly just above three leaves which have branched veins: *Trillium*.

C. Flowers (yellow or yellowish) hanging singly from the tips of stems which later continue growth so that the flowers seem to hang from the axils of leaves: *Uvularia*.

D. Flowers (pink, purple, green, or white) hanging from the axils of leaves, singly or in small clusters: *Polygonatum* (flower-stalks bent or curved); *Streptopus* (flower-stalks bent sharply).*

E. Flowers (white) in racemes (branched or unbranched) or spikes: *Smilacina* (stems arching; leaves broad; perianth of separate parts); *Maianthemum* (flower-parts in twos and fours); *Convallaria* (flowers white, hanging from an arched stem; perianth of joined parts); *Stenanthium* (raceme with slender branches; leaves folded lengthwise); *Chamaelirium* (stamens and pistils on separate plants in tall narrow clusters; leaves on stem grasslike); *Xerophyllum* (leaves stiff, narrow, very numerous and crowded, flowers many, small).

F. Flowers (brown or green) in branched racemes: *Veratrum* (leaves plaited); *Melanthium* (sepals and petals on stalks).

G. Flowers in umbels from the axils of leaves: *Smilax*.

II. *Leaves all from the underground stem or crowded on a very short erect stem.*

A. Flowers (white or yellow) borne singly, pendent: *Erythronium*.

B. Flowers (white, pinkish, or greenish) in umbels at the summit of the stem: *Allium* (with the odor of onions); *Nothoscordum* (leaves narrow, flowers creamy); *Clintonia* (leaves broad).

C. Flowers in racemes (branched or unbranched) or spikes; leaves at the base, not very numerous. This group is so large that it is convenient to divide it.

1. Flowers with parts of the perianth joined to form a bell: *Aletris* (flowers white or yellow; flower-cluster tall and narrow, the flowers pointing upward or outward); *Muscari* (flowers white or blue; inflorescence dense, the flowers pointing downward).

2. Flowers with the parts of the perianth separate. Of these the first four have three separate styles on the ovary; *Helonias* (flowers pink; seed-pod short, heart-shaped); *Amianthium* (flowers white, pink, or purplish; seed-pod tapering); *Tofieldia* (flowers white or greenish; leaves in two ranks); *Zigadenus* (perianth-parts with one or two glands near the base inside; flowers white or yellow). The remaining genera of this group have a single style on each ovary: *Camassia* (flowers from white to lavender; style longer than the ovary); *Ornithogalum* (perianth white with a green stripe in the middle of each part, on the outside; stalks of the stamens flat, white).

D. Flowers (white) in racemes; leaves numerous, crowded on a very short erect stem from which the tall leafless flower-stalk emerges: *Yucca*.

E. Flowers large, lilylike, orange or yellow, each lasting only one day, borne on forking stems: *Hemerocallis*.

THE LILIES (LILIUM)

Lilies – the great genus *Lilium* – grow all around the world, in and out of gardens. One authority lists eighty species that grow wild; about twenty in North America. The wild species are scarcely inferior in size and color to the many cultivated kinds. They are mostly tall plants (up to 9 feet) with many pointed leaves on a stem which grows from a bulb or scaly rhizome. The large flowers are borne at and near the summit. They are white, yellow, orange, red, or purple, often spotted with gold, brown, or purple. In our species the sepals and petals are all colored alike or nearly so, often mottled. The fruit is a pod (capsule) which splits open along three lines when mature. The seeds are flat, arranged in two columns in each of the three chambers of the pod.

Since earliest times lilies have had a place in mythology. They are mentioned in the Bible (though the "lilies of the field" of the New Testament were perhaps the scarlet anemones common in Palestine). The white lily of Europe was known to the ancients five thousand years ago, and used through classical times as a symbol of virginity and chastity. In early Christian times it was dedicated to the Virgin, finally (in the nineteenth century) becoming known as the Madonna lily. An old poem relates that the sweet fragrance of the flower changes to a foul odor when pollination is accomplished and it is thus fertilized. Even in recent times, lilies used as decorations in churches would be deprived of their stamens.

In medieval times the bulb was used medicinally. When pounded up with honey it was reputed good for ulcers and scurvy. Mixed with barley and baked into

*Asparagus may be looked for here; its flowers hang from the axils of branches instead of leaves; its leaves are replaced by needle-like branches.

cakes, it was used as a cure for dropsy. An infusion made by boiling it with vinegar or an ointment made from it would remove corns. Its mucilaginous quality has much to do with these supposed virtues; modern medicine fails to confirm them.

Many plants are known as lilies that are not species of *Lilium*. Lily-of-the-valley is *Convallaria*; it sometimes escapes to the wild. Corn-lily is *Clintonia*, described below. Fawn-lily is better known as dog-tooth-violet. Day-lily is *Hemerocallis*. Water-lily is not even in the lily family.

Five species are common in the northeastern United States. They may be distinguished as follows:

I.   *Lilies with Erect Flowers.*

WOOD LILY, L. PHILADELPHICUM (1–4 feet), is a familiar and beautiful woodland plant. The leaves are generally in circles. The flower may be single at the summit of the stem, or there may be two, three, or more in an umbel. The petals and sepals are narrowed to slender stalks. They are orange or red-orange, spotted with purple inside. In one form the perianth is yellow; in a more western variety it is an intense red. The latter variety has leaves mostly borne singly rather than in circles.

June to August: in woods and clearings (the red-flowered variety sometimes in prairies and swamps) from Maine to Ontario and southward to Maryland, North Carolina, and Kentucky (the variety extending westward to British Columbia and southward to Kentucky, Iowa, Nebraska, and New Mexico). *Plate 1*.

L. *bulbiferum*, the orange lily, resembles the wood lily, the narrow leaves being borne singly. There may be small bulblets (small bulbs) in the axils, as in the tiger lily. There is usually a single flower. This is a native of Europe, which has escaped from cultivation in scattered places (as roadsides and fields) in Quebec and New Jersey.

The southern L. *catesbaei*, leopard or pine lily, has been reported in wet ground in southeastern Virginia and southern Illinois.

The leaves are borne singly on the stem. There is but one flower, with red perianth.

II.   *Lilies whose Flowers hang on Curved or Hooked Stalks.*

FIELD LILY, L. CANADENSE (2–7 feet), has up to twenty flowers on a plant (rarely only one), in an umbel at the summit and from the upper axils. The petals and sepals curve outwards, but not backwards; they are yellow, orange, or red, with dark spots. The stamens and style are no longer than the petals.

June to August: in moist open ground from Quebec to Minnesota and southward to Virginia and Alabama. *Plate 1*.

TURK'S-CAP LILY, L. SUPERBUM (to 8 feet), is the largest and most floriferous of our lilies; forty flowers have been counted on one stem. The petals and sepals are orange or red, spotted; they are sharply bent back, the stamens and pistil being exposed.

July to September: in moist meadows and woods from Massachusetts to New Hampshire and southward to Georgia and Alabama. *Plate 1*.

TIGER LILY, L. TIGRINUM (2–4 feet), a common lily of gardens, is often found in the wild on roadsides and around old dwellings. Its leaves are borne singly; small black bulbs are generally present in the axils. The petals and sepals are strongly bent back; they are red or orange, mottled.

July to September: on roadsides, in thickets, etc., from New England to South Dakota and southward to Virginia. *Plate 1*.

Besides the above species, L. *michauxii* and L. *grayi* of the southern states may be found in Virginia. L. *michauxii* resembles L. *superbum*; its leaves are broadest towards their tips, and rather thick and leathery. It has few flowers. L. *grayi* also has few flowers (from one to three), only two or three inches long, with petals and sepals that spread slightly but are not bent back.

MEDEOLA

There is only one species of *Medeola*.

INDIAN CUCUMBER-ROOT, M. VIRGINIANA, has a slender stem up to 3 feet tall. Half-way up the stem is a circle of leaves, and at the summit three more, smaller leaves. The "root," which has the crisp texture of a cucumber and is edible, is really a rhizome or underground stem. The small flowers grow in an umbel from the summit of the stem, but their stalks curve so as to bring them below the three upper leaves, facing downwards. Each flower has a greenish-yellow perianth which is curled backwards.

The oddest feature of the flower is the three thread-like, brown stigmas which diverge at the top of the ovary. The fruit is a dark crimson berry; several of these usually are carried up, by the straightening of the stalks, to a position in the midst of the three upper leaves.

May and June: in woods and on mossy banks from Quebec to Minnesota and southward to Florida and Louisiana. *Plate 1*. The name of the genus is derived from that of Medea, a celebrated sorceress of ancient Greece; but there seems no record of magical qualities for the plant.

PLATE 1

Lilium canadense

Gray

Lilium tigrinum

Johnson

Lilium canadense

Johnson

Lilium philadelphicum

Johnson

Medeola virginiana

Rhein

Lilium superbum

Gottscho

THE MANDARINS (DISPORUM)

The genus *Disporum* contains two species of eastern North America; others grow in the West and in Asia. The flowers hang singly or in twos or threes, like bells, from the tips of forked stems. The fruit is a red berry. The botanical name of the genus refers to the two rudimentary seeds in each chamber of the ovary; if all develop, there are six seeds in the berry.

YELLOW MANDARIN, D. LANUGINOSUM (16–30 inches), has yellowish-green petals and sepals, nearly an inch long, much longer than the stamens,

slightly curved outwards.

May and June: in woods from New York to southern Ontario and southward to Georgia and Alabama. *Plate 2*.

NODDING MANDARIN, D. MACULATUM (8–24 inches), has white petals and sepals spotted with purple, often an inch long but shorter than the stamens, which project from the flower.

May: in woods in eastern Ohio and southward to Georgia and Tennessee; also in Michigan.

DOGTOOTH-VIOLETS or ADDER'S-TONGUES (ERYTHRONIUM)

The dogtooth-violets are welcome flowers of early spring throughout northeastern America, the yellow ones commoner towards the Atlantic, the white ones more abundant farther inland. To call a white or yellow flower a violet has offended some persons (though there are white and yellow violets!); among these persons was John Burroughs, who invented the names trout-lily and fawn-lily. Several English flowers have been called violets besides those of the genus *Viola*. All these are pink or purple, as is the European dogtooth-violet. The "dogtooth" part of the name refers to the little white bulb underground. The botanical name of the genus is from a Greek word meaning "red."

The plants are like miniature lilies with a single pendent flower on each stalk. The stalk is sheathed by a pair of glossy, often mottled leaves. Flower-stalk and leaves come from a small bulb deep underground.

This also sends out slim white underground branches which form new bulbs at their tips. Bulbs that are formed from these tips or from seed send up only single leaves for several years before they produce a flower-stalk. Patches of such single leaves, without any flowers, may often be found in the woods.

YELLOW DOGTOOTH-VIOLET, E. AMERICANUM (4–8 inches), has yellow sepals and petals which curve sharply upward; they are generally spotted with brown on the inside. The six brown stamens are in two circles of three, one group commonly a little shorter than the other. A number of varieties, differing by very minor details, have been named.

March to May: in wet woods and meadows from Nova Scotia to Minnesota and southward to Florida and Alabama; commoner eastward. *Plate 2*.

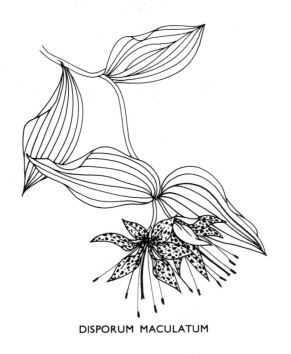

DISPORUM MACULATUM

ALLIUM TRICOCCUM

PLATE 2

Uvularia sessilifolia *Elbert*

Erythronium americanum *Johnson*

Uvularia perfoliata *D. Richards*

Erythronium albidum *Aborn*

Disporum lanuginosum *D. Richards*

Uvularia grandiflora *Johnson*

WHITE DOGTOOTH-VIOLET, E. ALBIDUM (4–8
inches), has a perianth more or less strongly bent
upwards. The petals and sepals are white inside with a
yellow base, and are usually tinged with lavender outside. A variety found on rocky bluffs in Iowa and Missouri and southwestward has a perianth that does not
curve outward, and leaves that are are not mottled.

April to June: in woods and thickets and on
bluffs from Ontario to Minnesota and southward to
Kentucky, Arkansas, and Texas; rare in the Atlantic
states. *Plate 2.*

E. propullans, with pink flowers and small leaves, is a much
rarer species which has been reported from Minnesota and Ontario.

BELLWORTS (UVULARIA)

The bellworts have pretty hanging yellow flowers
and leaves that droop at flowering time from a slender
forked stem. The petals and sepals, which are all
colored alike, are pointed and curved to one side: the
entire flower seems twisted. After flowering the stem
continues to grow, so that the leaves are no longer
bunched and drooping. The fruit is a three-lobed pod.

Bellworts should not be confused with bell-
flowers (*Campanula*). "Wort" is a word formerly given
to plants used for food or medicine; as a suffix it often
just means "plant."

I.   *In two species each leaf has basal lobes that meet
     around the stem; or, to put it differently, the stem
     seems to grow through the leaf ("perfoliate").*

U. PERFOLIATA (4–24 inches) has smooth leaves,
with a whitish bloom. The flowers are bright yellow. The inner surface of the perianth appears rough
with minute projecting glands.

April to June: in open woods, often acid, from
Massachusetts to Ontario and southward to Florida
and Louisiana. *Plate 2.*

U. GRANDIFLORA (6–30 inches) has leaves very finely
downy on the lower side, and not whitened with
bloom. There are usually no more than two leaves
below the first fork in the stem; sometimes none. The
flowers are bright yellow, rather larger than those of
U. perfoliata (up to 2 inches long). The perianth is
quite smooth inside.

April to June: in rich woods, often in limestone
regions, from Quebec to North Dakota and southward
to Georgia and Oklahoma. *Plate 2.*

II. *In the other common species the leaves are merely
     attached by their narrow base.*

MERRY-BELLS or WILD-OATS, U. SESSILIFOLIA, (4–
16 inches), is a delicate small plant. The flowers
are pale yellow, only about an inch long.

April to June: in woods and thickets from Quebec to North Dakota and southward to New England,
in the mountains to Georgia and to Alabama, Oklahoma, and South Dakota. *Plate 2.*

The southern *U. caroliniana* may be found in West Virginia
and Virginia and farther up the coastal plain. It is very similar to *U.
sessilifolia,* but the stem bears some minute hairs in lines.

THE TRILLIUMS (TRILLIUM)*

The trilliums are spring flowers mostly of moist
woods. The name, which is derived from the Latin
word for "three," describes the plants, which have all
their parts in threes. The stem grows each year from a
perennial underground stem, a rhizome. At its summit it bears three leaves, and, just above these, a single
flower with three green sepals, three petals, six stamens, and a three-chambered pistil with three stigmas; in most of the species there is no style, so that the
stigmas are situated directly on the ovary. The fruit is
a berry, often with three or six angles. The leaves are
unusual for this family in having a network of veins.

Our species may be conveniently distinguished
in several groups, as follows:

I.   *Trilliums whose flowers lack stalks (they are situ-
     ated immediately above the three leaves).*

TOADSHADE, T. SESSILE (4–12 inches), has leaves
usually mottled or blotched with brown. The

sepals and petals are rather narrow and the petals stand
nearly erect; the petals are either maroon or greenish-
yellow. This is a common midwestern species.

April to June: in woods from western New York
to Missouri and southward to Georgia and Arkansas.
Plate 3.

T. RECURVATUM (6–18 inches) may at a glance resemble *T. sessile.* Its petals are red-brown, purplish, or greenish-yellow. But the sepals bend down
towards the earth; the petals are more oval and are
narrowed at the base to a sort of stalk; and the leaves
are definitely stalked.

April, May: in woods from Michigan to Nebraska and southward to Alabama and Arkansas.
Plate 3.

Besides these, three southern species with flowers that lack
stalks may be found along our southern borders. *T. viride* has narrow
greenish petals, often an inch or more long, which taper to the base.
T. luteum (*Plate 3*) has yellow or greenish petals which do not taper

*If we translate Lilium into lilies, why not Trillium into 'trillies'?

PLATE 3

Trillium recurvatum   *Johnson*

Trillium nivale   *D. Richards*

Trillium cuneatum   *Rickett*

Trillium sessile   *Mayer*

Trillium luteum   *Rhein*

Trillium undulatum   *Johnson*

downwards. The flowers have a lemon odor. *T. cuneatum* (*Plate 3*) resembles *T. sessile* but is larger, the maroon or greenish petals up to 3 inches long.

II. *Trilliums with flowers on definite stalks (the flower may hang below the leaves but the stalk grows from the summit of the stem).*

A. Of these species with stalked flowers, two have leaves also with definite stalks.

PAINTED TRILLIUM, T. UNDULATUM (8–12 inches), is the most decorative of our trilliums: its petals are wavy-edged ("undulate") and white, marked towards the base with a red or purplish blotch and streaks. The tips of the stamens are pink. The flower-stalk may be 2 inches long and stands erect. The leaves taper to sharp points.
April to June: in acid woods and swamps from Quebec to Manitoba and southward to New Jersey and Wisconsin and in the mountains to Georgia and Tennessee. *Plate 3.*

DWARF WHITE or SNOW TRILLIUM, T. NIVALE (3–6 inches), is a smaller plant but bears a flower of about the same size as that of *T. undulatum.* The petals are white, sometimes streaked with pink. There is a style carrying the stigmas up away from the ovary. The leaves are blunt.
March to May: in rich woods from western Pennsylvania to Minnesota and Nebraska and southward to Kentucky and Missouri. *Plate 3.*

B. The remaining trilliums with stalked flowers have leaves with very short stalks or, more usually, no stalks. They include some of our commonest eastern species. It is a temptation to classify them by the color of the petals; but the white flowers often fade to maroon or pink, and the red-flowered species may have white flowers.

STINKING-BENJAMIN, T. ERECTUM (6–24 inches), is perhaps the commonest eastern trillium. Its flower is on a long stalk (to 4 inches long) which is straight but may be directed sharply to one side. The petals are typically maroon or dark red, but may be greenish, yellow, or white. The flower, as the English name suggests, is ill-scented.

April to June: in woods, usually moist, from Quebec to Ontario and Michigan and southward to Delaware and Ohio and in the mountains to Georgia and Tennessee. *Plate 4.*

LARGE WHITE TRILLIUM, T. GRANDIFLORUM (8–16 inches), has white petals about 2 inches long, with wavy edges; but they may be pink or green or striped with green. Forms have been reported with two instead of three leaves, sepals, and petals, and others with four or five of each. Indeed this is our most variable species, as well as one of the handsomest. It is often cultivated. The flower stands on a stalk up to 3 inches long.
April to June: in woods and thickets from Quebec to Minnesota and southward to Pennsylvania and Arkansas and in the mountains to Georgia. *Plate 4.*

NODDING TRILLIUM, T. CERNUUM (6–24 inches), is characterized by a "nodding" (or "cernuous") flower: that is, one that hangs from the end of its stalk with its opening directed downward. The stalk is curved so that the flower hangs beneath the leaves. The flower is small, the petals only about an inch long; they are white or pink. The tips of the stamens are pink, and the ovary of the pistil is white or pink. The leaves are up to 6 inches long and about as broad and have very short stalks.
April to July: in damp, usually acid woods from Newfoundland across Canada and southward to Delaware, Illinois, and Iowa, and in the mountains to Georgia and Tennessee. *Plate 4.*

T. FLEXIPES (6–24 inches) is a less-known, mainly midwestern species that has gone by several names (*T. declinatum, T. gleasoni*). It closely resembles *T. cernuum.* The flower hangs much as in that species. The tips of the stamens are white. Its leaves are larger than those of *T. cernuum,* up to 8 inches long and broad, and have no sign of a stalk.
April to June: in moist woods from central New York to Minnesota and southward to Maryland, Tennessee, and Missouri.

The southeastern *T. pusillum*, no more than 12 inches tall, with narrowish, blunt leaves and white petals about 3 inches long, and white petals which become pink with age, is found in southeastern Virginia. Closely related to this, and perhaps not to be separated from it, is the more robust *T. ozarkanum*. It grows in Missouri and Arkansas.

ONIONS (ALLIUM)

It may be a surprise to find these pungent vegetables in the lily family. But their flowers have a perianth of six parts and the usual six stamens and three-chambered pistil. What we use for food or seasoning is of course a bulb, consisting of circular, succulent leaf-bases seated on and concealing a small dome-shaped

stem. From the center of this dome arises, in nature or in the garden, a leafless stalk bearing at the summit a cluster (false umbel) of flowers, surrounded at first by one or more bracts. The leaves are narrow in most species, hollow in some.
We have five native species in the northeastern

PLATE 4

Trillium grandiflorum   *Gottscho*

Allium tricoccum   *Johnson*

Allium stellatum   *Johnson*

Allium cernuum   *Johnson*

Trillium erectum   *Rhein*

Trillium erectum   *Rickett*

Trillium cernuum   *Johnson*

states, besides a few that intrude from the south and west, and a number of cultivated species gone wild. There are many more species in the west, and in Asia. A number have pretty flowers and some are cultivated, especially in rock gardens, for their decorative quality. Some are noxious weeds, imparting a bad odor and taste to the milk of cattle that graze them.

I.   *One species may be immediately distinguished by its broad leaves or by the absence of leaves.*

WILD LEEK, A. TRICOCCUM (6–24 inches), has
    leaves usually more than an inch wide, often more than 2 inches, and up to a foot long. These appear in spring, and among them the flower bud pushes up; but the leaves wither and disappear before the flowers open. The numerous white flowers measure about $\frac{1}{4}$ inch, on stalks generally about $\frac{1}{2}$ inch long.

    June and July: in rich woods from Quebec to Minnesota and southward to Maryland, Tennessee and Iowa; in the mountains to Georgia. *Plate 4.*

II.   *The other species have narrow leaves, which are generally present at flowering time. They may best be separated by looking at the bracts which surround the entire group of flowers in bud and are still present, somewhat shriveled and papery, during the flowering period.*

    A. The garlics have a single long-beaked bract.
       In fact the word garlic means, in its etymology, a spear ("gar") borne on a leek ("lic").

FIELD GARLIC, A. VINEALE (1–4 feet), is an unplea-
    sant weed. The leaves are narrow, hollow cylinders, tapering gradually. The small flowers are greenish or purplish, on short stalks; they are often replaced by small bulbs, which generally end in slender "tails" extending upward.

    May to July: a weed in fields, roadsides, etc. from New England to Minnesota and southward to Georgia, Arkansas, and Kansas; a native of Europe. *Plate 5.*

    B. Our native species with narrow leaves have two or three bracts around the flower-cluster.

WILD GARLIC, A. CANADENSE (up to 2 feet), is so
    abundant in places as to appear like grass. The leaves are very narrow. The flowers are enclosed by two or three rather broad bracts. The flowers are small, pink or white, on slender stalks up to an inch long. Like those of *A. vineale*, they are frequently replaced by small bulbs, with or without long "tails"; in fact, in many places one never sees flowers. The English name is misleading, as this is not a true garlic.

    May to July: in open woods, meadows, and prairies from Maine to South Dakota and southward to Florida and Texas. *Plate 5.*

WILD ONION, A. CERNUUM (to 2 feet), is at once dis-
    tinguished by the crook in the flowering stem just beneath the flower-cluster, so that the cluster is directed sideways or even hangs downwards (it is "cernuous"). The leaves are narrow. There are two bracts around the flower-cluster. The flowers are pink or white, about $\frac{1}{4}$ inch long, on stalks up to an inch long.

    July and August: in gravelly or rocky places, often at high altitudes, from New York to British Columbia and southward to Georgia, Alabama, Missouri, and Arizona. *Plate 4.*

WILD ONION, A. STELLATUM (to 2 feet), resembles
    A. cernuum except for its straight flower-stalk. The flowers are pink.

    July to September: in prairies and open rocky places from Ontario to Saskatchewan and southward to Illinois, Missouri, and Texas. *Plate 4.*

WILD CHIVES, A. SIBIRICUM (to 2 feet or more), has
    slender hollow leaves shorter than the stem. The stout stem bears a dense cluster of pink flowers, at first enclosed in a pair of bracts which are also often pink or pink-veined. The flowers are $\frac{1}{2}$ inch long on stalks only about $\frac{1}{4}$ inch long.

    June to August: in rocky places, gravelly banks, etc., from Quebec to Alaska and southward to New England and New York, Minnesota, Colorado, and Washington.

    True chives are *A. schoenoprasum*, a native of Europe, cultivated in America and occasionally found growing wild. It differs only in detail from our *A. sibiricum*, which also grows in Europe and Asia; many botanists include *A. sibiricum*, as a variety, in *A. schoenoprasum*.

NOTHOSCORDUM

Other species of *Nothoscordum* are found in South America, Asia, and Africa.

FALSE GARLIC, N. BIVALVE, is an insignificant plant
    (not more than a foot tall) having some resemblance to a wild onion (a species of *Allium*) but without the characteristic onion odor. The leaves grow from a bulb; they are narrow, grasslike. The flowering stem is terminated by a small cluster of flowers on longish stalks that are generally unequal in length. The petals and sepals are somewhat greenish or yellowish, less than $\frac{1}{2}$ inch long.

    April and May: in prairies and open woods, on sandy banks, etc. from Virginia to Nebraska and southward to Florida and Texas. *Plate 5.*

PLATE 5

Allium vineale   *Rickett*   Allium canadense   *D. Richards*

Nothoscordum bivalve   *Rickett*

Clintonia umbellulata   *Gottscho*

Clintonia borealis   *Johnson*

Polygonatum pubescens   *Scribner*

Clintonia borealis   *Johnson*

WOOD-LILIES (CLINTONIA)

The genus *Clintonia* has two species in the eastern states, both found in woods in the mountains, one extending far to the north in bogs and other places. They are plants with a tuft of several broad, shining leaves and a leafless stalk, about a foot tall, bearing an umbel of small flowers, succeeded by berries.

BLUEBEAD, DOGBERRY, or CORN-LILY, C. BOREALIS, is frequent on mountains in the eastern states. There are up to eight flowers on one stem. The sepals and petals are greenish-yellow, about ¾ inch long. Two common names suggest that the bright blue berries may be more familiar than the flowers; they are more colorful and last for a longer time.

May to August (depending on latitude and altitude): in moist mossy or rocky woods and high meadows from Labrador to Manitoba and southward to New England and Wisconsin and in the mountains to Georgia and Tennessee. *Plate 5.*

SPECKLED-WOOD-LILY, C. UMBELLULATA, is of more limited distribution. It has up to thirty flowers on a stem. The sepals and petals are white spotted with green and purple and only about ⅓ inch long. The berries are black.

May to July: in rich woods from the mountains of New York to eastern Ohio and southward to Georgia and Tennessee. *Plate 5.*

SOLOMON'S-SEAL (POLYGONATUM)

These plants have almost always unbranched stems which usually arch or lean, the small flowers hanging singly or in small groups from the axils of the leaves. The leaves are elliptic or ovate, tapering to sharp points. They are attached singly and so disposed as to form two opposite ranks on either side of the stem. The flowers are tubular with spreading teeth, the petals and sepals being joined. The fruit is a dark blue berry.

The common name comes, it is said, from the circular scar left on the underground stem (rhizome) by the death and withering of the flowering stem; the scar somewhat resembles the seal impressed on wax on official documents, or on letters in former times. But why Solomon's seal, rather than another's? His seal would be the magical pentacle, a five- or six-pointed star. A completely different explanation is given by Gerard in his herbal; following Dioscorides, he writes: "The roots are excellent good for to seale or close up . . . wounds, broken bones, and such like"; and Solomon, to the herbalist, was a magician who could perform such acts of healing.

The botanical name is derived from two Greek words signifying "many" and "joints," from the form of the stem.

The species are somewhat confused; different authorities list three or four, which are not sharply distinct. The complicating factor is a tendency for the chromosomes, those hidden microscopic bodies that govern development, to double up, which is apt to make the plants larger in all their parts.

P. PUBESCENS has an arching stem from 1 to 3 feet long. The leaves have minute hairs (easily seen with a hand lens) on the lower surface, especially along the veins. There are generally only one or two flowers in each cluster (occasionally up to four), hanging on stalks that are sharply bent down. The flowers are yellowish-green, from ⅓ to ⅔ inch long, the perianth somewhat constricted just where the spreading points begin.

May and June: in woods from Quebec to Manitoba and southward to Maryland, Kentucky, and Iowa, and in the mountains to South Carolina. *Plate 5.*

P. BIFLORUM includes a wide variety of plants, with stems ranging from 8 inches to 6 feet in length, and leaves from 1 to 4 inches broad. The larger plants have been separated by many authors under the name *P. canaliculatum* (formerly *P. commutatum*); but every gradation exists in the characteristics that are supposed to separate the species. The larger plants (*P. canaliculatum*) are apparently more widespread; the smaller ones slightly more southern.

There are from one to three (or sometimes more) flowers in each cluster on the plants generally named *P. biflorum* (which means, of course, "two-flowered"); from two to ten or even more on the larger plants called *P. canaliculatum*. The flowers are greenish (deep yellow in a variety found in Michigan and Ontario), ranging in size from ½ to 1 inch in length; they hang on curved rather than bent stalks.

May and June: in woods, thickets, on roadside banks, etc., from New Hampshire to Manitoba and southward to Florida and Texas. *Plate 6.*

Besides these, the European *P. latifolium*, which has hairs on the stem, has been reported from Massachusetts.

PLATE 6

Streptopus roseus   *Gottscho*

Streptopus amplexifolius   *Rhein*

Polygonatum biflorum   *Justice*

Smilacina racemosa   *Rickett*

Streptopus amplexifolius   *Johnson*

Polygonatum biflorum   *Johnson*

Smilacina racemosa   *Johnson*

MANDARINS or TWISTED-STALKS (STREPTOPUS)

The twisted-stalks have usually forked stems which bear ovate, sharp-pointed leaves singly. The disposition of the flowers is curious and unusual. Instead of arising from the axil of a leaf, as many flowers do (e.g. those of Solomon's-seal), each flower-stalk grows from the side of the stem *away from the leaf* (placing the main stem apparently in the axil!). Then the flower-stalk at once doubles back *under* the leaf, and forms a single flower at its tip. Halfway along it is a sharp bend, directing the flower downward. It is to this that the name twisted-stalk refers; also the botanical name, which means "twisted foot"(the "foot," as usual among botanists, being the stalk). The fruit is a red berry.

Several published illustrations show the flowers wrongly attached.

Both of our species grow in cold moist woods, flowering from May to July.

WHITE MANDARIN or LIVERBERRY, S. AMPLEXI-
FOLIUS (4–36 inches), has leaves which "em-
brace" the stem (*amplexi-*); that is, they extend around the stem on either side at the point of attachment. The flowers are generally greenish-white, the petals and sepals about ½ inch long and sharply bent upwards. A variety with pink or purplish-flowers is found in the mountains of Maine and New Hampshire and adjacent Canada.

From Greenland and Labrador to Alaska and southward to New York and Wisconsin and in the mountains to North Carolina and Arizona. This species is also widespread in Europe. *Plate 6.*

PINK MANDARIN, S. ROSEUS (6–24 inches), has
leaves which do not "embrace" the stem but simply taper to the narrow base. The flowers are pink or purplish, the petals and sepals about ½ inch long and curved upwards only at the tips.

From Labrador to Ontario and Minnesota and southward in the mountains to New Jersey, Georgia, Kentucky, and Wisconsin. *Plate 6.*

FALSE SOLOMON'S-SEAL, FALSE SPIKENARD (SMILACINA)

The stem and leaves of most kinds of *Smilacina* resemble those of Solomon's-seal; hence the first rather unsatisfactory common name. The arching stem bears its elliptic or ovate leaves in two ranks. It grows from an underground stem (rhizome). The characteristic that distinguishes *Smilacina* from *Polygonatum* is the gathering of the flowers into clusters at the tip of the stem. The perianth is white. The fruit is a berry.

True spikenard is an Asian plant from which an aromatic ointment, nard, was prepared. American spikenard is *Aralia racemosa*.

The botanical name is a diminutive form of *Smilax*, but has no connection with the plant we now know by that name. The herbalists used *Smilax* for several vines in various genera.

We have three species, easily distinguished.

S. RACEMOSA, with stems 16–40 inches long, is the
commonest. The flowers are in a much-branched cluster (a compound raceme). The perianth is only ⅛ inch long or less. The berries are at first greenish-yellow speckled with brown, at maturity red.

May to July: in woods from Quebec to British Columbia and southward to Virginia, Tennessee, and
Missouri, and in the mountains to Georgia. *Plate 7.*

S. STELLATA is a smaller plant, the stem not more than
24 inches long. The flowers are less numerous and disposed in a simple raceme, that is, one composed of single flowers rather than clusters. The perianth is up to ¼ inch long. The mature berry is black or black-striped.

May to August: in gravelly thickets, meadows, etc., from Labrador and Newfoundland to British Columbia and southward to New Jersey, West Virginia, Ohio, Kansas, New Mexico, and southern California. *Plate 7.*

S. TRIFOLIA has a stem only 16 inches long or less and
bearing commonly three leaves (*trifolia*); some plants have from one to four leaves. The flowers are arranged in a simple raceme. The perianth is about ⅙ inch long. The mature berry is dark red.

May to August: in bogs and mossy woods from Labrador and Newfoundland to Mackenzie and southward to New Jersey, Ohio, northern Illinois, Minnesota, Saskatchewan, and British Columbia; also in Asia. *Plate 7.*

PLATE 7

Smilacina stellata *Elbert*

Yucca smalliana *Rickett*

Maianthemum canadense *Rickett*

Maianthemum canadense *Rickett*

Chamaelirium luteum *Rickett*

Chamaelirium luteum *Rickett*

Smilacina trifolia *Phelps*

MAIANTHEMUM

We have one species of this genus.

CANADA MAYFLOWER or WILD-LILY-OF-THE-VALLEY, M. CANADENSE, has leafy flowering stems 2–8 inches tall, growing from slender creeping underground stems (rhizomes), and often forming wide carpets of green under trees. From the underground stems grow also single long-stalked leaves, generally from the same points as the flowering stems; but these are usually withered and gone when the flowers appear. The flowering stems bear usually two or three leaves, each of which is heart-shaped, the two lobes projecting on either side of the stem and "clasping" it; some leaves, especially the lower ones, have short stalks. On most of our plants there are con-spicuous, raised cross veins connecting the lengthwise ones; on others there are no visible cross veins. Leaves of midwestern and western plants, with or without this network of veins, may bear minute hairs on their under surface.

The flower is unique in this family in having its parts in twos and fours: two sepals, two petals, four stamens, and a two-chambered ovary from which rises a two-parted style. The flowers are disposed in a short raceme. The fruit is a berry, at first greenish with dark speckles, finally red.

May and June: in woods, especially coniferous woods, from Labrador to British Columbia and southward to Delaware, Tennessee, and Iowa, and in the mountains to Georgia. *Plate 7.*

STENANTHIUM

There is only one species of this genus in our range.

FEATHERBELLS, S. GRAMINEUM, has grasslike leaves, rarely more than an inch broad, and folded lengthwise. The flowering stem (1–6 feet) is much branched, the drooping branches covered with small flowers which have practically no stalks. The sepals and petals are very narrow (*Stenanthium* means "narrow flower") and less than $\frac{1}{2}$ inch long; they may be white, greenish, or purplish. The flowers on the side branches may lack pistils. The fruit is a small pod with three beaks.

June to September: in moist woods and thickets from Pennsylvania to Missouri and southward to Florida and Texas. *Plate 10.*

CONVALLARIA

LILY-OF-THE-VALLEY, C. MAJALIS, is an Old-World plant, widely cultivated and quite often "escaping" into woods and thickets, where it may form dense mats. The stem arches, bearing a raceme of white, bell-like, sweetly fragrant small flowers which hang on short, curved stalks. There are generally two leaves on the stem a short distance above the ground. The same species, or one very much like it, is native in the mountains of Virginia and West Virginia and thence southward; some botanists consider it distinct, and it has been named *C. montana*. It differs in a number of minor details.

CHAMAELIRIUM

We have only one species of *Chamaelirium*.

BLAZING-STAR, DEVIL'S-BIT or FAIRY-WAND, C. LUTEUM, is a very slender plant with a tuft of basal leaves and a flowering stem (about 2 feet tall) which bears small leaves and a long spike-like raceme of small white flowers. The basal leaves are blunt and broadest near their tips; the leaves on the stem tend to be lanceolate. Southward one finds taller plants (up to 3 feet), often with round-bladed basal leaves. Leaves and stem grow from a perennial underground stem (rhizome). The plants are staminate and pistillate; that is, the flowers on one plant have either stamens or pistils, not both. The staminate spike tapers to the tip, which bends over and droops. The pistillate spike is shorter, straight, and equally thick up to its blunt tip. The sepals and petals are narrow. The fruit is a small pod which splits open into three parts, the dry empty shells remaining on the stem.

The names of this curious little species are unfortunate, except perhaps fairy-wand. Nothing about the plant "blazes" or is starlike; "devil's-bit" or "devil's-bite" is the name of a quite different plant in England; the devil is supposed to have bitten off its rhizome, and this is the subject of several superstitions. *Chamaelirium* means "dwarf lily," but the plant is not lily-like. *Luteum* means "yellow"; and the flowers are white.

June and July: in woods and bogs from Massachusetts to southern Ontario and Michigan and southward to Florida, Mississippi, and Arkansas. *Plate 7.*

BEAR-GRASS and RELATED SPECIES (YUCCA)

Yucca is characteristically a genus of the arid southwestern states, but several species are native along the southern borders of our range and may escape from cultivation farther north. The genus is unmistakable. The long, sharp-pointed leaves grow from a very short stem. From the tip of this arises the tall, leafless flowering stem. The numerous flowers are bell-like, white, quite large, in a raceme which is generally branched. The fruit is a pod (capsule).

Many of the species are much alike, and many in the Southwest are known as Spanish-bayonets.

ADAM'S-NEEDLE, Y. FILAMENTOSA, may raise its flowers to a height of 10 feet. The leaves are stiff, rough, and thick; their margins become numerous twisted threads; they are equally wide throughout or wider towards the tip. The petals are roundish with short, sharp tips.

June to September: on sandy beaches and dunes and in old fields on the coastal plain from southern New Jersey to Georgia; escaped from cultivation farther north.

ADAM'S-NEEDLE, Y. SMALLIANA, resembles *Y. filamentosa*, growing even taller. The leaves taper to sharp points. The petals also taper to points.

June to September: in sandy places, old fields, etc., from North Carolina and Tennessee southward to Florida and Louisiana; around abandoned dwelling sites, etc. farther north. *Plate 7.*

SOAPWEED, Y. GLAUCA, has a very short main stem which generally lies on the ground, from which the flowering stem rises not more than 6 feet, scarcely more than the leaves. The leaves are stiff and very sharp, only $\frac{1}{2}$ inch or less wide.

May to July: in prairies and on sand from Iowa to Montana and southward to Missouri and Arizona.

XEROPHYLLUM

Of this genus only one species occurs in the eastern states.

TURKEY-BEARD, X. ASPHODELOIDES, is a plant of unique appearance. Numerous narrow, stiff leaves about 6 inches long grow from the base. From their midst rises the stem (1–5 feet tall), bearing similar leaves and a large and dense raceme, a foot long, of many small white flowers. The fruit is a capsule.

May to July: in sandy pinelands from New Jersey to North Carolina and in mountain woods from Virginia and Tennessee to Georgia. *Plate 8.*

FALSE HELLEBORES (VERATRUM)

The false hellebores have broad leaves which are strongly plaited lengthwise, and a tall much-branched inflorescence of numerous small green or purplish flowers. The ovary is three-lobed, and from it rise three distinct styles. The fruit is a three-lobed pod (capsule). *All parts of the plant are highly poisonous.* Care must be used not to mistake it for skunk-cabbage.

The name *Veratrum* was apparently used for the true hellebore (*Helleborus*) in ancient times. The termination -*atrum* means "black" and may refer to the black flowers of *H. niger*, the Christmas-rose, or to its brownish-black rhizome.

FALSE HELLEBORE or INDIAN POKE, V. VIRIDE (2– 7 feet), has broad leaves on the flowering stem as well as at and near the base, all ovate. The flowers are green and fringed, almost without stalks; those on the lower branches may lack pistils.

May to July: in swamps, wet meadows, and other wet places, from Quebec to Minnesota and southward to Maryland, Tennessee, and Missouri, and in the mountains to North Carolina. *Plate 8.*

FALSE HELLEBORE, V. WOODII (2–5 feet), is more sparingly leafy, the upper leaves much narrower. The flowers are greenish-purple or purplish-black and not fringed.

July to September: in woods and on hillsides from Ohio to Iowa and southwestward to Missouri and Oklahoma.

BUNCHFLOWERS (MELANTHIUM)

Melanthium resembles *Veratrum* in many respects. The distinctions are that the leaves are narrower and not plaited, and the sepals and petals have narrow stalk-like bases to which the stamens adhere. A hand-lens will reveal two glands at the base of the blade of each sepal or petal. The flowers are green, becoming purplish or blackish as they age (the botanical name means "black flower").

BUNCHFLOWER, M. VIRGINICUM (2–5 feet), is the commonest species. The leaves are long and narrow, not more than an inch-and-a-half wide. The sepals and petals are flat.

June and July: in meadows and moist thickets and woods from New York to Minnesota and southward to Florida and Texas. *Plate 8.*

M. HYBRIDUM (up to 4 feet) is restricted to upland regions in the eastern states, and is not common. Its leaves are broader than those of *M. virginicum*, up to 2½ inches wide. The sepals and petals have wavy edges.

June and July; in open woods from Connecticut and New York to West Virginia and Georgia. *Plate 8.*

HELONIAS

There is only one species of *Helonias*.

SWAMP-PINK, H. BULLATA, is a rather rare and very handsome species. The leaves, about a foot long, grow in a tuft, and are evergreen. From among them rises in spring a hollow leafless branch (1–3 feet tall) bearing (besides a few bracts) a dense raceme of many pink flowers with blue-tipped stamens. The fruit is a capsule.

April and May: in swamps and bogs (the botanical name is derived from the Greek for swamp) on the coastal plain from southern New York to southeastern Virginia and in the mountains from Pennsylvania to Georgia. *Plate 8.*

ALETRIS

Other species of *Aletris* occur in the southeastern states and in Asia.

COLIC-ROOT or STAR-GRASS, A. FARINOSA, has a cluster of leaves about 8 inches long and ½ inch wide growing from a short, thick underground stem (rhizome). The flowering stem rises in the midst of these leaves and may reach a height of 3 feet. It bears a number of bracts and a raceme of small, short-stalked, white flowers. The sepals and petals are joined to make a tubular perianth, six-toothed at the rim, nearly ½ inch long. The fruit is a capsule.

May to August: in sandy and peaty soil in open woods and barrens from southern Maine to Minnesota and southward to Florida and Texas. *Plate 8.* The sepals and petals are covered on the outside with small projections which have suggested "mealiness"; whence *farinosa*.

The southern species *A. aurea*, with yellow, bell-shaped flowers, is found in Maryland and southeastern Virginia, and another southerner, *A. lutea*, is occasionally found northward.

AMIANTHIUM

There is but one species of this genus.

FLY-POISON, A. MUSCAETOXICUM, has mostly basal leaves, a foot long or more but usually less than an inch wide. There may be a few small bracts on the flowering stem. The flowers are in a dense raceme carried by the stem 3 feet or more above the ground. The sepals and petals are white, about ⅛ inch long. The ovary is very deeply three-lobed, each lobe tapering upwards into its style. The fruit is a pod or capsule with three beaks.

All parts of the plant are poisonous, but whether it has been used to poison flies is unknown. The English name is a translation of the Latin epithet *muscaetoxicum*, given by Thomas Walter in 1788.

June and July: in open woods from southern New York to Missouri and Oklahoma and southward to Florida, Mississippi, and Arkansas. *Plate 9.*

PLATE 8

Aletris farinosa *Ryker*

Helonias bullata *Gottscho*

Xerophyllum asphodeloides *Clark*

Veratrum viride *Elbert*

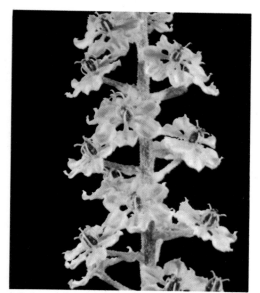

Melanthium hybridum *Rhein*

Melanthium virginicum *Rhein*

Aletris farinosa *Ryker*

THE FALSE ASPHODELS (TOFIELDIA)

These are small plants with a tuft of grasslike leaves and a flowering stem which grow from a rhizome. There is a small leaf or bract midway on the stem. The white flowers are in a dense raceme. The ovary bears three styles. The fruit is a pod (capsule).

The name *Tofieldia* is derived from that of an English botanist of the eighteenth century.

True asphodel is *Asphodelus*, a genus that grows in the lands around the Mediterranean — and, in classical mythology, also in the Elysian fields to which the most deserving mortals were transported after death.

T. GLUTINOSA grows from 8 to 20 inches tall. The name is derived from the glutinous dark glands on the flower-stalks. The flowers are singly attached to the stem.

June to August: in marshes, on shores, and in other wet places from Newfoundland to British Columbia and southward to New York, West Virginia, northern Illinois, and Minnesota, and in the mountains to Georgia; a related form in California. *Plate 9.*

T. RACEMOSA has a stem from 1 to 2 feet tall. It is very minutely downy in the inflorescence. The flowers are clustered mostly in threes and fours.

June to August: in wet soil on the coastal plain from New Jersey southward to Florida and westward to Texas. *Plate 9.*

CAMASS and CROW-POISON (ZIGADENUS)

The species of *Zigadenus* have grasslike leaves and a flowering stem growing from a bulb or rhizome; the flowering stem bears no leaves but a few bracts. The flowers are arranged in a raceme, simple or branched. The ovary and fruit resemble those of *Tofieldia*: three-lobed, each lobe tapering upward to a style. The flower differs from that of *Tofieldia* in having one or a pair of glands near the base of each sepal and petal.

Besides the species noticed below, a number of others are more southern or western; some of these may be found entering our range, but are not here described.

Probably all species of *Zigadenus* are poisonous. WHITE-CAMASS, Z. GLAUCUS, grows up to 3 feet tall. The flowers are cream-white, bronze or purplish on the outside.

July to September: on gravelly shores, in bogs, on cliffs, from Quebec to Minnesota and southward to New York, Ohio, northern Indiana, and Illinois, and in the mountains to North Carolina. *Plate 9.*

Z. LEIMANTHIOIDES is taller, up to 8 feet, but the flowers are smaller (perianth about $\frac{1}{6}$ inch long). The sepals and petals are creamy or yellow, each with a darker spot near the base; the two glands are small.

June to August: in sandy soil and bogs on the coastal plain from southern New York to Georgia and Louisiana and inland in the mountains from Virginia to West Virginia and Alabama. *Plate 9.*

QUAMASH or CAMASS (CAMASSIA)

We have one species of *Camassia*.

WILD-HYACINTH, C. SCILLOIDES, has a tuft of leaves commonly about a foot long but less than half an inch wide. These grow from a bulb, which also sends up the leafless flowering stem (1–2 feet tall or occasionally taller). The flowers are pale blue, the wide-open perianth about an inch across. A rather long bract stands under each flower. The fruit is a pod.

April and May: in prairies and open woodlands from western Pennsylvania to southern Michigan, Wisconsin, and Kansas and southward to Georgia, Alabama, and Texas. *Plate 9.*

There are several western species of *Camassia*, the bulbs of which were valued as food by the Indians. The name *Camassia* is derived from the Indian name, quamash, for these bulbs.

GRAPE-HYACINTHS (MUSCARI)

This is an Old-World genus, some species of which are widely cultivated in the United States. At least two species are occasionally found growing wild. They have bulbs from which arise narrow leaves and a leafless stem bearing a dense raceme of small, bell-like blue flowers. (White flowers also are known in cultivation.) Bluebottle, *M. racemosum*, has leaves almost round in cross section and drooping at the tip. Grape-hyacinth (*M. botryoides*; *Plate 10*) has flat leaves. Both species flower in April and May.

PLATE 9

Camassia scilloides *Mayer*

Zygadenus leimanthoides *Gottscho*

Tofieldia glutinosa *D. Richards*

Johnson

Tofieldia racemosa *Allen*

Amianthium muscaetoxicum

Zigadenus glaucus *D. Richards*

Amianthium muscaetoxicum *Uttal*

STAR-OF-BETHLEHEM, CHINKERICHEE (ORNITHOGALUM)

This is an Old-World genus, brought into gardens in America, and in many places escaped from cultivation. The narrow, grasslike leaves grow in a tuft from a bulb which also produces the leafless flowering stem. Conspicuous bracts accompany the flowers. The perianth is white, in our species striped with green outside. A distinguishing mark is the flat, white stalks of the stamens. The fruit is a capsule.

All parts of the plant are poisonous.

The botanical name is from the Greek words meaning "bird" and "milk"; but why these plants should be called "bird-milk" is unknown, at least to this writer. Handsome species from South Africa, known as chinkerichee, are in cultivation.

STAR-OF-BETHLEHEM, O. UMBELLATUM, grows in waste land, on roadsides, and such places. The stem rises from 4 to 12 inches tall. The flowers, in spite of the botanical name, are not in an umbel but in a raceme; the lower flower-stalks are much longer than the upper, so that a somewhat flat inflorescence is formed. Petals and sepals are less than an inch long.

April to June: on roadsides, waste land, etc., from Newfoundland to Ontario and Nebraska and southward to North Carolina, Mississippi, Missouri, and Kansas. *Plate 10.*

O. NUTANS is larger (1–2 feet tall). The flowers are in a more cylindric cluster, the lower flower-stalks not much longer than the upper. The sepals and petals are an inch or more in length.

April and May: occasionally escaped from cultivation in meadows, etc., from New York to Maryland; Missouri. *Plate 179.*

DAY-LILIES (HEMEROCALLIS)

The day-lilies resemble true lilies and are often mistaken for them. Underground is a cluster of root-tubers, from which leaves and stem arise. The leaves grow only at the base of the flowering-stem; they are in two ranks. The stem forks repeatedly, a flower appearing at each fork and opening only for a day or part of a day (*Hemerocallis* is from two Greek words meaning "beautiful" and "day").

Both the "species" named below are really hybrids between plants native in Europe and Asia, escaped from cultivation. They do not form fertile fruits, and propagate by their tubers.

ORANGE DAY-LILY, H. FULVA, sends its stem up from 2 to 6 feet. The orange color of the perianth is deeper towards the center; each of the three petals has a wavy margin. The open flowers are about 5 inches across. *Plate 10.*

May to July: common on roadsides and borders of fields in most parts of our range but more frequent eastward.

LEMON DAY-LILY, H. FLAVA, is not so tall. The flowers are yellow, about 4 inches across, and fragrant.

May and June: along roadsides, etc., in scattered places from New England to Michigan and southward to Pennsylvania. *Plate 10.*

CARRION-FLOWER and CATBRIERS (SMILAX)

The genus *Smilax* is composed mainly of woody vines, mostly thorny, with inconspicuous flowers in umbels. These vines, some of which are evergreen, are troublesome weeds in woods. Since they scarcely answer to our definition of wild flowers, they are not here described or illustrated. There are, however, several herbaceous species which may be mentioned here.

The flowers of all the species have either stamens or pistil, not both; and the two kinds are on different plants. The sepals and petals are only about $\frac{1}{4}$ inch long or less. The fruit is a black, blue, or red berry. The leaves are broad, veiny, generally with a pair of tendrils from the base of the stalk.

This is not the "smilax" of florists, who have applied the name to an ornamental asparagus.

CARRION-FLOWER, S. HERBACEA, climbs or trails over other plants, often forming a tangled mass. It has no thorns. The leaves are broad, ovate, tapering to a sharp or blunt tip, with stalks from 1 to 4 inches long. The ill-smelling flowers and later the dark blue or black berries are in umbels on erect stems from the axils.

April to June: in woods, thickets, and meadows, in the broad sense of the species from Quebec to Minnesota and Wyoming and southward to Georgia, Alabama, Oklahoma, and Colorado. *Plate 10.*

S. LASIONEURA differs from *S. herbacea* chiefly in having a minute down on the pale under surface of the leaves, and in having black berries.

May and June: in woods and thickets from On-

PLATE 10

Hemerocallis fulva *Johnson*

Phelps

Hemerocallis flava *Roche*

Muscari botryoides

Smilax herbacea *Rhein*

Stenanthium gramineum *Justice*

Hypoxis hirsuta *Johnson*

Ornithogalum umbellatum *Rickett*

tario to Saskatchewan and Montana and southward to Georgia, Oklahoma, and Colorado. *Plate 179.*

S. PSEUDO-CHINA, also called carrion-flower, differs from *S. herbacea* in the shape of the leaves, the margins of which tend to curve inward above the broad base; the tip is generally blunt with a small sharp projection. The flowering stems are often as long as or longer than the leaves. The sepals and petals are minute. The berries are blue or black.

May to July: in borders of woods, meadows, etc., mostly in damp soil on the coastal plain from southern New York to Georgia.

S. PULVERULENTA differs from *S. herbacea* in its leaves: they are slightly downy on the veins and not so pale underneath. Also the berries are black rather than blue and lack the whitish "bloom."

April and May: in open woods from Rhode Island to Minnesota and southward to Georgia, Tennessee, and Missouri.

S. ECIRRHATA grows up to 3 feet tall without clinging to a support, for it has few or no tendrils; it does lean on other plants. On the lower part of the stem there are only bracts, from the axils of which, as well as from the upper leaves, arise flower-stalks. The leaves have long stalks.

May and June: in woods from southern Ontario to South Dakota and southward to South Carolina, Alabama, and Missouri. *Plate 179.*

THE DAFFODIL FAMILY (AMARYLLIDACEAE)

The daffodil (or amaryllis) family contains not only the lovely host of daffodils, jonquils, narcissus (all in the genus *Narcissus*), but also the snowdrops and snowflakes of our gardens and the amaryllis, clivia, and other exotics of northern greenhouses, and the maguey of southwestern arid lands and Mexican agriculture. In the southern states there are some striking and beautiful wild members of the family, but in the northeastern region proper (excluding its southern margin) we can include only a couple of rather inconspicuous species.

The daffodil family is close to the lily family, differing chiefly in having an inferior ovary. (Indeed, various botanists have separated the two families in quite different ways.) There are six stamens and, in our native species, a radially symmetric perianth of six parts.

STAR-GRASS (HYPOXIS)

The genus contains only one truly northeastern species; several more occur in the south.

YELLOW STAR-GRASS, H. HIRSUTA, has a tuft of narrow, grasslike leaves usually about a foot tall, growing from a corm underground. In the midst of these rises a stem bearing a cluster (a false umbel) of small yellow flowers, not rising above the leaves. The parts of the perianth are all alike, yellow, pointed, spreading to form a six-pointed star. Both leaves and stem bear long, scattered hairs (they are "hirsute"), and similar hairs decorate the outer surfaces of the perianth. The fruit is a small pod that fails to open.

April to September: in grass and open woodland from Maine to Manitoba and southward to Florida and Texas. *Plate 10.*

CENTURY-PLANTS, FALSE ALOES, ETC. (AGAVE)

This large genus is composed of several hundred species native to the warmer and drier parts of America; the century-plant, which dies after producing its immense flowering stem (not necessarily after 100 years!), is well known. In Mexico many species, known as maguey, are grown for the production of the alcoholic beverage pulque. In general they have large, succulent leaves, often whitish with a bloom, and in some species formidably armed with marginal spines. We have but one species in the northeastern states.

FALSE ALOE, A. VIRGINICA (to 6 feet), has leaves in a tuft at the base of the stem; they are thick, pointed, rough on the edges, about a foot long. The flowers are in a loose spike; they are small greenish-yellow tubes with six teeth, only about an inch long. The fruit is a round pod.

June to August: on dry slopes and in woods from Virginia to Missouri and southward to Florida and Texas. *Plate 11.*

The lovely spider-lily, *Hymenocallis occidentalis*, of the South extends northward to southeastern Missouri, southern Indiana, and southern Illinois. And the equally beautiful Atamasco lily, *Zephyranthes atamasco*, may be found as far north as Virginia.

THE IRIS FAMILY (IRIDACEAE)

Everyone knows the iris of our springtime gardens, the fleur-de-lis of French royalty. But the family includes also plants of entirely different aspect: crocus, gladiolus, freesia, and many others familiar in cultivation. All these, apparently so diverse, share certain well-marked botanical features: especially the possession of six perianth-parts, three stamens, and an inferior ovary – the last two characteristics separating the family from the lilies. The leaves also of most species are distinctive. They are more or less grasslike, but folded lengthwise along their midrib and each enfolding the next younger leaf which faces toward it. This curious arrangement was called "equitant" by Linnaeus: each leaf seems to bestride the next as if riding horseback (especially when the whole tuft of leaves is cut across).

We have only three genera.

THE IRISES (IRIS)

Many wild irises grace our meadows, marshes, and streamsides, and some grow in woods and barrens. As a genus they are easily recognizable, resembling the cultivated plants; but some of the species are hard to distinguish. The flower has three sepals colored more or less like the three petals, but generally differing from them in shape, and slightly in color-patterns. In most species the sepals curve downward, the petals upward; but in some all six spread on the same level. Below they are joined, with the style and stalks of the stamens, into a slim tube. The sepals are in most species furnished with a "crest" or "beard" – a fringed or furry ridge, often of a conspicuous color. The flowers grow from a mostly papery envelope (spathe) of two or more small bracts.

Perhaps the most unusual feature of the flower is furnished by the style, which branches into three flat parts colored like petals. A stamen is concealed beneath each of these branches.

Iris in classical mythology was a goddess whose visible sign was the rainbow; the plants were so called for their rainbow hues. Several species are called flags – not to be confused with the sweet-flag. The royal emblem called fleur-de-lis represents an iris flower; but its derivation seems dubious. An inexplicably altered form of the name iris turns up as orris; orris root is the rhizome of one or several European species. It has the odor of violets and is used industrially for that property.

To assist identification, we may group our wild-growing species by the height of their stems.

I. *Irises with Stems more than 8 inches tall.*

In this group, the over-all color of the flower further separates the species.

A. Species with Yellow Flowers.

YELLOW FLAG, I. PSEUDACORUS (about 3 feet), has flowers 3 inches or more across. The sepals are marked with dark lines and flecks. The pod is six-sided.

April to August: in marshes and meadows, on stream-banks, and in wet open places in general, from Newfoundland to Minnesota and southward to Georgia. *Plate 11*. This is an immigrant from Europe. The rhizome has been used for dyeing: it yields a black ink.

B. Species with Tawny or Copper-colored Flowers.

COPPER IRIS, I. FULVA (to 5 feet), is a southern species found along our southwestern borders. The perianth spreads almost flat; it is colored tawny or coppery with green or blue lines. The pod is six-sided.

April to June: in wet, muddy places, either in the open or in woods, from southern Illinois and southern Missouri to Georgia and Louisiana.

C. Species with Blue, Lilac, Purple, or White Flowers.

The first three of the species described in this group have bluntly three-angled pods; the fourth, sharply three-angled pods; the last, six-sided pods.

BLUE FLAG or WILD IRIS, I. VERSICOLOR (about 3 feet), has a perianth about 3 inches across, variously colored, the sepals generally with dark blue lines and lighter towards the base. This is a common and beautiful flower of wet meadows and marshes. Unfortunately, the rhizome is extremely poisonous; confusion of this plant with the harmless sweet-flag, in the arum family, has sometimes had disastrous results.

May to August: in marshes, meadows and open wet places in general, from Labrador to Manitoba and southward to Pennsylvania and Wisconsin. *Plate 11*.

SOUTHERN BLUE FLAG, I. VIRGINICA (about 2 feet), differs from *I. versicolor* chiefly in its smaller size and the habit of both leaves and stem to lie down on the ground or water (the pod may actually mature under water). The sepals have a basal yellow blotch; they are slightly longer than the petals.

May: in marshes, shallow water, etc., on the coastal plain from Virginia to Florida and thence westward to Texas.

A more northern variety, sometimes distinguished as a separate species with the name *I. shrevei*, differs in being stiffer, in having a more branched flowering stem, and in forming a longer pod (4 inches as against 3 inches). It flowers from May to July from Quebec to Minnesota and southward to North Carolina, Alabama, Arkansas, and Kansas. *Plate 11*.

BEACH-HEAD FLAG, I. HOOKERI (to 2 feet), grows in dense clumps, with many fans of leaves up to 16 inches tall and about ½ inch wide. The sepals are violet with a white blotch at the base. The petals are small, rolled up into tubes.

This is by some considered only a variety of the Siberian *I. setosa*.

June to August: on rocky slopes, beaches, and banks, from Newfoundland and Labrador to Quebec and Maine.

SLENDER BLUE FLAG, I. PRISMATICA (3 feet), forms slender runners at the surface of the ground. From the tip of a last year's runner, rises, in the spring, leaves which grow to about 2 feet tall and only about ¼ inch wide, and a flowering stem which rises above them. The flowers are violet, with dark veins in the sepals. The capsule (and the stem beneath the flower that contains the ovary) is sharply 3-angled – almost winged on the angles.

May to July: in marshes, swamps, meadows, etc., near the coast, from Nova Scotia to Georgia. A variety with somewhat broader and grooved leaves is found in the southern Appalachian mountains. *Plate 11*.

LAURANCE IRIS, I. BREVICAULIS (16 inches), has a somewhat zigzag stem which may not stand erect. The leaves rise above the stem to a height of 2 feet or more; they are an inch or more wide. The flowers are lavender, blue, or purple, the sepals with greenish-white marks at the base and a yellowish

crest. The pod is six-sided.

May and June: in swamps, woods, and bottomlands from Ohio to Kansas and southward to Alabama and Texas. *Plate 11*.

II. *Irises with Stems less than 8 inches tall.*

These are the dwarf irises. The three species named below are much alike. The two first have crested sepals. Noticing where these grow aids materially in identifying a specimen. The sepals of the third lack crests.

CRESTED IRIS, I. CRISTATA (4 inches), has a rhizome almost at the surface and slender runners. The leaves grow finally to be more than a foot long and an inch broad. The short flowering stem is sheathed by overlapping leaves. The perianth is flat, colored lilac or purple except for the conspicuous crest on the sepals; this is whitish with a fringed purple outline. The capsule is sharply three-angled.

April and May: in rich woods and on bluffs from Maryland to Missouri and southward to Georgia, Mississippi, and Arkansas. *Plate 11*.

I. LACUSTRIS is very similar to *I. cristata*. The leaves are narrower (about ½ inch broad). The flower is smaller (2 inches across as compared with 3 inches).

May to July: on sandy and gravelly beaches, in bogs, etc., around Lakes Huron, Michigan, and Superior. *Plate 12*.

I. VERNA (6 inches) has slender rhizomes on the surface, bearing leaves which eventually reach more than a foot in height, but less than ½ inch wide. The perianth is 2 inches wide, violet, the sepals with an orange or yellow lengthwise band instead of a raised crest. The capsule is bluntly three-angled.

March to May: in sandy and peaty places and pine barrens from Maryland to Virginia and southward and southwestward to Florida and Mississippi. *Plate 11*. A distinct variety, with shorter rhizomes and therefore denser clumps, grows in the mountains of Pennsylvania and West Virginia and southward to Florida and Alabama.

BLUE-EYED-GRASS (SISYRINCHIUM)

The delicate small flowers of *Sisyrinchium* do not at first sight suggest relationship with the flamboyant iris; their six spreading petals and sepals recall rather the lily family. But when one notices the three stamens (joined to form, with the style, a central column), the swelling in the flower-stalk just below the perianth, which contains the inferior ovary, and the folded leaves, the family to which these plants belong is clear.

They are not, of course, grasses; and the "blue-eyed" is not always accurate, for forms are known with white and yellow flowers, besides blue, violet, and purple; some have a yellow center. The petals and sepals are generally tipped with a small point. The fruit is a small round pod. The stems of most species are flat and sharp-edged, resembling the leaves.

The species are separated by rather small details

PLATE 11

Iris prismatica   *Miller*

Iris cristata   *Gray*

Iris brevicaulis   *Johnson*

Iris virginica   *Johnson*

Iris versicolor   *Gottscho*

Agave virginica   *D. Richards*

Iris verna   *Uttal*

Iris pseudacorus   *Rickett*

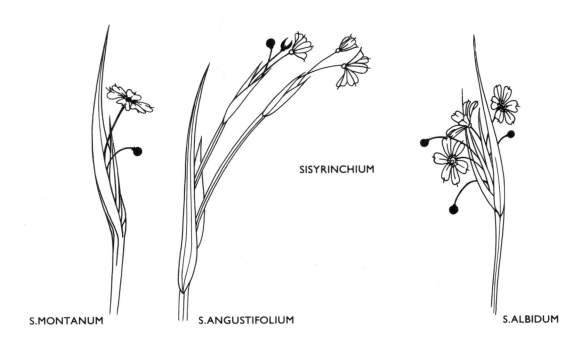

S.MONTANUM   S.ANGUSTIFOLIUM   S.ALBIDUM

SISYRINCHIUM

of structure. The flowers may be less helpful than the small fruits, and the naturalist who finds these small plants in flower should look carefully to see if fruits also are present.

This is one genus for which the naturalist will not find the technical manuals of much help, for the same species bears different names in different books and the same name is applied to different species. Even the technical terms used to describe the plants are given different meanings by different authors.

We may separate the species into two groups according as their stems are branched or not; but even those that are characterized by branched stems have also many that are unbranched, so that it is necessary to have a good-sized clump of stems for identification.

I.   *Plants with All Stems Unbranched.*

(There may be a *leaf* halfway up the stem.)

A. In the commoner species a single cluster of flowers terminates each stem. The cluster emerges from between folded scales or bracts: the outer bract seems to continue the stem, tapering to a narrow point. Within the fold of the outer bract is a smaller one, folded also, tapering inward; and within this another, often papery scale, not easily seen. (Compare B.)

S. MONTANUM (to 2 feet) has leaves and stems about $\frac{1}{3}$ inch wide, about equal in height. The outer bract of each flower-cluster tapers sharply to a long narrow spine. At the base, where it envelops the flowers, the two edges are joined for $\frac{1}{4}$ inch or less. The

flowers are blue-violet, about an inch across on rather short stalks. The pods measure up to $\frac{1}{4}$ inch in diameter; in the western and northern parts of the range (generally outside of our region) they are pale; in the eastern states, however, they are somewhat smaller and dark-colored.

May to July: in meadows and on shores, from Newfoundland to British Columbia and southward to Pennsylvania, Illinois, and Iowa, and in the mountains to North Carolina, Colorado, etc. *Plate 12.*

This is perhaps our commonest and most widespread species of *Sisyrinchium*. Its name signifies that it grows in mountains, and so it does; but it also grows in the plains and valleys.

S. MUCRONATUM (to 16 inches) has almost thread-like stems, with very narrow margins. The leaves are similar, only about $\frac{1}{12}$ inch wide, and shorter than the stems. The individual flowers are on longish stalks; they are violet, less than an inch across. The pods are pale in color, sometimes yellowish, about $\frac{1}{16}$ inch in diameter.

May and June: in meadows and open woods from Maine to Minnesota and southward to North Carolina, Michigan, and Wisconsin.

S. CAMPESTRE (20 inches) has a flat stem and leaves about $\frac{1}{8}$ inch wide, the leaves sometimes equal to the stems in height but often shorter. The flowers are light blue or white, less than an inch across. The pods are light-colored, only about $\frac{1}{6}$ inch in diameter.

April to June: in prairies, meadows, and open woods from Wisconsin to Manitoba and southward to

PLATE 12

Sisyrinchium angustifolium *Uttal*

Sisyrinchium campestre *Johnson*

Iris lacustris *Rhein*

Sisyrinchium albidum *D. Richards*

Belamcanda chinensis *Allen*

Sisyrinchium montanum *Smith*

Sisyrinchium angustifolium *Rickett*

Belamcanda chinensis *Roche*

Illinois, Louisiana, and Texas. This is perhaps the commonest species in the prairie regions of the Midwest. *Plate 12*.

> B. In two of our species there are mostly *two* clusters of flowers at the tip of each stem, close together, each with its pair of enveloping scales but both partly enfolded by the outermost, long-pointed bract. (See the accompanying drawings, page 50.)

S. ALBIDUM (to 16 inches) has flat stems and leaves up to $\frac{1}{4}$ inch wide; the stems are much longer than the leaves. The flowers are white or pale violet, about $\frac{2}{3}$ inch across. The pods are pale, about $\frac{1}{6}$ inch across.

May and June: in open places in dry soil from New York to North Dakota and southward to Georgia, Louisiana, and Oklahoma; mainly a southern species, first discovered in Kentucky by the brilliant but eccentric botanist Constantine Rafinesque. *Plate 12*.

The southern *S. capillare*, with threadlike leaves and stems and small flowers, is found in southeastern Virginia.

II. *Species with Some, at least, of the Stems Branched.*

The lower half of the stem seems to be prolonged upward into a leaf, and at the junction two or more slender branches bear the flowers. The flowers are in clusters enveloped by scales as in group I A, but the outer bracts do not much exceed the inner in length.

S. ANGUSTIFOLIUM (to 20 inches) has flat stems and leaves about $\frac{1}{4}$ inch wide or narrower, about equal in height. The flowers are pale blue or violet, about an inch across, on longish individual stalks. The pods, about $\frac{1}{4}$ inch in diameter, become dark when dry.

May to July: in meadows, damp woods, and thickets from Newfoundland to Minnesota and southward to Florida and Texas. A common and widespread species. It may be confused with *S. montanum*, but its long flower-stalks should distinguish it. *Plate 12*.

S. ATLANTICUM (to 2 feet) has narrow leaves and stems, less than $\frac{1}{4}$ inch wide. The stems are much longer than the leaves. The flowers are violet, about an inch across. The capsules are about $\frac{1}{6}$ inch in diameter, dark-colored.

May to July: in meadows, marshes, and low woods from Nova Scotia to Michigan and southward to Florida, Ohio, Mississippi, and Missouri.

S. ARENICOLA grows only in sandy soil on the coastal plain from Nova Scotia and Massachusetts to Florida and Alabama. It differs from *S. angustifolium* chiefly in forming tufts largely composed of the old bristle-like leaves. The pods do not exceed $\frac{1}{5}$ inch in diameter.

BELAMCANDA

Of this Asiatic genus we have only one species, not native to America but now quite at home in many places.

BLACKBERRY-LILY, B. CHINENSIS, grows to about 3 feet in height, with narrow leaves like those of an iris. Its flowers, however, with six equal petals and sepals, do not suggest an iris. The flower is salmon-orange with crimson spots, 2 inches across or less; each lasts only for a day, being then succeeded by another from the same cluster enclosed by the bracts (spathe). The English name is derived from the fruit. This is a pod which splits open to reveal a cluster of black, shining seeds in a mass that resembles a blackberry. (The segments of a blackberry, however, are not seeds but small individual fruits.)

June and July: in open woods, roadsides and dry places in general, from Connecticut to Nebraska and southward to Georgia, Missouri, and Kansas; introduced from Asia. *Plate 12*.

THE WATER-PLANTAIN FAMILY (ALISMATACEAE)

The water-plantains and their relatives the arrowheads grow in water, in swamps, or on muddy banks, or occasionally in wet sand. They are characterized by long-stalked leaves in clumps, with a flowering stem rising among them. The flowers have three green sepals and three white or pink-tinged petals, six or more stamens, and several or many pistils; the stamens and pistils may be in separate flowers.

We have three genera.

WATER-PLANTAINS (ALISMA)

One or possibly two species are found in the northeastern states.

A. TRIVIALE has elliptic blades, sometimes indented
at the base, on stalks a foot or more long. The flowers grow on a stem which may be shorter than the leaves or may rise above them; it has many branches in circles, these branches have further branches in circles, and at the end of each ultimate branchlet is a small flower, not more than ½ inch across and often less. The flower has three green sepals and three white (or pink) petals, six or more stamens, and many pistils.

June to October: in shallow or deep water, swamps, and wet mud from Nova Scotia and Quebec to British Columbia and southward to Florida, Texas, California, and Mexico. *Plate 13.*

Plants growing in deep water may not thrust all their leaves above the surface. The submerged leaves are ribbonlike, and even those that reach the air have narrower blades than the usual ones. Such plants are by some botanists considered a distinct species, *A. gramimeum.* Other plants, with smaller flowers, form a variety which also is often considered a separate species, *A. subcordatum (Plate 13).* Indeed, *A. triviale* itself was long treated as a variety of the Old World, *A. plantago-aquatica,* and some modern authorities still regard it as such.

The solid bulblike base of the plant was dried and eaten by Indians.

THE ARROWHEADS (SAGITTARIA)

The genus takes its name from the shape of the leaves of most species; but some species do not have such leaves, and for recognition it is best to get acquainted with the flowers. These have three green sepals, three white petals, mostly many stamens and pistils; in most species the upper flowers on each flowering stem have stamens with or without pistils, the lower flowers have pistils only. The pistils become flat, thin-margined achenes, in a tight round mass.

Beneath the surface of the mud or sand in which they are rooted the plants form long creeping stems, rhizomes, the ends of which develop into starchy tubers. These were a staple food of American Indians, under such names as wapato and katnis, and became familiar to the white settlers who called them duck-potatoes or swan-potatoes. Modern writers pronounce them palatable when properly cooked. The Indians used to raid muskrat houses, where the animals accumulated stores of these tubers!

There are a number of species; the differences between some are quite small and technical, involving the size and shape of the small fruits: not helpful when the plant has flowers only! The leaves of some common species are so variable in size and shape that they are worthless for identification. The range of some species is very limited, and this may help.

Besides the species listed below, several others intrude into our southern and western boundaries; and one, *S. planipes,* has been reported only in Dismal Swamp, Virginia.

To assist in identification, the species of our range are first grouped by the *general* shape of their leaves.

I. *Species regularly with arrowhead-shaped leaves. Some species of group II may have leaves of this shape, especially S. rigida; and some leaves of plants of this group may be lanceolate or ribbonlike.*

The four species here listed may be distinguished fairly well by counting the stamens and measuring the petals.

S. LATIFOLIA is our commonest species. The leaves
vary enormously, as is shown in the drawings, but are regularly provided with the two backward pointing lobes, the "barbs" of the arrowhead. The petals are from ⅖ to ⅘ inch long. The stamens number from twenty-five to forty.

July to September: in water, on mud or wet sand, in swamps, etc. from Nova Scotia to British Columbia and southward to Florida and Mexico. *Plate 13.*

S. ENGELMANNIANA has somewhat smaller leaf-
blades than *S. latifolia* (up to 10 inches long). The petals are from ⅓ to ½ inch long. There are from fifteen to twenty-five stamens.

July to October: in wet sand, bogs, shallow water, etc. from Massachusetts to Florida and Alabama. *Plate 13.*

S. CALYCINA exists in several forms. In the Atlantic
states it is likely to have leaf-stalks without blades or with small elliptic blades. In the central states and to the west and south the leaves have arrow-shaped blades which may be very large, the "barbs" of the arrowhead being rather long in proportion to the central part. In all forms the stem and leaf-stalks are rather thick and spongy. The petals measure from ⅓ to ⅗ inch. The stamens number from nine to fifteen.

June to October: in sloughs, ponds, tidal water and mud, etc. from Ohio to Minnesota and South Dakota and southward to North Carolina, Alabama, Louisiana, Texas, and California; also in Mexico.

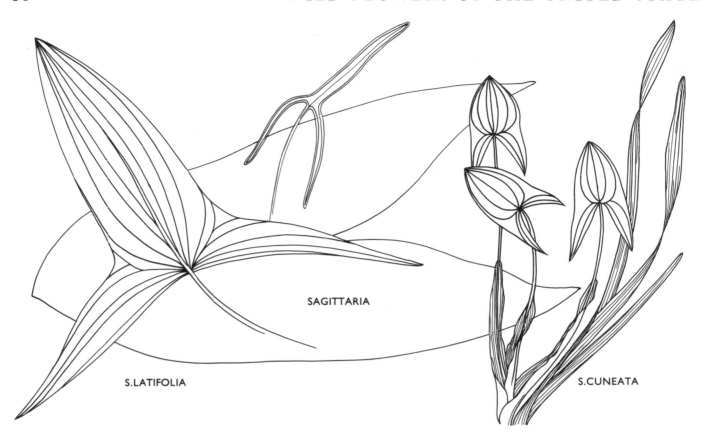

SAGITTARIA

S.LATIFOLIA

S.CUNEATA

S. CUNEATA is extremely variable in leaf shape. When
    it is growing in mud or shallow water the leaves
are generally arrowhead-shaped, with blades only 8
inches long or less. In deeper water the leaves may be
lanceolate or ribbonlike. The petals are about $\frac{2}{5}$ inch
long. There are from ten to eighteen stamens.

    June to September: on muddy shores, in shal-
low water, and other wet places throughout Canada
and southward to New Jersey, Indiana, Kansas, New
Mexico, and California.

II. *Species whose leaf blades are generally without
    backward-pointing lobes at the base; they may be
    lanceolate or ovate; or blades may be lacking, the
    leaves ribbonlike or stalk-like. The narrow shapes
    are more usual in submerged plants, but are normal
    for some species even on land.*

    The five species listed below are hard to distin-
guish. They have relatively few stamens as compared
with most plants in group I. The size of the petals,
with one or two other characteristics, is about the best
means of identification.

S. GRAMINEA is named for the grasslike leaves often
    present (*gramen* is Latin for "grass"). The blades,
however, vary from very narrow to ovate; or they may
be lacking, only the stalks being present. The petals
are very small, only about $\frac{1}{5}$ inch long.
    May to September: in wet sand, shallow water,

and muddy places from Newfoundland and Labrador
to Saskatchewan and southward to Florida and Texas.
Plate 13.

S. RIGIDA may have arrowhead blades, but with only
    small barbs; the more typical form is lanceolate
or elliptic; in deep water the blades may be lacking.
The flowering stem may be variously bent or even
prostrate. The petals are comparatively large, from $\frac{1}{2}$
to 1 inch long, or even longer.
    July to October: on mud or in water from Que-
bec to Minnesota and southward to Virginia, Tennessee, Missouri, and Nebraska. *Plate 13.*

S. FALCATA regularly has lanceolate leaf-blades. The
    petals measure from $\frac{1}{3}$ to $\frac{3}{5}$ inch. There may be
as many as thirty stamens – a large number for this
group of species.
    July to October: in swamps and on shores, along
the coast from Delaware to Florida and thence westward to Texas; also in Mexico and Central America.

S. SPATULATA is generally distinguished by having
    only one circle of flowers on the stem; but there
may sometimes be more than one. The leaves may
have small, narrow blades, but are more generally
only thick, spongy stalks. The petals are about $\frac{1}{5}$ inch
long.
    July to October: on tidal mud and in tidal mar-
shes from Quebec to Virginia.

PLATE 13

Sagittaria rigida *Johnson*

Sagittaria latifolia *Johnson*

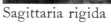

Sagittaria graminea *Rickett*

Alisma triviale *Rickett*

Sagittaria engelmanniana *Elbert*

Alisma subcordatum *Elbert*

S. SUBULATA has narrow, ribbonlike leaves, or sometimes leaves with elliptic or ovate blades which
float on the surface of the water. The petals are from
$\frac{1}{5}$ to $\frac{2}{5}$ inch long. The stamens are fewer than twelve —
the least numerous of those of any of these species.

July to September: on tidal mud, in brackish
marshes, in ponds, etc. mostly along the coast from

Massachusetts to Florida and westward to Alabama.
S. TERES has only, for leaves, round stalks with no
blades, those in deep water thick and spongy.
The petals are small, $\frac{1}{5}$ inch long or less. There are
only about twelve stamens.

July to September: on sandy shores, in swamps,
etc. along the coast from Massachusetts to Maryland.

BUR-HEADS (ECHINODORUS)

The bur-heads resemble *Sagittaria* in many ways,
and may be confused with those species of *Sagittaria*
that have lanceolate or ovate leaf-blades; the bur-
heads have no arrowheads. The chief differences are
that the flowers all have both stamens and pistils, and
that the fruits — achenes — have no thin flanges like
those of *Sagittaria*, but are pointed and form a somewhat prickly round mass or "bur."

E. BERTEROI is easily recognized by its large leaves
with mostly ovate blades often indented at the
base. The flowering stem is often branched.

June to October: in muddy bottomlands, ditches, etc. from Ohio to Nebraska; southward to Texas
and Mexico and California.

E. TENELLUS grows only to a height of 4 inches. The
leaves are lanceolate, mostly not more than 2
inches long. The petals are tiny, about $\frac{1}{16}$ inch long.

July to October: on sandy shores and in shallow
water, sparingly in Massachusetts, Illinois, and Missouri, and southward to Florida and Mexico; also in
the West Indies and South America.

E. CORDIFOLIUS is unique in having a creeping stem,
from which at intervals arise clusters of flowers
on slender stalks. The leaves are much like those of
E. berteroi.

July to October: in swamps, ponds, slow streams,
etc. from southeastern Virginia to Kansas and southward to Florida and Mexico.

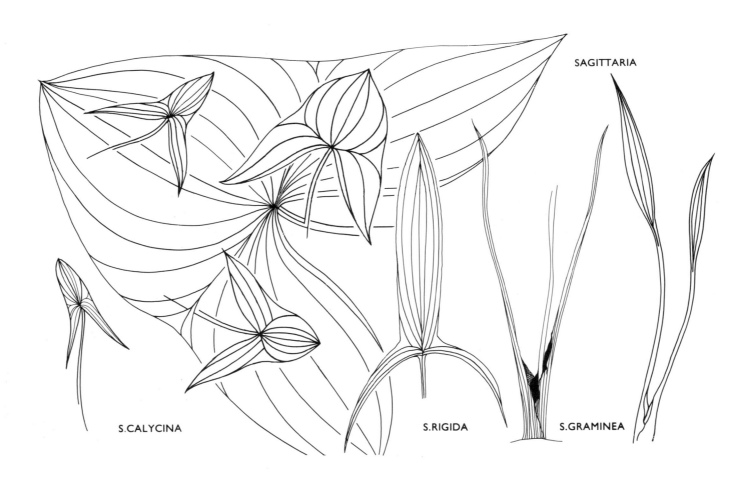

SAGITTARIA

S. CALYCINA   S. RIGIDA   S. GRAMINEA

THE EEL-GRASS FAMILY (HYDROCHARITACEAE)

Perhaps few persons will become acquainted with the eel-grass family; most species grow submerged in water, and some flower only rarely. Some are well-known in aquaria.

WATERWEED (ELODEA)

E. CANADENSIS is familiar in aquaria, both as decoration and as food for fish. The long trailing stems are covered with small, bright green leaves. Flowers are rarely seen. Pistils and stamens are in separate flowers on separate plants. The flowers are raised to the surface of the water on slender stalks. There are three sepals and three petals. The staminate flowers have from three to nine stamens.

July to September: in quiet waters practically throughout the United States. *Plate 179*. To many persons who have studied "general botany" in college, *Elodea* will recall examination of living cells in the microscope. In another species, *E. nuttallii*, the staminate flowers break away and float on the surface.

EEL-GRASS (VALLISNERIA)

V. AMERICANA has very long, grasslike, submerged leaves (it is also known as tapegrass) in a cluster from the roots. The pistillate flowers are raised to the surface on a slender leafless stem which may reach a length of 10 feet or more. The staminate flowers break loose and rise to the surface, gathering in numbers (by surface tension) round each pistillate flower. After fertilization, the stalks of the pistillate flowers coil spirally, drawing the pistil down under the surface where it becomes the fruit.

July to October: in water from Nova Scotia to North Dakota and southward to Florida and Texas.

One other family, the pondweed family (*Naiadaceae*), is composed entirely of aquatic plants. The numerous species of pondweeds (*Potamogeton*) send up their small green flowers in spikes that project above the surface. The leaves may be submerged or floating, and are of many shapes. These and the related ditch-grasses, grass-wrack, and naiads must be sought in the technical books; they will only rarely be collected as wild flowers.

A southern species, *Limnobium spongia*, very rarely reaches southern New York along the coast. It has stalked leaves with small ovate blades 2 or 3 inches long and nearly as broad. The plants commonly float in stagnant water.

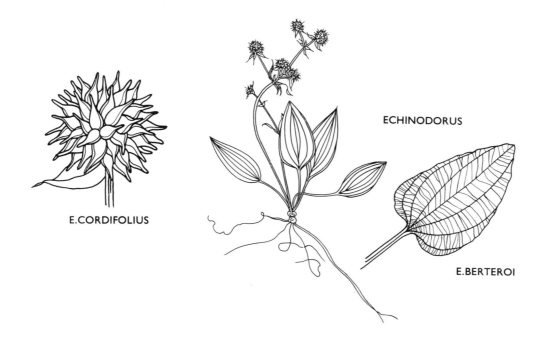

E.CORDIFOLIUS

ECHINODORUS

E.BERTEROI

GRASSES and SEDGES (GRAMINEAE and CYPERACEAE)

Grasses and sedges are deliberately omitted from this book, as being generally unattractive as flowers and too difficult for the amateur. However, it must be pointed out that, though their flowers are minute, many of them are graceful plants. Among the grasses we may notice the common reed (*Phragmites communis*) growing in swamps and other wet places and raising its feathery panicles to a height of 10 feet and more; and Canary reed grass (*Phalaris arundinacea*), also of wet places, and growing to 5 feet tall. The sedges, which are largely moisture-loving plants, include various graceful plants of the genus *Scirpus*, generally called bulrushes. The distinction between the families is not difficult. The lower part of a grass leaf is a sheath around the stem; this sheath is open down one side. The lower part of a sedge leaf is a closed sheath around the stem. The stem of many (not all) sedges is triangular and generally solid. The stem of most grasses is round and hollow. It is scarcely necessary to add that the grasses are of vast economic importance; one need only mention wheat, oats, barley, rice, and the bamboos, besides the pasture grasses. Others are bad weeds: crab grass, quack grass. Among the sedges the species of *Cyperus* from which the Egyptians made papyrus was once important. Some are troublesome weeds.

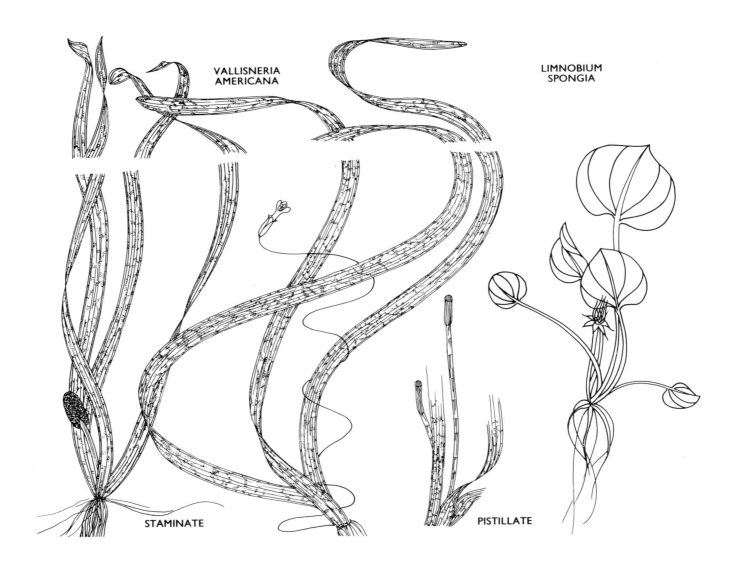

VALLISNERIA
AMERICANA

LIMNOBIUM
SPONGIA

STAMINATE

PISTILLATE

GROUP II

Sepals three, petals three; petals mostly separate, bilaterally symmetric. Stamens six, or else united with the style and stigma to form a "column" in the center. Leaves without teeth; veins running from base to tip without visible branches.

Exceptions; *Tradescantia* and *Heteranthera* have radically symmetric petals. Some orchids have apparently only two sepals.

I. *Plants with three or six stamens in a flower.*

   A. Plants growing on land: dayflower family.

   B. Plants growing in water: pickerel-weed family.

II. *Plants with stamens joined to the style forming a column in the center of the flower:* orchid family.

THE DAYFLOWER FAMILY (COMMELINACEAE)

The dayflowers and their relatives compose a chiefly tropical family, of both Old and New Worlds. They are characterized by a flower with three mostly green sepals and three petals; the symmetry may be radial or bilateral. There are six stamens, of which only three may bear pollen.

The flowers rise in clusters from an enveloping bract or pair of bracts. The leaves are rather thick, succulent. Only two genera extend into most of the northeastern states; a third, *Aneilema*, is found in the southeastern tip of Virginia. Its flowers are borne singly in the axils of leaves.

THE DAYFLOWERS (COMMELINA)

The dayflowers are known by their pretty blue flowers which stay open only for one morning. Two petals, usually bright blue, stand erect; the third, below, is smaller and in some species blue, in others white. There are three stamens with pollen, and three shorter, sterile stamens tipped with curious cross-shaped heads. The flowers bloom one at a time in each cluster; the cluster is enveloped by a special leaf (bract) which is folded lengthwise.

The genus was named by Linnaeus, with his usual humor, for the brothers Commelijn, two of whom (the two upper petals) were botanists of some repute, while the third (the insignificant lower petal) did nothing for the science.

C. COMMUNIS is an immigrant from Asia which has become a common and troublesome weed. Its stem creeps on the ground, rooting at the points where leaves are attached; fragments cut off by the gardener's hoe readily root again. The tip of the stem curves up and forms the cluster of flowers in its folded bract. The two upper petals are blue, narrowed at the base into stalks; the lower petal is much smaller and white.

June to October: in gardens, on roadsides, and in waste ground from Massachusetts to Wisconsin and Nebraska and southward to North Carolina, Alabama, Arkansas, and Kansas. *Plate 14*. A variety has only a rudiment of the lower petal.

C. VIRGINICA has an erect stem, up to 4 feet tall,
      growing from a creeping underground stem.
The sheathing parts of the leaves are fringed with
bristles. The two upper petals are stalked; the lower
is also blue and almost as large.

July to October: in moist woods and on shaded
banks from New Jersey to Kansas and southward to
Florida and Texas. *Plate 14.*

C. ERECTA is a very variable species. It sends up its
      more or less erect stems from a cluster of thick
roots. The sheathing part of the leaf is expanded into
a flange edged with hairs. The upper petals are blue,
the lower one white and much smaller.

June to October: in woodland, often in dry,
sandy soil, from southern New York to Kansas and
southward to Florida and Texas. *Plate 14.*

C. DIFFUSA is a creeping species with slender branch-
      ing stems which form mats. The sheathing part
of the leaf bears long hairs. The petals are all blue,
the upper two with broad blades on stalks, the lower
one smaller.

July to October: in bottomlands, marshes, and
moist woods from Delaware to Kansas and southward
to Florida and tropical America; also in tropics of
the Old World; and found as an occasional weed in
New England.

THE SPIDERWORTS (TRADESCANTIA)

The flowers of spiderworts are like those of the
dayflowers in being open only for a morning; those
of most species are blue or lavender. They differ in
being radially symmetric, the three petals all alike.
The six stamens also are all alike; their stalks are
covered by long hairs. The stems are mostly upright.
The leaves are characteristically folded lengthwise;
the upper two are smaller (often unequal) and may be
termed bracts, since they envelop the flower-cluster.

The hairs on the stamens are a favorite object of
microscopic study for students in botanical labora-
tories, easily mounted and providing a view of living
protoplasm.

Several species of *Tradescantia* adorn roadsides
and open woodlands and — of all places — the rocks of
railroad embankments, particularly in the Midwest.
Linnaeus named the genus for John Tradescant, who
was gardener to Queen Henrietta Maria of England
and a botanical explorer, and also founded a museum
of natural history in Lambeth.

There are six widely distributed species in our
range, distinguished by rather minor characteristics
such as the size and hairiness of sepals; though some
can be classed as southern or northern. Besides these
there are three species known chiefly from the dry
rocky hills of southern Missouri, and southwestward
into Oklahoma and Texas.

I.   *Spiderworts with narrow leaf-blades — less than an*
       inch wide; no wider than the sheath which embraces
       the stem (compare II).
          To distinguish these species with certainty it is
       necessary to examine the hairs on the sepals, if any,
       with a magnifier. If the hairs are tipped with minute
       globes, they are said to be glandular.

A. Species with narrow leaves characterized by

sepals without glandular hairs, or without
hairs at all.

T. VIRGINIANA is a common and handsome spider-
      wort, growing to a foot or more tall. Stem and
leaves are smooth or nearly so. The sepals and flower-
stalks are hairy. The flower-stalks do not exceed $1\frac{1}{2}$
inches in length. The petals are about $\frac{3}{4}$ inch long;
they are blue or purple.

April to July: in woods and meadows and on
roadsides from Maine to Minnesota and southward
to Georgia, Tennessee, and Missouri. *Plate 14.* Often
cultivated and escaped from cultivation. A form is
known with white petals.

T. THARPII is much lower, the stem at flowering time
      less than 3 inches tall, elongating later. The
flower-stalks are relatively long, 2 inches or more.
They and the sepals are hairy, as well as stem and
leaves. The petals approach an inch in length; they
vary from blue and purple to pink.

April and May: in rocky prairies and woods
from Missouri and Kansas to Texas.

T. OHIENSIS is recognizable by the whitish bloom on
      its smooth stems and leaves. It grows up to 4
feet in height. The flower-stalks are short, not more
than an inch long. The sepals may have a tuft of
hairs, a "beard," at the tip but are otherwise smooth.
The petals, about $\frac{1}{2}$ inch long, vary from rose to blue.

April to June: in meadows and woods and on
roadsides and railroad embankments, etc. from Massachusetts to Minnesota and Nebraska and southward to Florida and Texas. *Plate 14.* Often cultivated
and escaped from cultivation beyond this range.

Many wild flowers have white forms; they are
too numerous to be all mentioned in these pages. One
of the prettiest is a white *T. ohiensis* with the stamen-
hairs of the usual bright blue.

PLATE 14

Commelina virginica   *Brodeen*
Gottscho

Tradescantia occidentalis   *Johnson*

Commelina communis

Tradescantia bracteata   *Johnson*

Commelina erecta   *Uttal*

Tradescantia virginiana   *Johnson*

Tradescantia ohiensis   *Johnson*

B. Species with narrow leaves and glandular hairs on the sepals (in some mixed with non-glandular hairs).

T. BRACTEATA has smooth or almost smooth stem and leaves (they may bear a very fine down). The stem grows to 2 feet in height. The flower-stalks and sepals are hairy, some of the hairs being glandular. The flowers are rose or blue.

May to July: in prairies and on roadsides, railroad embankments, etc. from Michigan to Montana and southward to Indiana and Kansas. *Plate 14.*

T. OCCIDENTALIS is, as the name suggests, a western species; it comes into the westernmost states of our range. It is commonly about 2 feet tall. The stem and the narrow leaves are very smooth; the flower-stalks and sepals are sparsely beset with glandular hairs. The flowers are rose or blue.

May to July: in prairies, rocky places, etc. from Wisconsin to Manitoba and southward to Iowa and Mexico. *Plate 14.*

T. LONGIPES is a low species, the stem only about 4 inches tall at flowering. The stem is densely hairy; the leaves also are hairy. The flower-stalks are very short; they and the sepals (which are purplish) bear both glandular and non-glandular hairs. The flowers are rose or blue.

May: on dry hills in Missouri. *Plate 15.*

II. *Spiderworts with leaf-blades wider than the sheath; from ¼ inch to more than an inch wide.*
These are southern and southwestern species, only the first at all widespread.

T. SUBASPERA may reach 40 inches in height. The stem is often somewhat zigzag. Stem and leaves are essentially smooth but may bear scattered hairs. The sepals bear hairs, glandular, non-glandular, or both mixed. The flowers are blue.

June and July: in moist woods from Virginia to Missouri and southward to Florida and Alabama. *Plate 15.*

T. OZARKANA has a stem up to 2 feet tall. It resembles *T. subaspera* in many ways, but the sepals bear only glandular hairs and the petals vary from mauve to white.

April to June: in rocky woods from southern Missouri and Arkansas to Oklahoma. *Plate 15.*

T. ERNESTIANA, another southwestern species, has a stem some 20 inches tall, smooth or with scattered hairs. The leaves are smooth or very finely downy. The flower-stalks are hairy and the sepals downy but not glandular. The petals are deep blue.

April and May: in rocky woods from southern Missouri and Arkansas to Oklahoma. *Plate 15.*

THE PICKEREL-WEED FAMILY (PONTEDERIACEAE)

The *Pontederiaceae* are a small family of aquatic plants, mainly of warmer regions. They include some strange and beautiful flowers and some less conspicuous but widely distributed species. Like the species of the lily family, these have a perianth of six parts, all colored alike; the flowers may be radially or bilaterally symmetric. In our genera there are either three stamens, or six of which three are shorter than the others.

Besides the species described below, the beautiful nuisance called water-hyacinth (*Eichhornia crassipes*), a native of tropical America, extends as far as southern Virginia.

Only one species, *P. cordata*, is widely distributed in the northeastern states. A second species, *P. lanceolata*, comes up from the South as far as Delaware and Missouri. It is very variable, and differs from *P. cordata* mainly in bearing small glands in the inflorescence.

PICKEREL-WEED, P. CORDATA, has leaves whose blades are borne above the surface of the water on long stalks. The blades are extremely variable in shape, typically being indented at the base and tapering to a point (i.e. "cordate"), but often lacking the indentation, and even sometimes being entirely lacking (only the leaf-stalks present). The flowers are in a dense spike up to a foot above the water. The perianth is deep blue, the younger flowers bearing white hairs. The three upper parts are joined, the middle one bearing two yellow spots. The three lower parts are separate. There are three long, projecting stamens, and three very short stamens which are often imperfect. The ovary has three chambers but only one matures a seed; the fruit is seedlike (an achene).

June to November: in shallow, quiet water and on muddy banks from Nova Scotia to Minnesota and southward to Florida and Texas. *Plate 15.*

PLATE 15

Tradescantia subaspera   *Johnson*

Cypripedium acaule   *Gottscho*

Pontederia cordata   *Rickett*

Tradescantia ozarkana   *Robyns*

Tradescantia ernestiana   *Johnson*

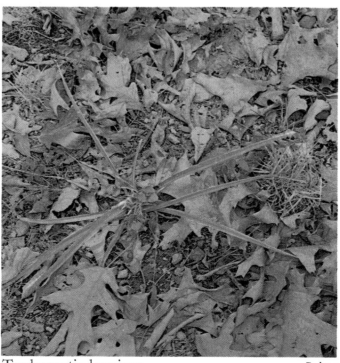

Tradescantia longipes   *Robyns*

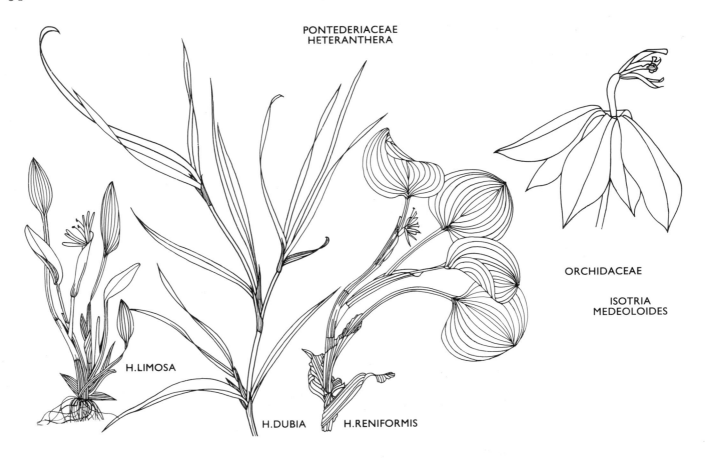

PONTEDERIACEAE
HETERANTHERA

H.LIMOSA

H.DUBIA   H.RENIFORMIS

ORCHIDACEAE

ISOTRIA
MEDEOLOIDES

HETERANTHERA

The species of *Heteranthera* grow in America and Africa, in mud or shallow water. The flowers emerge from a delicate bract. They have a perianth of six like parts and three stamens.

MUD-PLANTAIN, H. RENIFORMIS, has leaf blades
rather broader than long, indented at the base, on long stalks, the whole reaching up to 8 inches. The small white or pale blue flowers, about $\frac{2}{5}$ inch across, emerge from the base of the leaf-stalk.
August to October: creeping in mud or floating in water from Connecticut to Nebraska and southward to Florida and Mexico; also in tropical America.

MUD-PLANTAIN, H. LIMOSA, is similar to the preceding species, with larger, blue flowers, about $\frac{4}{5}$ inch across.
July to September: in muddy places from Illinois and Minnesota to Colorado and southward to Florida and Mexico; also in tropical America.

WATER-STARGRASS, H. DUBIA, is usually submerged. Its leaves are long, narrow, pointed. The pale yellow flowers are about $\frac{1}{2}$ inch across.
June to September: in water from Quebec to Minnesota and Oregon and southward to Florida and Mexico; also in tropical America.

THE ORCHID FAMILY (ORCHIDACEAE)

The orchids have been called the royal family of flowering plants. Certainly for flamboyant display, fantastic form, and gorgeous color no other family can rival them. They may compose the largest family of plants with flowers – they dispute that title with the daisy family. Brilliant

cattleyas are familiar in corsages. Orchids of many hues and diverse shapes adorn the branches of tropical trees, and the glasshouses of orchid fanciers. But orchids grow also in northern bogs and meadows and woodlands, and these are not all conspicuous for size or color. In fact, the flowers of some of our native orchids – even some semi-tropical species – are tiny, greenish, and not particularly attractive.

All these diverse flowers form a single family by virtue of certain peculiar and easily seen characteristics. As in the lily family, there are three sepals and three petals; but the symmetry is markedly bilateral, one petal, usually the lowest as the flower stands, differing from the other two in size, shape, or color, or often in all three; this petal is called the "lip". Second, the center of the flower is occupied not by recognizable separate stamens and pistil but by a "column" formed of style, stigma, and one or more stamens all joined, often brightly colored and petal-like. The ovary is inferior, embedded in the end of the stem that supports the rest of the flower; it contains very minute ovules (seeds to be) in great numbers.

These two peculiarities, the lip and the column, distinguish the orchid flower from all others and unite in one family thousands of flowers that differ in almost every other respect. One further peculiarity of most orchid flowers is that during their development they twist on their stalks so that what was originally the lowest petal or sepal becomes the uppermost. The lip of an orchid flower, generally the lowest petal when the flower is open, starts as the uppermost petal. This condition the botanist describes by the word "resupinate" – a technical way of saying "upside down."* A few of our native orchids, however, either fail to twist or twist through a complete

circle so that the lip is displayed in the usual uppermost position.

The parts of the perianth other than the lip are not especially remarkable. The remaining two petals, to right and left as you face the flower, are the "lateral petals." These are in many species like the sepals, which are rarely green like the sepals of roses or snapdragons. In some species lateral petals and sepals are joined, or they "connive" to form a hood over the column.

The genera of orchids native in the northeastern United States are not difficult to distinguish, and the guide that follows should enable the amateur naturalist to place an unknown orchid in its correct genus.

The family is divided into two subfamilies (or tribes, according to some botanists), the first of which comprises only the lady's-slippers (*Plates 15, 16*). This group scarcely needs description: the flowers are easily recognized by the large slipper-like or pouch-like lip. Among our natives, the only possibility of confusion is with *Calypso*, the fairy slipper (*Plate 16*); in this, however, the form of the "slipper" is quite different. Technically, the lady's-slippers are characterized by two fertile stamens, seen as two masses of pollen, one on each side of the column; and a third, sterile stamen which forms a shieldlike object at the tip of the column. In the second subfamily, in which are found most orchids, there is generally but one stamen, forming its pollen just beneath the tip of the column.

Guide to Genera of Native Orchids

Subfamily 1. The lady's-slippers (see above): *Cypripedium*.
Subfamily 2. All other genera.

I. *Orchids with a single flower (rarely two) at the tip of the stem.*

  A. One genus has no well-developed leaves at flowering time: only small sheathing leaves – bracts. One narrow leaf appears after flowering. The flower is generally pink, the lip with a yellow crest: *Arethusa*.

  B. One genus, with a very beautiful pink flower and a mottled, saclike lip, has a single leaf at

the base of the flowering stem: *Calypso*.

  C. Two genera have a single leaf on the flowering stem, and often one or more long-stalked leaves at the base: *Pogonia* (lip flat with yellow hairs); *Cleistes* (lip trough-shaped).

  D. One genus has usually five (sometimes more) leaves in a circle just below the flower: *Isotria*.

II. *An orchid with usually three flowers, each on a long curved stalk which grows from the axil of a small leaf; the leaves are attached singly:* Triphora.

III. *Orchids with generally more than three flowers (rarely fewer) in spikes or racemes.*

  A. A genus with two leaves paired on the flowering stem: *Listera*.

*Curiously, in some of the most modern technical manuals, the term has been exactly reversed in meaning, so that orchids with the lip uppermost are erroneously called resupinate.

B. A genus with generally a single leaf on the flowering stem, sometimes with two leaves not paired but close together; the flowers are tiny, greenish: *Malaxis*.

C. Two genera with a single leaf at the base of the flowering stem, formed the preceding autumn and withering just before or during the flowering season: *Aplectrum* (lip rounded); *Tipularia* (lip narrow, pointed).

D. Two genera with no green leaves at any time: *Corallorhiza* (lip generally less than ½ inch long); *Hexalectris* (lip about ⅗ inch long).

E. Orchids not fitting under heads A to D.

1. Genera with a hollow tube or "spur" at the base of the lip: *Orchis* (lateral petals with upper sepal or all sepals forming a hood; spur flaring at open end), *Habenaria* (lower sepals spread horizontally; flowers numerous).

2. Genus with no spur; leaves on the flowering stem: *Epipactis*.

3. Genera with no spur; leaves at or near the base of the flowering stem: *Spiranthes* (small white flowers in a spike which is often twisted); *Goodyera* (small white flowers in a spike; leaves usually white-veined, at the base); *Calopogon* (lip uppermost in the flower; flowers few, comparatively large); *Liparis* (lip flat, lateral petals threadlike).

THE LADY'S-SLIPPERS (CYPRIPEDIUM)

The lady's-slippers are perhaps our most familiar native orchids. The large lip, white, pink, yellow, or variegated, gives the English name to the genus; and the botanical name refers to the sandal or slipper (*pedilum*) of Aphrodite, the goddess of love and beauty, who was born on the island of Cyprus. Botanically, the lady's-slippers differ from all other orchids in having two pollen-bearing stamens, to be seen at either side of the column near the opening of the "slipper"; the rudiment of a third stamen, which forms no pollen, is the glistening, shieldlike object in the center of the flower. The stigma projects downward into the cavity of the lip. The lower two sepals of most species are joined so that there seem to be only two instead of three. A single green bract, much like the foliage leaves but smaller, stands just behind each flower.

The leaves of lady's-slippers are broad and marked by conspicuous veins which run from base to apex without branches.

The several species of *Cypripedium* native in the northeastern United States may be characterized as follows.

I. *The "stemless" lady's-slipper. The stem is underground; leaves and flower-stalk arise together from this underground stem. The flower-stalk normally bears a single flower.*

PINK LADY'S-SLIPPER or MOCCASIN-FLOWER, C. ACAULE (to 20 inches), has two leaves at the base of the flower-stalk, generally set at a slight angle to each other (i.e. not exactly opposite). The pink lip has a cleft rather than an aperture, with the edges turned in. The sepals and lateral petals are brownish or greenish.

A form with white lip is not uncommon.

April to July: in dry or moist woodlands, bogs, etc. from Newfoundland to Alberta and southward to Georgia, Alabama, and Minnesota. *Plate 15*.

II. *The other native species have stems that bear both leaves and flowers.*

YELLOW LADY'S-SLIPPER, C. CALCEOLUS (to nearly 3 feet), is a very variable species, ranging from Europe and Asia into North America. The American plants were formerly thought of as two species, *C. pubescens* (lateral petals greenish-yellow) and *C. parviflorum* (smaller; lateral petals purplish-brown); but such is their variability that they are now considered merely varieties of *C. calceolus*, and some botanists do not even distinguish them as two but lump them all into one. The stem generally bears from three to five leaves and one or two flowers. The lip is yellow. The lateral petals are usually spirally twisted. The sepals are similarly colored but broader.

Calceolus means, somewhat redundantly, a "small shoe."

April to July: in bogs, swamps, and woodlands from Newfoundland to British Columbia and southward to New Jersey, the mountains of Georgia and Tennessee, Missouri, Texas, New Mexico, and Washington. *Plate 16*.

SHOWY LADY'S-SLIPPER, C. REGINAE (to 3 feet), is well named; it is the most brightly colored of our native cypripediums. The lip is white suffused with pink and streaked with rose-purple or sometimes entirely rose-purple or occasionally all white. The lateral petals and the sepals are white; the broad upper sepal arches over the lip and column. The leaves are broad and strongly plaited. The whole plant is hairy; the hairs can cause a rash on the skin of some persons.

PLATE 16

Cypripedium calceolus *Rhein*

Cypripedium reginae *Mayer*

Cypripedium candidum *Rhein*

Arethusa bulbosa *Rhein*

Calypso bulbosa *Rhein*

Cypripedium arietinum *Rhein*

Cypripedium calceolus *Johnson*

May to August: in mossy swamps, bogs, and damp woodlands, from Newfoundland to Manitoba and southward to New Jersey, the mountains of Georgia and Tennessee, and Missouri. *Plate 16*.

The botanical name means "lady's-slipper of the queen"; doubtless fit for a queen.

WHITE LADY'S-SLIPPER, C. CANDIDUM (to 16 inches), is a rare species. The lip is white; the rest of the perianth greenish-yellow, often marked with crimson lines. The white form of the pink lady's-slipper is sometimes mistaken for this species; but the white lady's-slipper has from three to five leaves on the flowering stem, not at the base; and the lip is only an inch long or less.

May and June: in wet prairies and meadows, swamps, etc. from New York to North Dakota and southward to New Jersey, Kentucky, and Missouri. *Plate 16*.

RAM'S-HEAD LADY'S-SLIPPER, C. ARIETINUM (to 16 inches), is the most curious of our cypripediums. The lip, from which it gets both English and Latin names, has a large pointed pouch projecting downward; this is only about $\frac{1}{2}$ inch long, white marked with a network of crimson lines. The sepals and lateral petals are greenish or crimson; the three sepals are all distinct.

May and June: in damp, mossy coniferous woods and bogs from Quebec to Manitoba, and southward to New York, Michigan, and Minnesota; rare in the United States. *Plate 16*.

ARETHUSA

We have only one species of *Arethusa*. Another grows in Japan.

SWAMP-PINK, A. BULBOSA, bears a single lovely blossom at the tip of a stem a foot or more tall. No leaves are present at flowering time, only some scales or bracts that sheathe the stem. From the axil of the uppermost of these scales protrudes, as the flower vanishes, a single leaf only about $\frac{1}{5}$ inch wide. The stem grows from a corm underground. The magenta-pink sepals and lateral petals, up to 2 inches long, stand almost erect, their ends arching over the column. The broad lip bends sharply down, suffused with pink, streaked with darker pink or crimson, and bearing several rows of yellow or white hairs (the so-called "beard").

This plant may possibly be confused with snake-mouth (*Pogonia*), which was, indeed, placed in the same genus by Linnaeus. It, however, has an ovate or elliptic leaf midway on the stem.

May to August: in bogs and peaty meadows from Newfoundland to Ontario and Minnesota and southward to Maryland, the mountains of South Carolina, Ohio, northern Indiana, and Wisconsin; locally abundant but becoming rare in the United States. *Plate 16*. In Greek mythology Arethusa was a nymph whom the goddess Artemis transformed into a spring of water so that she might escape the amorous advances of a river-god. The connection with our orchid is not clear, but the nymph was doubtless as beautiful as the flower. It is also called, less pleasingly, dragon's-mouth.

CALYPSO

There is but one species of *Calypso*, growing around the world in northern latitudes.

FAIRY-SLIPPER, C. BULBOSA, forms its fantastic flower at the tip of a stem about 8 inches tall. At the base of this stem is a single broad leaf about $2\frac{1}{2}$ inches long; it was formed the preceding autumn and lived through the winter (but it sometimes withers before the flowering stem appears). Leaf and stem grow from a tuber, below which there may be a branched rhizome. The lip is slipper-like (Dr Fernald says "resembling a sugar-scoop"), about an inch long, the end covered by a delicate "apron" which is whitish with brown-purple blotches. The lateral petals and the sepals are narrow and pointed, standing erect to form a spiky top to the flower.

May to July: in cool mossy woods and open woodlands across Canada and southward to New York, Michigan, Wisconsin, Arizona, and California; commoner in the West. *Plate 16*. In Greek mythology Calypso was the queen of Ogygia. Odysseus was detained by her — willingly — for seven years on his way home from Troy. The plant has also been named *Cytherea*. This was one of the several names of Aphrodite who, in one version, was born from sea-foam and landed on the island of Cythera.

POGONIA

This small genus is represented in the United States by only one species.

ROSE POGONIA or SNAKE-MOUTH, P. OPHIOGLOS-
SOIDES (to 2 feet), somewhat resembles the swamp-pink (*Arethusa*), but its stem bears an ovate or elliptic leaf, about 4 inches long, midway on the stem at flowering time (the grasslike leaf of *Arethusa* emerges after flowering). There are often also long-stalked

leaves at the base of the stem. The single flower is pink; the sepals and petals are much alike, rather narrow, diverging in several directions, about an inch long. The flat lip bears three rows of fleshy hairs tipped with yellow or brown (the "beard").

May to August: in bogs, peaty soil, wet shores, and glades from Newfoundland to Ontario and southward to Florida, Pennsylvania, Tennessee, and Minnesota; on the coastal plain west to Texas. *Plate 17.*

CLEISTES

Cleistes has but one species.

SPREADING-POGONIA or ROSEBUD ORCHID, C.
DIVARICATA, is at once recognized by the tubular form of the flower. The tube, about 2 inches long, is formed by the trough-shaped lip and the lateral petals, "conniving"; these are a showy pink, or white. The sepals are narrow, brown or purplish, up to 3

inches long. The stem, up to 2 feet tall or even taller, bears one oblong or elliptic leaf about midway, and a leaflike bract just behind the single flower. From the cluster of fleshy roots grows a long-stalked basal leaf.

June and July: in pine-barrens, peaty places, etc. on the coastal plain from New Jersey to Florida and Texas and inland to Kentucky and Tennessee. *Plate 17.*

THE WHORLED-POGONIAS (ISOTRIA)

There are two species of *Isotria*, both American, one very rare. They are marked by a circle of five or more leaves on the stem just below the flower. The lip is small; the sepals are longer than the petals. The genus is not really distinct from *Pogonia*.

WHORLED-POGONIA or FIVE-LEAVES, I. VERTICIL-
LATA, has a stem up to 16 inches tall growing from a cluster of hairy roots. About 12 or 14 inches from the ground is a circle of elliptic or oblong leaves up to 4 inches long. From their midst rises the one flower (or rarely two flowers) on a slender stalk. The flower is remarkable for its three brown-purple, very narrow sepals, about 2 inches long or even longer.

The lateral petals are yellowish-green, only about an inch long. The lip also is greenish, with purple streaks, about the same length.

May and June: in woods from Maine to Michigan and southward to Florida and Texas. *Plate 17.*

LESSER FIVE-LEAVES, I. MEDEOLOIDES, reaches a
height of 10 inches, its leaves less than 4 inches long, and its sepals only an inch long, not much longer than the petals.

May to July: in woodlands from New Hampshire and Vermont and southward through New York, New Jersey, and Pennsylvania to North Carolina; also in southeastern Missouri; very rare. (See page 64.)

TRIPHORA

This is a small genus of American orchids, only one being found in the northeastern United States.

THREE-BIRDS or NODDING-POGONIA, T. TRIAN-
THOPHORA (to 1 foot), is distinctive among our native orchids in having small ovate leaves attached singly on the stem. The leaves sheathe or clasp the stem at their base. The stem grows from a tuber underground. Three (usually) flowers grow from the axils of the three uppermost leaves, one being at the

tip of the stem. Each flower hangs on a curved stalk. They are pink or white, with sepals and lateral petals much alike, about $\frac{3}{5}$ inch long. The lip has crinkled edges and bears three toothed ridges.

August and September: in woods from Maine to Wisconsin and southward to Florida and Texas. *Plate 17.*

Three-birds, like many other orchids, goes underground for years at a time — failing to produce any flowering stem above ground.

THE TWAYBLADES (LISTERA)

The twayblades are named for the pair of leaves midway on the stem. (They share this name with our species of *Liparis*, whose two leaves are at the base of the stem.) The flowers of *Listera* are small and greenish or purplish, growing in a raceme.

HEART-LEAVED TWAYBLADE, L. CORDATA, does not exceed a foot in height, the raceme being only about 4 inches long. The purplish-green sepals and petals are alike and only $\frac{1}{8}$ inch long or less. The lip, similarly colored, is slightly longer and deeply cleft into two prongs.

May to August: in mossy woods throughout Canada and southward to Maryland, the mountains of North Carolina and West Virginia, Wisconsin, New Mexico, and Oregon. *Plate 17*.

BROAD-LEAVED TWAYBLADE, L. CONVALLARIOIDES, is similar to *L. cordata*. It is easily distinguished by the round, not indented, base of the leaves, by the yellow-green color of the flowers, and by the shape of the lip which is slightly indented at the end, not cleft. The upper parts of the plant are whitened by a down.

June to August: in damp peaty or mossy woods, swamps, etc. from Newfoundland across Canada and southward to northern New England and the mountains of North Carolina and Tennessee.

Another essentially Canadian species, *L. auriculata*, comes south into the mountains of New Hampshire; the lip is deeply notched but not cleft. The southern twayblade, *L. australis*, is found northward in a few places in New York and eastern Canada; it resembles *L. cordata* in its cleft lip. Another southern species, *L. smallii*, extends north into the mountains of Pennsylvania and West Virginia; the lip is deeply lobed but scarcely cleft.

THE ADDER'S-MOUTH ORCHIDS (MALAXIS)

These orchids resemble the twayblades in having a short raceme of small greenish flowers. There is generally only one leaf in our northeastern species, the base sheathing the stem; if two, they are not paired. The stem grows from a corm.

GREEN ADDER'S-MOUTH, M. UNIFOLIA, grows to a little over a foot tall. There is generally a single leaf (*unifolia*) with the blade (about 3 inches long) midway on the stem (the sheathing part extending down some distance). Rarely there is a second leaf,

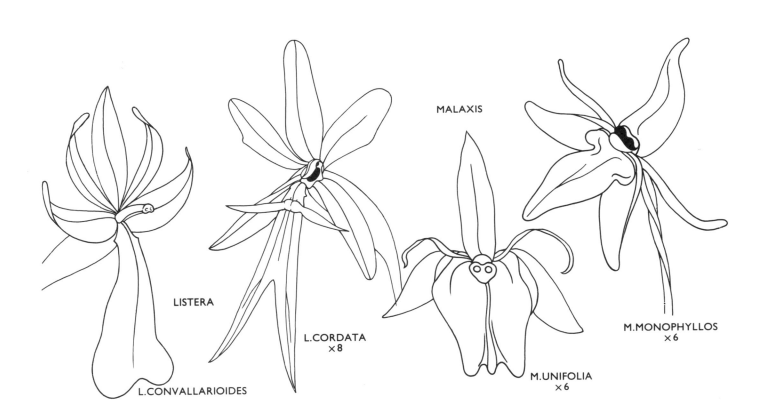

LISTERA

L.CONVALLARIOIDES

L.CORDATA
×8

MALAXIS

M.UNIFOLIA
×6

M.MONOPHYLLOS
×6

PLATE 17

Cleistes divaricata *Allen*

Pogonia ophioglossoides *Rhein*

Triphora trianthophora *Justice*

Aplectrum hyemale *Johnson*

Isotria verticillata *Fogelson*

Malaxis unifolia *D. Richards*

Listera cordata *Phelps*

slightly higher on the stem. The tiny flowers grow in a raceme which may reach a length of 6 inches. The sepals, only ⅛ inch long or even less, are narrow. The lateral petals are threadlike and curled. The lip is lobed or toothed at the tip. The whole perianth is green.

May to August: in woods, on slopes, and in the borders of swamps from Newfoundland to Saskatchewan and southward to Florida and Texas. *Plate 17.*

WHITE ADDER'S-MOUTH, M. BRACHYPODA, is similar in all dimensions to *M. unifolia*. The raceme is narrow, the flowers often distant from each other. The flowers are greenish-white. The petals are narrow and bent back but not threadlike. The lip tapers to a sharp point.

June to August: in damp gravels, peats, bogs, etc. from Labrador to Manitoba and southward to New Jersey, Tennessee, Minnesota, Texas, and California; also in Japan.

This may be considered only a variety of *M. monophylla*, which grows in northern Europe and Asia and in Canada. The difference is that the flower of typical *M. monophylla* twists in its development through a complete circle, bringing the lip into its original uppermost position (it is not resupinate), while in most plants of the United States it makes the usual half-circle twist (and is resupinate). *M. monophylla* also often has two leaves (in spite of its name, which means in Greek exactly what *unifolia* means in Latin, "one-leaved").

APLECTRUM

There is but one species.

PUTTYROOT, A. HYEMALE (to 2 feet), sends up its leafless flowering stem from a corm, a round, solid underground stem. Then this corm sends out from one side a slim rhizome which at its tip forms a second corm. From this rises, in autumn, a single broad leaf from 4 to 6 inches long. This lasts through the winter and withers before the new flowering stalk

grows from near its base. There are from seven to fifteen flowers in a raceme, each about half an inch long. The lip is white with purple marks, the rest of the perianth brownish or purplish.

This is also called Adam-and-Eve because of the two corms side by side.

May and June: in woods from Quebec and Vermont to Saskatchewan and California and southward to Georgia, Tennessee, and Arkansas. *Plate 17.*

TIPULARIA

We have but one species of this genus; the only other known species grows in Asia.

CRANE-FLY ORCHID, T. DISCOLOR, gets its odd name from the appearance of the flower, which resembles the small insect called a crane-fly. All parts of the perianth are narrow (⅛ inch or less wide) and relatively long (⅓ inch), and the lip bears at its base a hollow tube or "spur" nearly an inch long. The color is greenish, yellow, or purplish, often mottled. The

flowers are in a raceme up to 10 inches long. The single leaf is formed in autumn, lives through winter, and withers in the spring before the flowers appear. The flowering stem grows from the same corm that formed the leaf. This corm then develops another corm, to one side, which is responsible for the next leaf and stem.

July and August: in woods from Massachusetts to Illinois and southward to Florida and Texas; rare northward. *Plate 18.*

CORALROOTS (CORALLORHIZA)

The orchids of the genus *Corallorhiza* are among those few flowering plants that have no green color at any time. They support themselves, as do the mushrooms and toadstools, on the dead remains of other plants, in the soil. The "coral root" is not a root but an underground stem or rhizome, much branched, toothed, pink, and in general coral-like. The flowering stem which grows from this is sheathed by several scale-like

vestiges of leaves. The stem and the flowers are yellowish or brown or purple. The flowers are in a raceme. Sepals and lateral petals are much alike. The two lower sepals are joined together at the base and in some species make a small sac which is joined to the stem beneath the perianth; this is rather amusingly called a *mentum* — "chin." To distinguish some of the species it is necessary to examine the lip carefully with a lens.

PLATE 18

Hexalectris spicata — *D. Richards*

Corallorhiza trifida — *Johnson*

Tipularia discolor — *D. Richards*

Corallorhiza odontorhiza — *Elbert*

Corallorhiza wisteriana — *Elbert*

Corallorhiza striata — *Rhein*

Corallorhiza maculata — *Rhein*

SPOTTED or LARGE CORALROOT, C. MACULATA
(to 30 inches), has a brown-purple or yellowish stem. The sepals and lateral petals are crimson-purple, about 3 inches long. The lip has two narrow lobes near the base; it is white spotted ("maculate") with crimson-magenta. The mentum is scarcely developed.

June to August: in woods from Newfoundland across Canada and southward to Virginia, the mountains of North Carolina and Tennessee, Wisconsin, South Dakota, Colorado, and California. *Plate 18.*

AUTUMN CORALROOT, C. ODONTORHIZA (to 20
inches), has a light brown or purplish stem which is thick and bulb-like at the base. The sepals and lateral petals are about $\frac{1}{6}$ inch long; they are purple or greenish. There is no mentum. The lip is as wide as long or wider, often notched at the outer edge, more or less crinkled along the sides, narrow at the base; it is white spotted with magenta-crimson.

August to October: in dry woods from Maine to Minnesota and southward to Georgia, Mississippi, and Arkansas; also in Mexico and Central America. *Plate 18.*

STRIPED CORALROOT, C. STRIATA (to 20 inches),
has a purplish stem and a flower all parts of whose perianth are pinkish, yellowish, or whitish striped with purple. The flowers are large for a coralroot, sepals, lateral petals, and lip each about $\frac{1}{2}$ inch long. The lip is elliptic and not lobed.

May to August: in woods from Quebec to British Columbia and southward to New York, Minnesota, Colorado, and California. *Plate 18.*

NORTHERN CORALROOT, C. TRIFIDA (to 15 inches),
has a yellow stem. The raceme is only about 3 inches long. Sepals and lateral petals are yellowish-white to greenish or purple, the sepals about $\frac{1}{4}$ inch longer, the petals a little shorter. The upper sepal and the lateral petals "connive" to form a hood. The lip may be unlobed or it may have a small projection on each side near the base (thus being "trifid"). It is white, with or without purple spots.

May to July: in damp woods, swamps, etc. across Canada and southward to New Jersey, the mountains of Georgia and Tennessee, Missouri, Colorado, and Oregon. The southern *C. Wisteriana* (*Plate 18*) is found along our southern borders.

THE COCKSCOMB ORCHIDS (HEXALECTRIS)

Hexalectris is a genus of American orchids, all resembling coralroots in lacking green color and therefore living on organic matter in the soil. Only one species is found in the northeastern United States.

CRESTED-CORALROOT or COCKSCOMB, H. SPICATA,
resembles a coralroot in being leafless and lacking green color, but is a more imposing plant, its stem sometimes reaching a height of 3 feet. The flowers, which are in a loose spike (*spicata*), are yellowish with purple or brown-purple streaks. The lateral petals and sepals are about $\frac{3}{4}$ inch long. The lip (about the same length) is three-lobed, the lobes at each side curving upward around the column. The name of the genus means "six cockscombs" in reference to a number of fleshy ridges, often but not always six, that adorn the surface of the central lobe of the lip.

June to August: in dry woods from Maryland to Kentucky, Arkansas, and Arizona, and southward to Florida and Texas; also in Mexico. *Plate 18.*

ROUND-LEAVED AND SHOWY ORCHIS (ORCHIS)

Our northeastern species of *Orchis* have one or several leaves at the base of the leafless flowering stem. Leaves and stem grow from a cluster of thick roots. Lateral petals and sepals are similar (the petals smaller), all "conniving" together to form a hood over the column. At the base of the lip is an easily visible hollow, tubelike extension, the "spur," about as long as the rest of the flower, extending downward and slightly backward.

English species of *Orchis* were studied by Charles Darwin, who showed how their complex floral structure results in cross pollination.

The "long-purples" of Ophelia's garland were *O. mascula*, the early purple orchid of Britain. This species was since earliest times thought to possess astonishing medical properties, and in consequence gathered an equally astonishing array of English names. Bloody-man's-fingers, fried-candlesticks, poor-man's-blood, dead-man's-finger, are only a few of the more picturesque.

SHOWY ORCHIS, O. SPECTABILIS (to a foot tall), usually has two leaves at the base, but there are sometimes three — the third perhaps always in association with a second flowering stem. The leaves are broad, blunt-ended, sheathing the base of the stem, up to 8 inches long. The flowers are backed by long, pointed, green bracts which are almost foliage leaves. Sepals

PLATE 19

Habenaria fimbriata   *Elbert*

Orchis spectabilis   *Johnson*

Habenaria peramoena   *Rhein*

Habenaria peramoena   *Rhein*

Habenaria lacera   *V. Richard*

Habenaria psycodes   *Johnson*

Habenaria lacera   *Gottscho*

are $\frac{4}{5}$ inch long; lateral petals a little smaller; both are pink, lilac, or purplish. The lip is white.

April to June: in woods and on moist slopes from Quebec to Minnesota and southward to New Jersey, the mountains of Georgia and Alabama, Arkansas, and Kansas. *Plate 19.* This species was my introduction to orchids; I was roundly scolded by a venerable botanist for picking a flowering stem. Like other orchids, it may lie dormant, not showing above the ground, for several years together then appearing unexpectedly in groups.

ROUND-LEAVED ORCHIS, O. ROTUNDIFOLIA (to 16 inches), is a more slender plant than *O. spectabilis*, with only one leaf which is roundish and about 4 inches long. The sepals may be $\frac{2}{5}$ inch long, the lateral petals about $\frac{1}{4}$ inch, both white or pinkish-purple. The lip is usually three-lobed, white with purple spots.

June and July: in mossy woods and swamps from Greenland across Canada to Alaska and southward to New York, Michigan, Wisconsin, Minnesota, and Wyoming; very rare in the northeastern United States.

REIN ORCHIDS AND FRINGED ORCHIDS (HABENARIA)

Many species of *Habenaria* fail to live up to the popular concept of an orchid, their flowers being small and some of them green and inconspicuous. All these flowers, however, have the complex structure explained in the introduction to the family, if on a small scale. And a glance at the accompanying photographs will show that small size does not necessarily negate fantastic form and beautiful color. The lateral petals and the upper sepal usually make a hood over the column. The lip takes a variety of forms, and is the most useful identifying feature. It has a "spur," a tubular hollow structure at the base, extending downward. The stem rises from a cluster of thick roots. The leaves (one or more) of some species grow singly on the stem; in others they are paired at the base of the stem.

The name is from the Latin *habena*, a "rein," and apparently alludes to the long spur; but some say it refers to the narrow, strap-shaped lip of certain species.

There are many species, about twenty in our region. They are grouped below by characteristics of the lip, to observe which a hand magnifier may be necessary.

I. *Plants with a three-lobed lip, all the lobes being deeply cut into narrow, almost hairlike divisions. (Compare II, III, and IV.) In this group we may distinguish the species largely on the color of their flowers.*

    A. Plants with a three-lobed and deeply cut lip and lilac or purple (or white) flowers.

LESSER PURPLE FRINGED ORCHID, H. PSYCODES (to 3 feet), is one of the most beautiful species, with lilac or pink-purple flowers and beautifully fringed lip. There may be as many as five lanceolate or elliptic leaves on the stem, and, rising from these, a dense raceme of many flowers. The sepals and lateral petals are up to $\frac{1}{3}$ inch long, the lip about $\frac{1}{2}$ inch. A form with white flowers is known.

June to August: in meadows, swamps, open woods, etc. from Newfoundland to Ontario and Minnesota and southward to New Jersey, the mountains of Georgia and Tennessee, Indiana, and Arkansas. *Plate 19.*

A variety of this species with larger flowers (the perianth up to $\frac{1}{2}$ inch long, the lip to $\frac{3}{4}$ inch) is sometimes treated as a separate species with the name *H. fimbriata (Plate 19).* It may be called the large purple fringed orchid. It flowers a bit earlier than typical *H. psycodes*, and is found over much the same range but does not extend so far westward.

    B. Plants with a three-lobed and deeply cut lip and greenish or yellowish flowers.

RAGGED FRINGED ORCHID, H. LACERA (to 30 inches), is perhaps the commonest species of this genus in our region. The stem bears several rather narrow leaves on the stem, up to 8 inches long. The flowers are pale green or yellowish, the sepals and lateral petals rather less than $\frac{1}{4}$ inch long. The lip is more than $\frac{1}{2}$ inch long. The spur may be nearly an inch long.

June to September: in marshes, meadows, thickets, woods, etc. from Newfoundland to Minnesota and southward to Florida and Texas. *Plate 19.*

PRAIRIE FRINGED ORCHID, H. LEUCOPHAEA (to 4 feet), is a tall and stout species of the prairies. The leaves, growing singly on the stem, are up to 8 inches long and elliptic or lanceolate. The flowers vary from creamy white to greenish, and are sweetly fragrant. The lateral petals and sepals are $\frac{1}{2}$ inch long or longer; the lip may be nearly $1\frac{1}{2}$ inches. The spur is curved, somewhat club-shaped, and 2 inches long or even longer.

June to August: in wet prairies and open swamps from Ontario to South Dakota and southward to New York, Ohio, Louisiana, Kansas, and Nebraska.

II. *Plants with a three-lobed lip, the lobes being toothed but not cut into narrow divisions; the flowers rose-purple.*

PURPLE FRINGELESS ORCHID or PRIDE-OF-THE-
PEAK, H. PERAMOENA (to 40 inches), resembles *H. psycodes* except that the lobes of the lip are not so deeply cut, merely shallowly toothed. The color is rose-purple or lavender. The lateral petals and sepals are about $\frac{1}{3}$ inch long, the lip about $\frac{1}{2}$ inch, the middle lobe notched at the end. The spur may reach 1 inch in length.

June to August: in meadows, bogs, moist woods, wet banks, etc. from New York and New Jersey to Missouri and southward to Maryland, Georgia, Alabama, and Arkansas. *Plate 19.*

III. *Plants whose lip is not lobed or divided but has its margins deeply cleft into a hairlike fringe. These may be grouped by the color of their flowers.*

A. Flowers white or cream-colored.

WHITE FRINGED ORCHID, H. BLEPHARIGLOTTIS
(to nearly 4 feet), is mainly a species of the coastal plain, but extends inland. The leaves vary from ovate to elliptic or lanceolate. The raceme (in the north) is dense and thick. The flowers are less than $\frac{1}{2}$ inch long, the rather narrow lip about $\frac{1}{2}$ inch long, with a 1-inch spur (in the North; longer southward).

June to September: in meadows, marshes, bogs, peaty places from Quebec to Michigan and southward to Florida, thence west to Mississippi and Texas. *Plate 20. Blephariglottis* is from two Greek words meaning "eyelash" (referring to the fringe) and "tongue" (the lip).

B. Flowers yellow or orange.

CRESTED or YELLOW FRINGED ORCHID, H. CRIS-
TATA (to 3 feet), is rare in our region, commoner southward. It is a slender plant with several very narrow, sharp-pointed leaves on the stem and a dense spike of small flowers, the sepals and lateral petals only about $\frac{1}{6}$ inch long; the lip may be $\frac{1}{4}$ inch long, with a spur averaging about the same.

July to September: in bogs, low meadows, swamps, pine-barrens, etc. from Massachusetts to Florida and thence to Texas on the coastal plain; inland to Arkansas; rare northward. *Plate 20.*

ORANGE-PLUME or YELLOW FRINGED ORCHID,
H. CILIARIS (to 40 inches), is known not only by the color of its flowers but also by the very long slender flower-stalks which are nearly an inch long. Except in color it resembles *H. blephariglottis.* The leaves on the stem are lanceolate, sharp-pointed, up to a foot long. The sepals and lateral petals are about $\frac{2}{5}$

inch long, the fringed lip about $\frac{1}{2}$ inch. The spur is an inch or $1\frac{1}{4}$ inches long.

July to September: in bogs, swamps, meadows, thickets, pine-barrens — a great variety of situations — from Massachusetts to Ontario and Wisconsin and southward to Florida and Texas. *Plate 20.*

IV. *Plants with an unlobed lip, the edges toothed or plain, but not cut into a fine fringe.*
These plants may be readily separated into two groups (A and B) by the position of their leaves.

A. Plants with leaves (from one to four) at or near the base of the stem; the flowers are greenish or yellowish. (Compare B.)

ONE-LEAVED REIN ORCHID, H. OBTUSATA (to 16
inches), usually has one leaf at the base, rarely two. The leaf is blunt or round at the end, tapering down to the base so that the broadest part is above the middle. The lateral petals and sepals are only about $\frac{1}{4}$ inch long, forming a hood; the long narrow lip is about $\frac{2}{5}$ inch long. The spur about equals the lip.

June to September: in wet places, in coniferous woods, bogs, swamps, etc. across Canada and southward to New York, Michigan, Minnesota, Colorado and Utah; also in Norway.

ROUND-LEAVED REIN ORCHID, H. ORBICULATA (to
2 feet), has two basal leaves up to 10 inches long and 8 inches broad — almost round, with a blunt point; they lie flat on the ground. The sepals are $\frac{3}{5}$ inch long, the lateral petals $\frac{1}{2}$ inch; they are all distinct, extending straight out or even backwards. The lip is very narrow, up to an inch long, with a spur reaching nearly 2 inches in length.

June to August: in woods from Newfoundland to Alaska and southward to New Jersey, the mountains of Georgia and Tennessee, Illinois, Montana, and Oregon. *Plate 20.* The larger plants of this species, with leaves 10 inches long and spur nearly 2 inches long, have by some botanists been considered a separate species, *H. macrophylla.* They are found through the northeastern parts of the range of *H. orbiculata.*

HOOKER'S ORCHID, H. HOOKERI (to 16 inches),
has two leaves much like those of *H. orbiculata,* but not so large, up to 6 inches long and 5 inches wide. The raceme has fewer flowers and these do not stand out from the stem, so that the effect is of a more slender plant. Sepals and lip are about $\frac{1}{2}$ inch long, the lateral petals much shorter. The spur, which tapers to a very narrow end, may reach an inch in length.

May to August: in woods from Quebec and Ontario to Minnesota and southward to New Jersey,

Ohio, and Iowa. *Plate 20*. Sir William Jackson Hooker was a famous British botanist, the first Director of the Royal Botanic Gardens at Kew.

> B. Plants with an unlobed and uncut lip and several leaves on the flowering stem (rather than only at the base); above the leaves proper there are smaller appendages called bracts. The flowers are greenish or white, or in one species yellow or orange.
>
> First come two southerners.

SNOWY ORCHID, H. NIVEA (to 3 feet), has usually two or three long, narrow leaves on the lower part of the stem. The raceme has many small snow-white flowers. The distinctive feature of this species is that the lip is uppermost. The spur extends sideways, but is bent so that the end points upward.

August and September: in pine-barrens, meadows, and bogs from New Jersey southward on the coastal plain to Florida and thence westward to Texas. *Plate 20*.

SOUTHERN YELLOW ORCHID, H. INTEGRA (to 2 feet), has several narrow leaves sheathing the lower half of the stem; the upper are much smaller than the lower, and resemble the bracts below the raceme. This is the only fringeless rein orchid of our region with yellow or orange flowers. The flowers are very small but numerous and densely clustered. The lip is toothed along the sides.

August and September: in pine-barrens, bogs, and wet meadows, from New Jersey southward on the coastal plain to Florida and thence westward to Texas; also in the mountains of North Carolina and Tennessee; very rare in our range.

The remaining five species may be difficult to distinguish. All have small white, green, or yellowish flowers. The first two are northern and western, the third southern with a northern variety; the fourth is known by its conspicuous bracts; the fifth is our commonest of this group.

TALL BOG-ORCHID or BOG-CANDLE, H. DILATATA (to 4 feet), has several narrow leaves which sheathe the lower part of the stem. The flowers are white (or greenish or yellowish). The botanical name refers to the narrow, oblong lip, which is broader ("dilated") at the base. The spur about equals the lip, nearly $\frac{1}{2}$ inch long.

June to August: in meadows, bogs, wet woods, etc. throughout Canada and southward to New Jersey, Michigan, Wisconsin, South Dakota, Colorado, New Mexico, and California. It grows at high altitudes in the West. *Plate 20*.

This and the following species interbreed, producing hybrid plants.

NORTHERN GREEN ORCHID, H. HYPERBOREA (to 40 inches), has several lanceolate or oblong leaves. The flowers are green or yellowish. The lip also is lanceolate, tapering to a point; it is nearly $\frac{1}{2}$ inch long. The spur is shorter than the lip. The flower is sweet-smelling.

May to July: in bogs, thickets, meadows, and woods, etc. throughout Canada and southward to New York, Pennsylvania, Illinois, Minnesota, South Dakota, New Mexico, and California (often at high altitudes); also in Iceland and Asia. *Plate 21*. The more northern plants are often much smaller.

SOUTHERN REIN ORCHID, H. FLAVA (to 2 feet), has typically only two leaves; they are oblong or lanceolate. The bracts under the flowers are quite conspicuous. The flowers are yellowish-green. The lip is broad for this group, only about $\frac{1}{4}$ inch long, generally with a tooth on each side near the base. The spur is longer than the lip. The flower is sweet-smelling.

June to September: in swamps, wet thickets, bottomlands, etc. from Maryland to Missouri and southward to Florida and Texas. *Plate 21*. A variety with broader leaves is found from Nova Scotia to Ontario and Minnesota and southward to North Carolina, Indiana, Illinois, and Missouri.

LONG-BRACTED or FROG ORCHID, H. VIRIDIS (to 2 feet), has several leaves, the lower ones ovate, the upper lanceolate. The flowers are green (*viridis*). The lip, nearly $\frac{1}{2}$ inch long, is almost strap-shaped, with two or three teeth at the squared-off end. The spur is only about half as long as the lip, or less.

May to August: in damp woods, meadows, and shores from Newfoundland through Canada and southward to Maryland, the mountains of North Carolina, to Iowa, Nebraska, New Mexico, Utah, and Washington; also in Iceland and northeastern Asia. *Plate 21*. Our plants form a variety distinguished from Old-World plants by the long bracts under the flowers.

SMALL GREEN ORCHID, WOOD ORCHID, FROG-SPIKE, H. CLAVELLATA (to 18 inches), is the commonest rein orchid of our range. It has usually only one leaf (rarely two) midway on the stem; a very tapering narrow leaf. The flowers are very small, greenish-white or yellowish-white. The lip is oblong, only about $\frac{1}{4}$ inch long, and has three blunt teeth or tiny lobes at the square end. The spur is longer than the lip. Lip and spur extend sideways so that the flower seems to be distorted.

July to September: near water in woods, bogs, swamps, and wet meadows from Newfoundland to Minnesota and southward to Florida and Texas; also in Montana. *Plate 20*.

PLATE 20

Habenaria ciliaris *Rhein*

Habenaria cristata *V. Richard*

Habenaria hookeri *Johnson*

Habenaria clavellata *Rhein*

Habenaria dilatata *Rhein*

Habenaria orbiculata *Justice*

Habenaria nivea *Rhein*

Habenaria blephariglottis *Ryker*

EPIPACTIS

Epipactis is a genus mainly of Europe and Asia. Two species are North American, one in the northeastern United States.

HELLEBORINE, E. HELLEBORINE, is a leafy-stemmed orchid reaching 4 feet in height. The leaves may be 7 inches long and vary greatly in width; they may clasp the stem at their base, or they may have a short, narrow, stalk-like portion. The flowers are in a tall raceme, each in the axil of a long narrow bract. The sepals and lateral petals are about ½ inch long, green suffused with madder or rose. The lip forms a sac, with a triangular lip which is bent back under the sac.

June to September: in woods and thickets and on roadside banks from Quebec and Ontario southward and southwestward to New Jersey, the District of Columbia, and Missouri; in Europe and Asia. *Plate 21*. This is the only orchid which has been introduced from the Old World (no one knows how) and has spread across the northeastern United States.

LADIES'-TRESSES (SPIRANTHES)

The ladies'-tresses are delicate little plants, not generally recognized as orchids, with small white (or greenish or yellow) flowers in a narrow spike and leaves at or near the base of the flowering stem. The flowers of many species spiral around the stem, whence the botanical name. The stem grows from a cluster of roots which are generally thick and tuber-like. The flowers are small (from ⅕ to ⅖ inch long, mostly). The lateral petals adhere to the uppermost sepal, forming a sort of hood over the column. The lip of most of our species flares at the end with its edges crisped and glistening (as seen through a hand magnifier). With one exception, our species flower in the second half of the year.

This is a large genus, several hundred species being known in all the continents except Africa. Some twenty-five are reported from North America, but only eight of these concern us here.

The species are not easy to distinguish: the small size of the flowers necessitates the use of a hand magnifier and attention to minute details. The flowering periods in many species may seem unduly extended; this is because of their wide range. Plants growing in Florida may flower in January, those of the same species in Maine, in March. The plants grow mostly in open places, often on roadsides.

I. *One species may at once be separated by the color of its lip, which has a broad yellow stripe.*

S. LUCIDA is a small plant reaching a foot or a bit more in height. The leaves, on the lower part of the stem, are narrow and rather thick. The flowers are crowded in several spirals.

May to July: on moist gravelly shores and slopes and in thickets, bogs, and meadows from New Brunswick to Minnesota and southward to Delaware in the mountains to North Carolina and Tennessee, Illinois, and Kansas.

II. *Three of our species have a rather dense, cylindric spike of flowers — the flowers ascend the stem in several spiral ranks.*

NODDING LADIES'-TRESSES, S. CERNUA, is a robust species, whose stems may reach 4 feet in height, with flowers which curve downwards (they "nod"; they are "cernous"). It is downy in the upper parts; the leaves are mostly at the base, narrow, generally broadest towards the tip, up to a foot long. The flowers are white or greenish or straw-color or creamy, about ½ inch long.

July to January (in the various parts of its wide range): in open places, bogs, thickets, etc. from Quebec to Minnesota and South Dakota and southward to Florida and Texas. *Plate 21*. The larger plants form a distinct variety, commoner in the south, by some considered a separate species named *S. odorata*. The flowers have the odor of vanilla.

S. ROMANZOFFIANA grows up to 20 inches tall. The leaves are very narrow, often broadest near the tip; they may be 8 inches long. The spike is very dense, with bracts longer than the flowers; the flowers are white or creamy, about ½ inch long. A distinguishing mark that is seen with a hand magnifier is that the lip is indented at each side so that the mid-portion is narrower than the end.

July to October: in swamps, meadows, and thickets from Labrador across Canada and southward to New York, Ohio, Iowa, South Dakota, Utah, and California. *Plate 21*.

S. OVALIS is a comparatively rare southern species with smaller flowers than the two preceding. Its stem may be 16 inches tall, with leaves up to 6 inches long, broader towards the tip. The flowers are white, about ⅕ inch long.

August to November: in woods from Virginia to Missouri and south to Florida and Texas.

PLATE 21

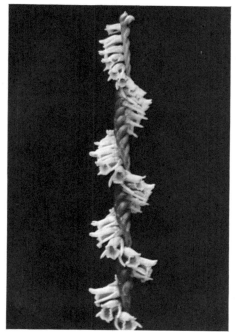

Spiranthes grayi   *Mayer*

Epipactis helleborine   *V. Richard*

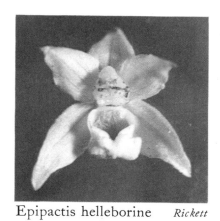

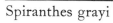

Epipactis helleborine   *Rickett*

Spiranthes romanzoffiana   *Scribner*

Spiranthes cernua   *Gottscho*

Habenaria flava   *Johnson*

Habenaria viridis   *Elbert*

Habenaria hyperborea   *Rhein*

III. *Our remaining species of* Spiranthes *have their flowers in a single rank extending up the stem on one side or spiraling around it. The general impression is thus of a very slender plant.*

The first two species below generally have leaves of an ovate or elliptic type on a short stalk; the leaves of the last two are grasslike.

LITTLE LADIES'-TRESSES, S. GRAYI, is a very slender plant with basal leaves about 2 inches long or more and a smooth stem up to 2 feet tall. The flowers are white and very small — only $\frac{1}{6}$ inch long — usually in a close spiral.

March to October: in sparse woods, on well-drained slopes, etc. from Massachusetts to Michigan and southward to Florida and Texas. *Plate 21*. It is named for the famous American botanist Asa Gray.

SLENDER LADIES'-TRESSES, S. GRACILIS, is similar in general aspect to *S. grayi*, but the flowers are larger — to $\frac{1}{4}$ inch long. They almost always form a spiral on the stem. The sepals and petals are white, the lip marked with a central green stripe (a southern variety has a yellow stripe).

June to October: in sandy soil in open woodland, grassy places, etc. from Nova Scotia and Quebec to Minnesota and southward to Florida and Texas. *Plate 22*.

NORTHERN SLENDER LADIES'-TRESSES, S. LACERA, has a very slender spike of flowers, reaching up to 20 inches above the ground, with flowers along one side or partly spiraling. The perianth is white, tubular with a trough-shaped lip which has a flaring, crisped end. The leaves are all at the base.

June to September: in meadows, fields, and thickets from Quebec across Canada and southward to Virginia, North Carolina, Tennessee, Wisconsin, and Minnesota.

SPRING LADIES'-TRESSES, S. VERNALIS, is distinguished from the above species by being downy in its upper parts. The stem grows to nearly 4 feet tall. The leaves are narrow, more or less lanceolate, up to a foot long or even more; they grow at the base and often also on the lower part of the stem. The spike of flowers is spiral. The flowers are yellowish or white, nearly $\frac{1}{2}$ inch long, and fragrant.

January to August: in wet meadows, bogs and marshes, moist pine-barrens, etc. from Quebec to Nebraska and southward to Florida and New Mexico; also in Mexico and Guatemala.

S. PRAECOX is a southern species with a limited occurrence in our range. It grows to about 30 inches tall with very narrow, often threadlike leaves 10 inches long. It may be slightly downy. The spike of flowers may be spiral but often the flowers are in a straight rank on one side of the stem. They are white, sometimes veined with green, nearly $\frac{1}{2}$ inch long. The lip is green-veined and wavy.

March to September: in wet pine-barrens, swamps, bogs, meadows, etc. from New Jersey in the coastal plain to Florida and Texas; westward to Arkansas; also in Rhode Island.

S. LACINIATA is thought to be a hybrid between the two preceding species. There is more downy hair in the inflorescence. There are more leaves on the stem. The flowers are more scattered. The end of the lip is jagged ("laciniate").

July to September: in bogs and marshes and shallow water from New Jersey to Florida and thence westward to Texas. *Plate 22*.

RATTLESNAKE-PLANTAINS (GOODYERA)

The genus *Goodyera* contains twenty-five or thirty species scattered over the world; four grow in the northeastern United States. All these have small ovate leaves in a circle at the base of the stem; in our plants they are dark green with white lines forming a network. The small white or greenish flowers are in a slender spike, which is downy and glandular. The upper sepal is joined at its edges to the lateral petals, forming a hood. The lip has the shape of a short sac or pouch with a sort of beak at its mouth. Stem and leaves grow from a small underground stem (rhizome). Like many orchids, these species grow in the organic matter of forest floors.

The genus commemorates an English botanist, John Goodyer, of the seventeenth century. It is not related to the plantains (*Plantago*) — nor to rattlesnakes. The leaves, with their network of white lines, were thought to resemble snakeskin, and therefore, if chewed, to be effective against snakebite.

Because of the smallness of their flowers and because of their variability, the species are difficult to distinguish without recourse to minute technical details. They are all northern plants: *G. pubescens* extends far southward, *G. repens* nearly to the southern edge of the northeastern states; the other two only reach our northern states. *G. oblongifolia* has the largest flowers. *G. pubescens* has a cylindric spike of flowers; *G. repens* has flowers in one row on one side of the stem; the other two have flowers either on one side or in a spiral row.

PLATE 22

Goodyera pubescens   *V. Richard*

Calopogon tuberosus   *Gottscho*

Spiranthes gracilis   *Elbert*

Spiranthes laciniata   *Rhein*

Goodyera repens   *Elbert*

Goodyera tesselata   *Scribner*

DOWNY RATTLESNAKE-PLANTAIN, G. PUBESCENS
(to 18 inches), is the most densely downy of these species. The leaves may reach 3 inches in length or even more. The flowers are generally white, small, about ⅕ inch long; they grow on all sides of the stem forming a dense cylindric spike.

May to October: in coniferous and deciduous woods from Newfoundland and Quebec to Minnesota and southward to Georgia, Alabama, and Arkansas. *Plate 22*.

CREEPING RATTLESNAKE-PLANTAIN, G. REPENS
(to 14 inches), has small leaves (reaching 2 inches in length) which are marked with dark instead of white veins; but in our range we find only a variety of this mainly Canadian, European, and Asian species, a variety with white-bordered veins, much like those in the other species. The plants produce slender runners: hence the name. The flowers are very small, about ⅛ inch long, white, greenish, or sometimes pink-tinged; they grow along one side of the stem.

June to September: in damp cool woods, usually mixed with moss, also in bogs and swamps, throughout Canada and southward to New York, in the mountains to North Carolina and Tennessee, to Minnesota, New Mexico, and Arizona; also in Europe and Asia. *Plate 22*.

G. OBLONGIFOLIA (to 18 inches) may have leaves unmarked with a white network or only partly so marked; they reach a length of 4 inches. The flowers are white (sometimes greenish), about ⅖ inch long, either along one side of the flowering stem or forming a spiral around it.

June to September: in dry or moist woods from Nova Scotia to Alaska and southward to Maine, Michigan, Wisconsin, South Dakota, Wyoming, New Mexico, Arizona, and California.

G. TESSELATA (to a foot tall) is densely downy. The leaves are about 3 inches long. The flowers are white, about ¼ inch long; they are rather loosely arranged along one side of the flowering stem or spiraling round it.

July to September: in dry coniferous or deciduous woods from Newfoundland to Ontario and Manitoba and southward to Maryland, Michigan, Wisconsin and Minnesota. *Plate 22*.

GRASS-PINKS (CALOPOGON)

There are only four species of *Calopogon*, of which only two are found in the northeastern United States. They make up in beauty what they lack in numbers. These orchids are among those that do not twist their flowers into an upside-down posture. The lip is the *uppermost* petal, and the column extends downwards and forward. This may not be evident at first glance, for the column has thin, petal-like wings on either side. The prominent hairs (the "beard") on the lip, however, identify it. *Calopogon* is from two Greek words meaning "beautiful beard."

Our two species are plants of bogs and swamps and other wet places. They are known as grass-pinks because of their narrow, grasslike leaves; they are also called swamp-pinks. (They are not, of course, related to the true pinks.)

C. TUBEROSUS is the species usually found in the
northeastern states. It sends up, from a round underground stem (a corm), a stem which may reach 4 feet or more in height, and, at the base of this, a single grasslike leaf (rarely two) up to 20 inches tall. From two to ten flowers (rarely only one or more than ten) are arranged in a raceme on the stem. The sepals and lateral petals are much alike, pink or rose-purple or magenta-crimson (rarely white), about an inch long. The lip may be pointed or indented at the tip. It bears club-shaped hairs which have cream-colored or white or flesh-colored stalks mostly tipped with orange. The column is colored like the perianth and could easily be mistaken for a petal.

May to August: in bogs and peaty meadows, margins of swamps, and along streams from Newfoundland and Quebec to Minnesota and southward to Florida and Texas. *Plate 22*. I have seen it growing in a swampy roadside in central Wisconsin, with the royal fern.

C. PALLIDUS is a smaller plant, rarely exceeding 2 feet. The flowers are (as the name indicates) pale in color, varying from rose-pink to white. The sepals and petals are from ½ to ⅗ inch long.

June to August: in damp pine-barrens, swamps, and other wet places from Virginia to Florida and Louisiana.

TWAYBLADES (LIPARIS)

Our two orchids by this name are members of a large genus, best represented in tropical Asia. The two leaves from which they take their English name are at or near the base of the stem, not halfway up as in *Listera* (also called twayblades). The stem grows from a roundish underground stem (corm). The sepals are lanceolate, the petals threadlike. The lip is comparatively broad, almost spadelike. The botanical name is from a Greek word meaning "fat," from the succulence of the leaves.

L. LILIFOLIA may grow to be a foot tall. The two ovate or elliptic, rather thick leaves may be 6 inches long or longer. The flowers are in a raceme. The sepals are greenish-white, rolled up lengthwise, about $\frac{1}{2}$ inch long. The lateral petals are brown-purple, threadlike and curved. The lip is brown-purple or lavender-purple.

May to July: in woods, on stream-banks, and in clearings from Maine to Minnesota and south to Georgia, Alabama, and Arkansas; also in China. *Plate 23.* The botanical name refers to such members of the lily family as the dogtooth-violets, which have somewhat similar leaves.

L. LOESELII resembles *L. lilifolia*, with leaves up to 8 inches long. The small flowers are yellowish-green; the lateral petals are rolled lengthwise; the lip is narrow.

June and July: in bogs and swamps and on moist slopes and shores from Nova Scotia and Quebec to Manitoba and Washington and southward to Maryland, the mountains of North Carolina, to Alabama, Missouri, Kansas, and North Dakota. *Plate 23.* The name refers to the French botanist Loiseleur-Deslongchamps.

GROUP III

Flowers minute, many packed together in a cylindric or spherical mass. Leaves without teeth on their edges; veins branched or not branched.

I. *Flower-mass generally enveloped by or associated with a bract which may be petal-like:* calla family.

II. *Flowers forming a long brown cylinder, tipped with a tapering lighter-colored group which soon withers; leaves narrow, grasslike:* cat-tail family.

III. *Flowers in spherical masses at intervals on a stem which is often zigzag:* bur-reed family.

THE CALLA FAMILY (ARACEAE)

The calla family is large and tropical, with a few species coming north into temperate America. It is familiar also to those who grow plants on their window sills or in greenhouses, for it includes the philodendrons, Chinese evergreen (*Aglaonema*), the ceriman (*Monstera deliciosa*), the anthuriums, dumb-cane (*Dieffenbachia*), and the calla-lilies (which are, of course, not lilies). One species of *Colocasia* yields the edible tuber called taro, an important source of food throughout the Pacific tropics.

The plants of this family are of diverse sizes and forms, some herbs, others vines, others treelike. They are brought into one family by their flowers and inflorescence. The flowers are small, with no perianth or with from four to six sepals.

Many are crowded together on a thick stem, either at its base only or extending up to and over its tip. Below this inflorescence there is generally a large bract, in some species leaflike but in others variously colored and having the appearance of a huge petal; this may extend up at one side of the flowers or even completely envelop them. Two special terms are useful here: the spike or knob of tiny flowers is a spadix; the bract is a spathe (this term is used also for bracts in certain other families – *Iridaceae*, *Commelinaceae* – and may refer to a *pair* of bracts as well as to one).

Our few species mostly grow in shallow water or in wet places; some are woodland plants. They offer no difficulties in identification.

SYMPLOCARPUS

There is but one species of this genus.

SKUNK-CABBAGE, S. FOETIDUS, usually has the honor of being the first flower of spring wherever it grows. The flowers are actually formed underground in the autumn, and the whole inflorescence, surrounded by its spathe, pushes up early in the following spring, generating such heat in its rapid growth that it thaws the soil around it and comes up often through snow or ice. The cabbage-like leaves appear as the spathe withers; their large veiny blades may reach 3 feet in length. The flowers are on a dome-shaped spadix; each has four sepals, four stamens, and a pistil.

February to May: in shallow water, swampy woods, and wet meadows from Quebec to Manitoba and southward to Georgia, Tennessee, Illinois, and Iowa; also in Asia. *Plate 23.* In spite of the unpleasant odor (often exaggerated; it does not perfume the landscape), the leaves may be eaten as greens; they must first be cooked in several changes of water, to which

PLATE 23

Symplocarpus foetidus *Rickett*

Liparis lilifolia *Allen*

Calla palustris *DeVoe*

Arisaema triphyllum *Rickett*

Arisaema triphyllum *Rickett*

Liparis loeselii *Rhein*

Arisaema dracontium *Johnson*

Peltandra virginica *Roche*

baking soda has been added. The rhizome also, after suitable treatment, was used by the Indians as a source of flour. NOTE: enthusiasts for eating native plants must carefully distinguish skunk cabbage from the very poisonous Indian poke (*Veratrum viride*) which grows with it and somewhat resembles it.

ARISAEMA

The genus *Arisaema* has flowers only at the base of the spadix. The spathe is green, more or less marked by brown lines. The flowers have no perianth. The stamens and pistils are in separate flowers, the staminate flowers above the pistillate (sometimes only one kind is present on a spadix). The inflorescence and the leaves grow from a corm underground.

INDIAN-TURNIP or JACK-IN-THE-PULPIT, A. TRI-
PHYLLUM, has usually a single leaf on a stalk up to 2 feet tall, the blade divided into three. The spathe forms the "pulpit," within which Jack, the top of the spadix, may be seen. The flowers are hidden in the base of the spathe.

April to June: in moist woods and swamps, from New Brunswick and Quebec to Manitoba and southward to Florida, Louisiana, and Kansas. *Plate 23.*

The corm is the "turnip," which is palatable and was eaten by the Indians, but only after cooking. In the raw state all parts of the plant contain innumerable needle-like crystals of calcium oxalate which can cause an intense burning sensation in the mouth and throat. The crystals are removed by proper cooking.

The species has by some botanists been divided into three or more by differences in the shape of the segments of the leaf, the color and striping of the spathe, and other details.

GREEN-DRAGON or DRAGON-ROOT, A. DRACON-
TIUM, is less common than *A. triphyllum*. It is easily recognized by the leaf, whose blade is divided into from five to fifteen segments; and by the spadix, whose long tapering tip — the dragon's snout? — protrudes from the end of the spathe.

May and June: in woods from Quebec to Minnesota and southward to Florida and Texas. *Plate 23.*

ACORUS

We have but one species of *Acorus*. Another grows in Asia.

SWEET-FLAG or CALAMUS, A. CALAMUS, has grass-
like leaves 5 feet tall or taller, growing from a rhizome. The stem that bears the flowers resembles the leaves, being flat. The spathe prolongs this stem, and the spadix, covered with flowers, projects from its base. The flowers form a pattern of diamonds on the long narrow spadix. Each has six sepals, six stamens, and a pistil.

The English name sweet-flag refers to the sweetish, aromatic odor and taste of the leaves and especially of the rhizome. This underground stem has been used in making candy.

May to August: in wet meadows, swamps, banks of streams, etc. from Nova Scotia to Oregon and southward to Florida and Texas. *Plate 179.*

CALLA

There is a single species of *Calla*.

WATER-ARUM or WILD-CALLA, C. PALUSTRIS,
sends up from its underground stem or rhizome a cluster of leaves, having broad blades, indented at the base, on long stalks; they are about a foot tall altogether. The flowers also are on a long stalk. The spathe is white and rather flat, with the spadix plainly visible at one side. The flowers have no perianth, six stamens, and a pistil.

April to August: in swamps, bogs, and shallow water from Newfoundland across Canada and southward to New Jersey, Indiana, Wisconsin, and Minnesota; also in the Old World. *Plate 23.*

PELTANDRA

We have only one species of *Peltandra*; several others grow in the southeastern states.

ARROW-ARUM, P. VIRGINICA, has arrowhead leaves which may be mistaken for those of *Sagittaria*; but the course of the veins is distinctive. The spathe is long, slender, and sharp-pointed, with a constriction about a fourth of the way up. The upper part disappears gradually, exposing the staminate flowers on the upper part of the spadix inside. The pistillate flowers are on the lower part, below the constriction.

April to July: in swamps and on the borders of streams, etc. from Maine to Michigan and southward to Florida and Texas. *Plate 23.*

PLATE 24

Comandra umbellata   *Johnson*

Orontium aquaticum   *Gottscho*

Comandra richardsiana   *Johnson*

Saururus cernuus   *Johnson*

Typha latifolia   *Rickett*

Typha angustifolia   *Rickett*

ORONTIUM

The genus contains only one species.

GOLDEN-CLUB, O. AQUATICUM, has leaves a foot tall or more, growing from a stem – a rhizome – beneath the surface. The blades are elliptic; they are on stalks as long as themselves. The flowering stems rise from among the leaves and often surpass them in height. Each bears a spadix at its tip covered with bright yellow flowers – the golden club. There is no spathe, only the vestige of one, a ring at the base of the spadix.

April to June: in shallow water and on wet banks from Massachusetts to Kentucky and southward to Florida and Louisiana. *Plate 24.*

THE CAT-TAIL FAMILY (TYPHACEAE)

The cat-tails are familiar plants of ditches, wet meadows, and swamps, but may not be thought of as flowering plants. The tall brown "cat's tail" is composed of thousands of minute flowers, each little more than a single pistil. Above them is a more slender spike of staminate flowers, lighter in color. When the pollen is shed, these upper flowers disappear, leaving only the withered stem that bore them. The pistils become small seedlike fruits, with long hairs growing from their stalks – and with their growth the whole brown cylinder bursts into a downy mass.

The botanical name is taken from the classical Greek name for the same genus. They are also known in England as bulrushes, a name applied in America to various sedges and horsetails.

TYPHA

T. LATIFOLIA is the common species, with leaves (*folia*) ½ inch wide or wider (*lati-*), and no space between the pistillate and staminate parts of the inflorescence.

May to July: throughout North America, and in Europe and Asia. *Plate 24.*

T. ANGUSTIFOLIA has narrower (*angusti-*) leaves, not more than ⅓ inch wide, and a short space of bare stem between pistillate and staminate flowers.

May to July: from southern Maine to Ontario and southward to South Carolina, Kentucky, Missouri, and Nebraska; California; Europe and Asia. *Plate 24.* Most abundant near the coast. Said to hybridize with the preceding species, producing plants to which various names have been given.

T. DOMINGENSIS is a tropical American species that has spread into North America. It is like *T. angustifolia* but has more numerous leaves (more than ten) and a pale brown spike.

June and July: from Delaware to Florida along the coast and thence westward to southern California; in the interior to Kansas, Utah, and Nevada.

THE BUR-REED FAMILY (SPARGANIACEAE)

The bur-reeds form an aquatic family with minute flowers. The erect stems grow from a rhizome underground. They bear leaves which sheathe the stem at the base. On the upper part of the stem the flowers form dense round masses, the staminate above, the pistillate below; this part of the stem may be branched and is often zigzag. The staminate flowers disappear when their pollen has been shed and that part of the stem withers. The pistils become small hard seedlike fruits with sharp beaks, each mass of them forming a bur.

SPARGANIUM

There are many species, identification of which is impossible without attention to minute characteristics. Three of the commonest in our range are *S. eurycarpum* (with two stigmas on the pistil) (*Plate 25*), *S. androcladum* (with stiff leaves), *S. americanum* (with soft leaves), and *S. fluctuans* (*Plate 179*).

GROUP IV

SEPALS present or absent, petals lacking. Flowers not minute. Stamens fewer than twenty.

I. *Plants with flowers in spikes.*

   A. Flowers with no perianth: lizard's-tail family.*
   B. Flowers with sepals (white, pink, or green); from three to nine stamens: smartweed family.*

II. *Plants with flowers in branched clusters; five stamens: sandalwood family.*

III. *Plants with flowers singly in axils of leaves:* Dutchman's-pipe family*; crowberry family.*

IV. *Plants with flowers in racemes; ten stamens:* pokeweed family.*

V. *Plants with several flowers enclosed in a circle of bracts or nectaries which look like sepals or petals.*

   A. Flowers with a tubular calyx: four-o'clock family.*
   B. Flowers with no perianth, each a single pistil or a single stamen: spurge family.

Besides the families named above, many species of the buttercup family lack petals; see group V. See also in the "guide to the families" (page 14) the list of plants in other groups that lack petals, or that *seem* to lack petals or perianth because of the early fall of the sepals.

THE LIZARD'S-TAIL FAMILY (SAURURACEAE)

We have but one genus and one species of this family, which is related to the tropical pepper family, a vast family of Central and South America.

SAURURUS

LIZARD'S-TAIL or WATER-DRAGON, S. CERNUUS, is a plant of wet places. Its creeping stems (runners) send up erect branches bearing long-stalked leaves with heart-shaped blades, and one or more slender, tapering spikes of small white flowers (the lizard's tails). The spikes regularly droop at their tips (this is the meaning of *cernuus*). There is no perianth, the white color being due to the stalks of the several stamens.

June to September: in shallow water and swamps from Quebec to Minnesota and southward to Florida and Texas. *Plate 24.*

THE SANDALWOOD FAMILY (SANTALACEAE)

In the sandalwood family we have only one genus common in the northeastern states. Several others include shrubby plants of the South that may just enter our southern borders. The English name has apparently nothing to do with footwear, but is derived from the Arabic name of a tree, transcribed into *Santalum* by Linnaeus (who classed it among "barbarous" names).

*Families represented in our area by only one or a few species, and readily identified by the illustrations of these.

91

BASTARD TOAD-FLAXES (COMANDRA)

The tip of the flower-stalk of *Comandra* flares into a small funnel, on the margin of which stand five white sepals. There are no petals. There are five stamens, and a pistil whose ovary is joined with the surrounding funnel (it is therefore inferior). The plants grow from underground creeping stems (rhizomes) and are parasitic on the roots of various woody plants. The leaves, borne singly, are narrow, blunt, without teeth. The name is from Greek words signifying "hair" and "male," because the stamens are hairy. Why they are likened to toad-flax (*Linaria*) I do not know.

C. UMBELLATA has a rhizome deep in the ground.

The leaves are pale on the lower surface. The fruit is a small nut.

April to July: in dry ground from Maine to Ontario and Michigan and southward to Georgia and Alabama. *Plate 24.*

C. RICHARDSIANA has a rhizome just beneath the surface. The leaves are green on both sides. The fruit is a small nut.

May to August: in stony and sandy soils, wooded or open, from Newfoundland and Labrador across Canada and southward to New York, Tennessee, Arkansas, Kansas, and Oregon. *Plate 24.*

C. LIVIDA has shorter, more triangular sepals. The flowers are on shorter stalks, in the axils of leaves. The rhizome is very slender. The fruit is red and partly succulent. On account of this distinctive fruit, this species is by some botanists treated as composing a distinct genus, *Geocaulon*.

May to August: in wet moss or humus from Labrador to Alaska and southward to the mountains of New England and New York, to Ohio, Michigan, and British Columbia.

THE DUTCHMAN'S-PIPE FAMILY (ARISTOLOCHIACEAE)

This is a small family, mostly tropical, characterized by a lack of petals and by sepals, separate or joined, that may resemble petals. There are either three separate sepals or a calyx that takes the form of the "Dutchman's pipe." Our species have either six or twelve stamens. The ovary is embedded in the tubular end of the flower-stalk.

BIRTHWORTS (ARISTOLOCHIA)

These are the "Dutchman's-pipes," from the shape of the calyx. The botanical name is said to be derived from Greek words signifying "best delivery," referring to childbirth. This is perhaps an example of the doctrine of signatures (see under *Hepatica*), the flower suggesting the pregnant womb. There are many tropical species, some with enormous and ill-smelling flowers of fantastic forms.

VIRGINIA SNAKEROOT, A. SERPENTARIA, grows up to 2 feet tall, from an underground stem. The leaf-blades are shaped much like arrowheads with blunt "barbs." The flowers are on branches from the base of the leafy stem, less than an inch long. The "pipe" flares at the end into a brownish-purple, slightly three-lobed disk. Inside are six stamens and a pistil with a broad stigma and an inferior ovary.

May to July: in woods from Connecticut to Kansas and southward to Florida and Texas. An inconspicuous little plant, not rare but often overlooked. The English name refers to the supposed value of the "root" (rhizome) as a cure for snakebite.

A. tomentosa and *A. durior*, called pipe-vines, are southern species which are found along our southern borders, the first from southern Indiana to Missouri, the second from southern Pennsylvania to Kentucky. Both are woody vines with ovate leaf-blades indented at the base. The flowers do not differ essentially from those of *A. serpentaria*.

ASARUM

The plants of the genus *Asarum* have heart-shaped leaf-blades (ovate, indented where they are joined to the stalk), and small, brownish or reddish flowers borne close to the ground. The flowers have three sepals, twelve stamens, and an ovary joined with the surrounding cup-shaped base (receptacle).

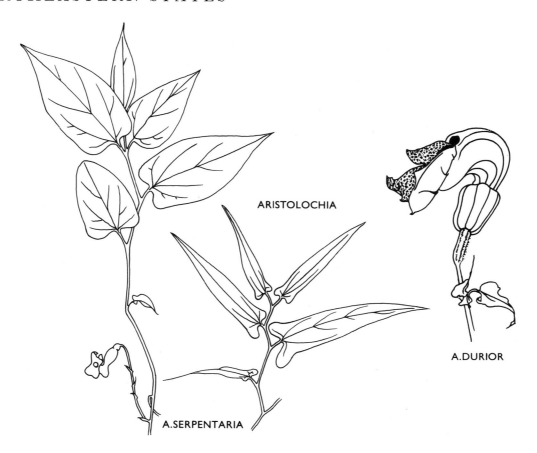

WILD-GINGER, A. CANADENSE, consists largely of
two large, heart-shaped, downy leaves (the stalks
are shaggy), between which, near the ground, grows
the single flower on a short stalk. The sepals are red-
brown and pointed; the pistil has one style with six
stigmas. All this grows from a thick stem (rhizome)
just beneath the surface.

April and May: in woods, especially on shaded
banks, from Quebec to Manitoba and southward to
North Carolina, Alabama, Arkansas, and Kansas.
Plate 25. Several varieties have been recognized, differing in the shape and position of the sepals; some
botanists consider them distinct species. When broken, the rhizome has a strong aromatic smell something like that of ginger. If cooked with sugar, it is
said to make an acceptable substitute for the real
thing. (True ginger is from a plant of a tropical
family.)

HEARTLEAF, A. VIRGINICUM, has several heart-
shaped, evergreen blades rather blunt at the tip,
on stalks up to 4 inches long. The flower is an inch
long or less. Leaves and flower-stalk arise close together from the tip of the slender rhizome. The ovary
has six styles, each with a stigma and each bearing
two horns at the tip.

March to May: in woods from Virginia to Kentucky and southward to Georgia and Alabama. *Plate
25.* This and the following species have by some botanists been placed in a separate genus, *Hexastylis.*

A. SHUTTLEWORTHII is very similar to the preceding species, differing chiefly in its larger flowers,
which may reach 2 inches in length.

April to July: in upland woods from Virginia
and West Virginia southward to Georgia and Alabama. *Plate 25.*

Two other southern species reach Virginia, West Virginia,
and Kentucky: *A. arifolium* (*Plate 25*) and *A. ruthii.* These have
more triangular leaf-blades. The first has a "flask-shaped" flower
about an inch long, the sepals flaring; the second, an egg-shaped
flower less than an inch long with sepals extending straight forward.

THE SMARTWEED FAMILY (POLYGONACEAE)

As the English name indicates, this family,
at least in eastern North America, consists largely
of weeds. Most of these, having inconspicuous
flowers, are not treated in this book. A few species of smartweeds, however, are striking enough
to attract the naturalist; the docks, as a group,

have some interesting points; and two other genera contribute wild flowers with some pretensions to beauty. Cultivated species are not numerous but familiar: buckwheat and rhubarb (both sometimes found growing wild).

The family is easy to recognize by the stipules at the base of the leaves, which generally take the form of a sheath (usually cylindric) around the stem. (This is missing in one of the species here described.) The flowers are small but generally numerous, with no petals but a varying number of sepals (from three to six) and several stamens (from three to twelve). The pistil has two or three styles, and becomes a one-seeded grain (achene), generally with two or three angles, and in some genera permanently enclosed in the calyx.

THE SMARTWEEDS AND KNOTWEEDS (POLYGONUM)

The smartweeds are rather attractive small plants with spikes* of pink or white flowers and mostly lanceolate leaves. The knotweeds are mostly creeping weeds with minute flowers; not mentioned further in this book.

Among the many species, the most attractive or common are presented here. All are rather difficult to identify without attention to the minute features emphasized in the technical books.

All flower in summer, and, weather permitting, on into autumn.

PINKWEED, P. PENSYLVANICUM, is a common smartweed in fields, moist waste ground, on shores, etc. It is tall for this genus, reaching 4 feet in height. The upper part of the stem bears stalked glands (visible under the hand lens). The spike of flowers is erect and dense, up to $\frac{1}{2}$ inch thick. The flowers are generally bright pink, though there is a white-flowered form. The achenes are two-edged.

From Quebec to Minnesota and South Dakota and south to Florida and Texas. *Plate 25.*

LADY'S-THUMB, P. PERSICARIA, is a similar weed in similar situations practically throughout the continental United States, an immigrant from Europe. It is about 3 feet tall, smooth, its sheaths fringed with bristles, the flower-spike dense and nearly $\frac{1}{2}$ inch thick but often only about an inch long. The flowers are pink. The achenes are mostly two-edged. The leaves often have a dark blotch in the middle of the blade, which has led to the local English name Virgin's-pinch: the Virgin picked the leaf. It is also called, in Scotland, useless — the Virgin threw it away! *Plate 25.*

P. CESPITOSUM is another immigrant, from Asia, which has formed bright-flowered masses in waste places in the Atlantic states. It has thinner spikes (about $\frac{1}{4}$ inch) and long, conspicuous bristles on the edges of the sheaths. The achenes are three-angled. *Plate 26.*

P. LAPATHIFOLIUM is a very widespread native species, occurring in damp places and cultivated ground practically throughout the country. It may be 6 feet tall or even taller. It is recognized by its slender flower-spikes (about $\frac{1}{4}$ inch thick) which have drooping tips. The flowers vary from green or white to pink. The achenes are two-edged.

WATER-PEPPER, P. HYDROPIPER, gives a name to the group, for it is both acrid and peppery in taste and causes smarting of sensitive skin on contact. This is also true of *P. persicaria* and other species. *P. hydropiper* is a native of Europe, naturalized in damp places throughout this country. The stems may be erect or lean outwards. The flowers are greenish-white or pink-tipped, in slender spikes which usually curve. The achenes have either two or three edges.

WATER SMARTWEED, P. AMPHIBIUM, is a species that grows in different forms around the world. As the name indicates, it is at home both on land or in water, and its form varies accordingly. In water the elliptic leaf-blades float; they are attached to the stem by long, slender stalks. On land the leaves are much like those of other species, and the plant may be hairy. The flower-spikes are dense, rather thick (more than $\frac{1}{2}$ inch), and erect. The flowers are pink. The achenes are two-edged. *Plate 26.*

P. COCCINEUM is another water smartweed with terrestrial and aquatic forms, found throughout the country. On land the leaves have elliptic or lanceolate blades on short stalks. In water the blades tend to be broader and deeply indented at the base. The land form is downy. Both forms have rather slender but handsome spikes of pink or red flowers. The species is found on damp and dry prairies and in or near ponds and streams. *Plate 26.*

*The flowers are arranged along the sides of a stem, densely or at intervals, in a form which is actually neither a spike nor a raceme as those terms are usually defined but is here called a spike for convenience.

PLATE 25

Asarum virginicum   *Phelps*

Asarum canadense   *Rickett*

Asarum arifolium   *Justice*

Asarum shuttleworthii   *Gottscho*

Sparganium eurycarpum   *Rhein*

Polygonum persicaria   *Elbert*

Polygonum pensylvanicum   *Johnson*

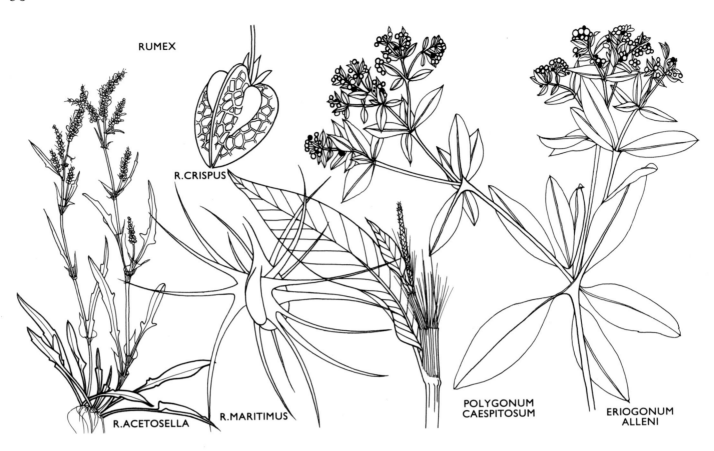

RUMEX

R. CRISPUS

R. ACETOSELLA   R. MARITIMUS

POLYGONUM
CAESPITOSUM

ERIOGONUM
ALLENI

PRINCE'S-FEATHER, P. ORIENTALE, is the handsomest species of the genus, with heart-shaped
blades on long stalks and mostly drooping spikes
of bright rose-colored flowers. This is a native of
India, brought to this country as a garden plant, and
escaped from cultivation in places. Another name, of
unexplained significance, is kiss-me-over-the-garden-
gate. *Plate 26.*

VIRGINIA KNOTWEED or JUMPSEED, P. VIRGIN-
IANUM, is a common woodland plant with lanceolate or ovate leaves and small greenish-white flowers
borne at intervals in a slender spike. There are four
sepals and two styles which bend downward.
From Quebec to Minnesota and Nebraska, and
south to Florida and Texas. *Plate 27.*

P. TENUE may serve as an example of the numerous
weedy species. It grows about a foot tall. The
leaves are narrow and sharp-pointed. The flowers are
strung out along the upper part of the stem in the
axils of small bracts. The sepals are whitish or pale

pink, and remain attached around the three-cornered
black achene ("seed").
June to October: in dry open places from Maine
to Minnesota and southward to Georgia and Texas.
Plate 27.

CLIMBING FALSE BUCKWHEAT, P. SCANDENS, is a
common weed which clambers in fencerows
among other plants. The leaves are commonly heart-
shaped, with a pointed tip and indented base. The
flowers are in erect racemes. Their outer three sepals
bear narrow projecting "wings" on their outer sides;
these give the whole cluster the appearance of small
fluttering leaves.
August to November: in thickets, roadside ditches, etc. throughout our range. *Plate 26.* There are
several other twining or struggling species of *Polygonum.* Black-bindweed, *P. convolvulus,* lacks the
wings on the sepals. Tear-thumb, *P. sagittatum,* has
leaves like arrowheads and a stem armed with hooked,
sharp prickles. These and others are widespread in
North America.

THE DOCKS (RUMEX)

The docks are distinctly weeds and get no full
descriptions or illustrations here. Yet they are conspicuous and, in several of their features, interesting.

The flowers have six sepals in two circles (should the
inner circle be termed petals?). The inner three of
these enlarge as the fruit (a three-cornered achene)

PLATE 26

Polygonum orientale   *Ryker*

Polygonella articulata   *V. Richard*

Polygonum amphibium   *Johnson*

Polygonum scandens   *Gottscho*

Polygonum amphibium   *Gottscho*

Polygonum coccineum   *Johnson*

Polygonum caespitosum   *Rickett*

develops, becoming joined at their edges so as to form an outer covering of the grain. They take various forms, some developing marginal teeth or fingers: it is by such peculiarities that the species are identified.

Two common and widespread species are *R. crispus*, sourdock, and *R. maritimus*. The little *R. acetosella*, red-sorrel or sheep-sorrel, is a familiar and pernicious weed of fields and lawns.

JOINTWEEDS (POLYGONELLA)

These little plants of sandy, mostly dry places have tiny pink or white flowers in their spikes and narrow leaves on branched stems; but the flowers are numerous enough to make an attractive showing. There are five sepals and eight stamens. The sepals form a loose covering around the grain.

P. ARTICULATA grows to about 2 feet tall. The stem and branches are wiry and the leaves almost threadlike. It flowers in summer on sandy beaches and dunes from Maine to Minnesota and southward to North Carolina, northern Indiana, and Iowa. It is sometimes, mistakenly, called heather. *Plate 26.*

ERIOGONUM

This is a vast genus in the West, but only one species is at all widely distributed in the Northeast.

UMBRELLA-PLANT, E. ALLENI, has a branching stem, up to nearly 2 feet tall, bearing stalked leaves with oval blades at the base and in circles where it forks.

The whole plant is densely downy or woolly with white hairs. The flowers are numerous, in many small clusters with a sort of cup of bracts beneath each cluster. There are six yellow sepals and nine stamens.

July to September: on rocky slopes and in barren places in Virginia and West Virginia.

THE FOUR-O'CLOCK FAMILY (NYCTAGINACEAE)

The garden four-o'clock, from tropical America, has given its name to the family. Several species of the same genus are native in North America.

UMBRELLA-WORTS (MIRABILIS)

The generally weedy nature of these plants is mitigated by the small clusters of pink or purple flowers. Several (in the wild species) small flowers are seated in a green, cup-shaped, five-lobed involucre (formed from a circle of joined bracts); this might possibly be mistaken for the calyx of one flower. The individual flowers are formed of five sepals joined to make a tubular pink calyx, less than $\frac{1}{2}$ inch long, with five teeth at the end. There are from three to five stamens. The fruit is a small achene enclosed by the calyx. The leaves are paired.

M. NYCTAGINEA is a smooth plant up to about 5 feet tall, with stalked leaves, the blades more or less heart-shaped. It grows in all sorts of places — on prairies, river-banks, etc. — from Wisconsin to Manitoba

and south to Alabama and Texas; sometimes wandering also eastward. It flowers in summer. *Plate 27.*

M. HIRSUTA is hairy, especially on the stem where leaves emerge. It grows up to 3 feet tall. The leaf-blades are lanceolate, often narrowly so, with short stalks or none. In dry places from Wisconsin to Saskatchewan and Wyoming and south to Missouri, Texas, and New Mexico.

M. ALBIDA is whitened with fine hairs, appearing smooth. The leaves are narrowly elliptic, rather blunt. It stands about 3 feet tall. In dry places, prairies, bluffs, etc. from South Carolina to Kansas and south to Georgia and Texas

Mirabilis jalapa is the common species of gardens.

THE POKEWEED FAMILY (PHYTOLACCACEAE)

The *Phytolaccaceae* are a mostly tropical family. We have only one species.

PHYTOLACCA

POKEWEED or POKEBERRY, P. AMERICANA, is a
widely branched, smooth plant which may reach
a height of 10 feet but is more often 5 or 6 feet tall.
The stem is frequently red, especially late in the season. The small greenish-white or pinkish flowers are
in racemes which are borne opposite the leaves. There
are five sepals which could be mistaken for petals, a
variable number of stamens, and an ovary composed
of a number of segments in a ring, each with its own
style and stigma. The ovaries become purple-black
berries in a raceme which now hangs down.

July to October: in moist woods, on roadsides,
and in fields and waste places from Maine to Minnesota and south to Florida and Texas. *Plate 27.* The
crimson juice of the berries was used as a pigment by
the Missouri painter Bingham. They are reputed to
be poisonous, but have been used to color foods and
wines; the name pigeonberry suggests that they are
or were eaten by birds. The very large root is indeed
dangerously poisonous. The young shoots (before
the crimson color appears) are, however, harmless and
palatable when cooked as greens.

THE SPURGE FAMILY (EUPHORBIACEAE)

The spurge family is a vast family of mostly
tropical and semitropical plants, some of which
yield important foods, oils, drugs, and rubber,
while others are highly poisonous. In temperate
regions we find many common weeds and a few
cultivated species. Some of the most familiar are
manihot, which provides the staple food of many
South Americans and the tapioca of our own
shops; the castor-oil plant; the rubber tree; the
tung-oil tree; the shrubs with decorative foliage
known as croton; poinsettias; and crown-of-thorns.
From even this brief list the great diversity of the
plants is evident. In the great genus *Euphorbia*
many species of hot, dry regions take forms
curiously like those of cacti.

The flowers also are various, but always very

small, and always limited to stamens or pistils,
never having both. There may or may not be a
calyx (none in the species described below); there
are no petals. Stamens vary from one to many
(only one in the wild species here described): a
flower may consist entirely of one stamen! There
is one pistil, usually with three styles. A number
of these simplified flowers may be enclosed in a
sort of cup formed of bracts or nectaries, in some
species with petal-like appendages, and all easily
mistaken for a single flower. Or clusters of flowers without perianth may be surrounded by
leaves of various colors, as in poinsettia. The species described below have milky juice, which is
quite general but not universal in the family. Many
other species have small green flower-clusters.

THE SPURGES (EUPHORBIA)

Spurge is derived from the Latin for "purge,"
the milky juice of many species having that effect as
part of its poisonous qualities. There are said to be
about 1,600 species. Some botanists have divided the
genus into many genera. In the northeastern United
States thirty-six or thirty-seven species are known,
many of them common weeds.

FLOWERING SPURGE, E. COROLLATA, has white,
petal-like appendages on the bracts around each
flower cluster, so that the cluster is easily taken for a
single flower. The plant grows up to 3 feet tall, forming many branches. The leaves are narrow and blunt
at the end. The whole plant is smooth.
June to October: in fields, roadsides, woods, and
prairies from Massachusetts to Minnesota and Nebraska and southward to Florida and Texas. *Plate 27.*

FIRE-ON-THE-MOUNTAIN or WILD-POINSETTIA, E.
HETEROPHYLLA, is a low plant, sometimes at-
taining 3 feet in height, bearing leaves (*phylla*) of very
diverse (*hetero*) aspect. They may be ovate, fiddle-
shaped, or very narrow (see the drawings). The flowers are clustered at the tip of the stem and usually surrounded by leaves that have a red or white blotch at
the base or in the lower half.
August and September: in waste places, open or
wooded, from Virginia to Minnesota and South Dakota and south to Florida and Texas. *Plate 28.*

SNOW-ON-THE-MOUNTAIN, E. MARGINATA, is a
plant of the West which is cultivated in eastern
gardens and has escaped into neighboring roadsides
and fields. Its names derive from its leaves, which are
bordered with white. It grows some 2 or 3 feet tall.

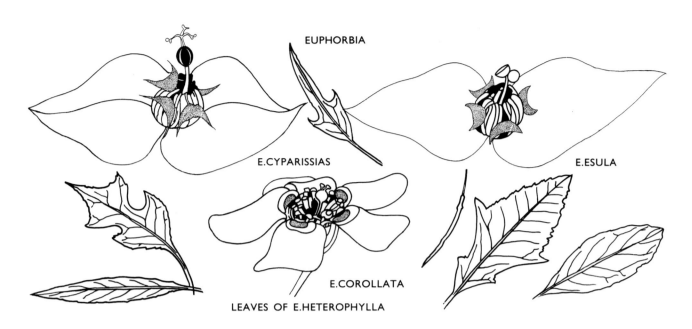

EUPHORBIA

E.CYPARISSIAS

E.ESULA

E.COROLLATA

LEAVES OF E.HETEROPHYLLA

June to October: in fields and prairies from Minnesota to Montana and southward to Missouri and New Mexico; in waste places elsewhere. *Plate 27.*

EYEBANE, E. MACULATA, may serve as an example
of the many weedy species. It has creeping stems with small paired leaves, often forming mats. The leaves frequently bear a crimson spot (*macula*). The flower clusters are small but numerous, each surrounded by bracts with white or red appendages. The photograph shows pistils (each constituting one flower) in various stages of development into fruits; and here and there the two-lobed yellow tip of a stamen appears.
June to October: in dry soil of roadsides, fields, waste ground, etc. from Quebec to North Dakota and south to Florida and Texas. *Plate 28.*

CYPRESS SPURGE, E. CYPARISSIAS, grows usually in
dense masses, the stems about 2 feet tall, bearing great numbers of needle-like leaves. The tiny flowers at the summit of the stems are embraced by waxy, yellowish glands (see the photograph) and by one or more pairs of broad, pointed bracts colored a bright greenish-yellow. A field covered with these plants is carpeted with gold, and many a highway is gilt-edged. These bracts may turn red as they age.
April to August: on roadsides, in fields, ceme-

teries, etc. from Maine to Minnesota and Colorado and southward to Virginia and Missouri; an immigrant from the Old World, now well established here. *Plate 28.*

LEAFY SPURGE, E. ESULA, resembles *E. cyparissias*,
but is generally taller, with broader (but still narrow) and less numerous leaves. The glands around the flowers bear two distinct horns. This also is an immigrant, which has become in places a troublesome weed. The season and range are much the same as those of cypress spurge but it extends westward to the Pacific. *Plate 28.*

E. LUCIDA, another naturalized species, resembles *E.
esula* but is taller (4 feet or more), with shining ("lucid") leaves an inch broad. It is found along roads and in fields and waste places from New York to Ontario and Iowa. *Plate 28.*

E. ZINNIFLORA does indeed suggest a small zinnia;
but it is the white appendages of a circle of glands that we see, not the ray-flowers of a composite. This is a southern species that is found along our southern borders. It grows in sandy and rocky places in open woodlands from Virginia to Kentucky and Arkansas and southward to Florida and Texas, flowering from June to September. *Plate 28.*

THE BOX FAMILY (BUXACEAE)

Of this small family, which includes the cultivated box, one species of the genus *Pachysandra* grows wild in the southeastern United States.

ALLEGHENY-SPURGE, P. PROCUMBENS, is a plant
only a foot or so tall with several evergreen leaves

near the tip of the stem and one or more spikes of greenish or purplish flowers from near the base. The

PLATE 27

Phytolacca americana   *Johnson*

Phytolacca americana   *Rickett*

Euphorbia corollata   *Johnson*

Mirabilis nyctaginea   *Elbert*

Euphorbia marginata   *Rickett*   Polygonum tenue   *Johnson*   Polygonum virginianum   *Rickett*

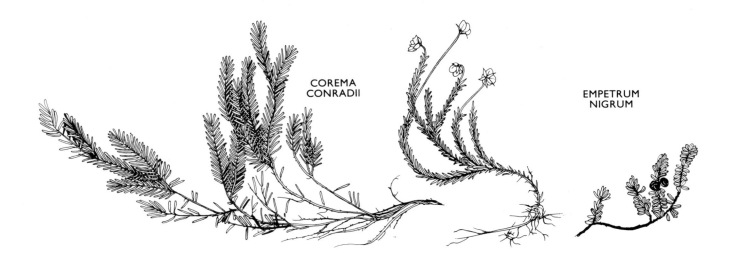

flowers in the upper part of the spike lack pistils, having a calyx of four sepals and four stamens; the flowers below lack stamens, having a pistil and several sepals. The white stalks of the stamens are the most conspicuous part of the flowers.

Allegheny-spurge grows in woods from Kentucky to Florida and Louisiana, flowering from March to May. *Plate 28*. Another species of *Pachysandra*, *P. terminalis* from Asia, is much planted as a ground cover, and is occasionally found wild.

THE CROWBERRY FAMILY (EMPETRACEAE)

This is a very small family, the relationships of which puzzle the botanists; it has some of the aspect of heather, being composed of shrubby plants with narrow, evergreen leaves.

EMPETRUM

There are only two or three species.

BLACK CROWBERRY, E. NIGRUM, has creeping branches bearing numerous narrow leaves. The flowers, in the axils of leaves, are inconspicuous, with three petal-like sepals, no petals, and either three stamens or a pistil. The pistil becomes a black or dark purple stone-fruit.

E. RUBRUM is very similar, but has hairy stems.

E. nigrum may be found, in our range, only on the high mountains of New England and New York, and in northern Michigan and Minnesota; it has been found also on Long Island, New York. *E. rubrum* has a similar range. They flower during the summer.

COREMA

BROOM-CROWBERRY or POVERTY-GRASS, C. CONRADII, is a small bush with tiny needle-like leaves, only $\frac{1}{4}$ inch long, up to 2 feet tall. The flowers are in small scaly clusters at the ends of branches, with three or four purplish sepals, no petals, and either three or four purplish stamens or a pistil. The fruit is a very small, dry, stone-fruit.

This curious little plant occurs in pine-barrens and on rocky plateaus from Newfoundland to New Jersey, flowering in April and May.

PLATE 28

Euphorbia cyparissias *Rickett*

Euphorbia esula *Johnson*

Euphorbia heterophylla *Gillis*

Euphorbia lucida *Elbert*

Pachysandra procumbens *Rhein*

Euphorbia maculata *Johnson*

Euphorbia zinniiflora *Elbert*

GROUP V

Sepals two or more, petals four or more; petals separate and radially symmetric. Stamens more than twenty.

Exceptions: *Cabomba* and *Brasenia* have three or four petals and from three to eighteen stamens. *Delphinium* and *Aconitum* are bilaterally symmetric. Some species of *Hypericum* and *Hudsonia* have fewer than twenty stamens. Many of the buttercup family lack petals.

I. *Plants growing in water, with round or oval leaf-blades:* water-lily family.

II. *Succulent plants, some with spines; petals indefinite in number:* cactus family.

III. *Plants typically with two sepals that fall as the flower opens and four or eight petals to a flower; leaves lobed or cleft; sap colored:* poppy family.

IV. *Plants with leaves shaped like hollow vases or pitchers:* pitcher-plant family.

V. *Plants typically with four or five petals to a flower, mostly growing on land (if in water not with round-bladed floating leaves), not succulent.*

   A. Flowers usually with many pistils; stamens growing from below the pistils: buttercup family.

   B. Flowers with usually several pistils; stamens on the margin of a disk or cup; leaves borne singly, with stipules, commonly lobed, cleft, or divided: rose family.

   C. Flowers with one pistil; stamens joined to form a sheath around the pistil: mallow family.

   D. Flowers with one pistil which has from three to five styles; leaves paired, not lobed or divided: St.-John's-wort family.

   E. Flowers orange, with one pistil; plant sticky: Loasa family.

THE WATER-LILY FAMILY (NYMPHAEACEAE)

The water-lilies and their kin all have stems (rhizomes) in the soil under the water and long-stalked leaves and flowers that reach the surface or project above it. The leaf-blades are round or oval, attached to the stalks in the center or at a notch in the margin; they float on the surface or stand above it. The number and form of the floral parts vary greatly.

WATER-LILIES (NYMPHAEA)

The flowers of water-lilies are composed of four green sepals and many rows of colored petals – white or pink in our species. The inner petals are narrower and form pollen at their tips; the outer stamens have broad white stalks like petals; there is no sharp distinction (here or in many other families) between petals and stamens. The ovary bears many stigmas radiating from the center; there is no style.

The flowers of the first two species open morn-ings for three or four successive days. Those of the third species open in the afternoon. The flowering period is from June to September. All these species grow in ponds or other quiet waters.

FRAGRANT WATER-LILY, N. ODORATA, has leaves and sepals colored red or purplish on the lower side. The petals are mostly sharp-pointed. This species grows almost throughout the country. *Plate 29.*

104

PLATE 29

Nuphar variegatum *V. Richard*

Nelumbo nucifera *Rhein*

Nelumbo lutea *Rickett*

Nymphaea tuberosa *Johnson*

Nelumbo lutea *Rickett*

Nuphar advena *Smith*

Nymphaea odorata *Smith*

N. TUBEROSA lacks fragrance, or almost lacks it. The leaves and sepals are green on both sides. The petals are blunt at the end. It grows from Quebec to Minnesota and Nebraska and southward to Maryland, Ohio, Illinois, and Arkansas. *Plate 29.*

N. TETRAGONA has more oval leaf-blades, often mottled. The flowers, which are odorless, are not much more than 3 inches across. The petals have crimson lines. This is found from Quebec to Minnesota, Idaho, and Washington, extending southward into Maine and Michigan; also in Asia.

YELLOW POND-LILIES (NUPHAR)

The conspicuous part of the yellow pond-lilies is the calyx, composed of five or six concave sepals which form a globe open at the top. The petals are numerous but small, like scales. The stamens also are very numerous. As in *Nymphaea*, the ovary bears many radiating stigmas. The various species grow in water at the margins of ponds and streams and in swamps, flowering from May or June until October.

COMMON SPATTERDOCK or COW-LILY, N. ADVENA, thrusts its leaf-blades above the water; they stand more or less erect. The outer sepals are green, the inner ones yellow. This species is found throughout the eastern half of the United States. *Plate 29.*

BULLHEAD-LILY, N. VARIEGATUM, is distinguished by its flat leaf-stalks. Many leaf-blades float on the surface. The sepals are generally red on the inner side. The range is across Canada and southward to Delaware, Ohio, Iowa, and Montana. *Plate 29.*

N. MICROPHYLLUM is named for its small leaf-blades, not more than 4 inches long; the leaf-stalks are like narrow ribbons. The flowers also are small, only about an inch across. The stigmas are red.

This is a northern species, found from Newfoundland and Quebec to Manitoba and extending southward to New Jersey, Pennsylvania, Michigan, Wisconsin, and Minnesota.

N. RUBRODISCUM is generally supposed to be a hybrid between *N. microphyllum* and *N. variegatum*. It has leaves and flowers of intermediate size, flat leaf-stalks, red stigmas, and inner sepals suffused with red on the inner side. It has about the same range as *N. microphyllum*.

Besides these species there are some restricted to isolated places: *N. fraternum* in New Jersey, with flowers only an inch across; and *N. ozarkanum* in Missouri, with floating leaves and flowers red inside.

LOTUS (NELUMBO)

Many plants in many lands have been called lotus, and our *Nelumbo* has no special right to the name. It is not the lotus of Homer, nor that of ancient Egypt (which was a *Nymphaea*). It is distinguished among our aquatic plants by the peculiar inverted cone in the middle of the flower. This has several holes in its flat upper surface, and within each hole is a pistil. The sepals and petals are numerous, with no sharp distinction between them. The leaves have round blades attached by their center to the stalk.

WATER CHINQUAPIN, N. LUTEA, has pale yellow (*lutea*) flowers commonly 6 or 8 inches across.

Both flowers and leaf-blades are raised above the water. The plants inhabit rivers and ponds from New England to Ontario and Minnesota and southward to Florida and Texas. It is not so common as *Nymphaea* or *Nuphar*, but in certain rivers — notably the Mississippi between Wisconsin and Iowa — forms colonies stretching for miles throughout the wide valleys, in quiet water. The flowers are seen from July to September. *Plate 29.*

N. NUCIFERA is a native of the Old World which has become naturalized in certain places, as in New Jersey. It has pink flowers. *Plate 29.*

BRASENIA

There is only one species of this genus.

WATER-SHIELD, B. SCHREBERI, has leaves like those of *Nelumbo*, but much smaller, only about 4 inches across. The lower surface is coated with a sort of jelly. The small flowers are purple, with three sepals

and three petals; there are from twelve to eighteen stamens, and about as many separate pistils.

Water-shield is found in quiet waters from Quebec and Nova Scotia to Minnesota and southward to Florida and Texas; from Idaho to British Columbia and California; and in the Old World. *Plate 30.*

CABOMBA

We have one species of *Cabomba* in North America, but several others occur in the warmer parts of this hemisphere.

FANWORT, C. CAROLINIANA, has leaves differing from those of other species of this family in being mostly submerged and cleft into numerous fine, threadlike parts; a few leaves have small round blades, less than an inch across, floating on the surface. Like the water-shield, this species has three sepals and three petals. The stamens and pistils are less numerous, not more than six of each. The flowers are white with yellow spots at the base of the perianth. It is found in ponds and quiet streams from New Jersey to Missouri and southward to Florida and Texas; it is naturalized in some places farther north and east.

THE BUTTERCUP FAMILY (RANUNCULACEAE)

The buttercup family is composed mostly of herbaceous plants, most abundant in the North Temperate Zone, and including many familiar wild flowers. Some of these appear in early spring; few are characteristic of late summer or autumn. Some genera have both sepals and petals; others lack petals but have sepals colored like petals. The stamens are usually numerous, and in most species there are several or many pistils to a flower (in two of our genera there is but one pistil). The pistils become berries, pods that split down one side (follicles), or small seedlike fruits that do not open (achenes). Leaves grow at the base of the flowering stem, singly upon it, or in some genera in pairs or threes; the blades may be divided into several or many small segments on one stalk.

At first sight there may seem to be little in common between a buttercup or anemone and a delphinium, aconite, or columbine. But when flowers are dissected and studied under magnification, the criteria mentioned above will be seen in all of them. Delphiniums and larkspurs are perhaps the most familiar garden plants in the family. Aconites, anemones, columbines, some buttercups, and species of several other genera are also cultivated in our borders. Many species are poisonous in various degrees, some, such as aconite, deadly; some are used in medicine.

This is a large family and well represented in our range; we have nineteen genera in the northeastern United States. They are not difficult to identify.

We may first group the genera according to the presence or lack of petals (i.e. whether the perianth consists of two circles of parts or only of one). Care must be used in making this distinction, since (1) when petals are lacking the sepals often have the appearance of petals; (2) when petals are present the sepals may fall as the flower opens so that there is but a single circle of parts which may then be mistaken for sepals; and (3) the petals when present may be small and not of the usual form of petals (see *Myosurus, Delphinium, Trautvetteria*). One should try to see unopened buds. *Hepatica* has three small leaves (bracts) a short distance below the flower which may be mistaken for sepals; but they are not parts of the flower. The colored parts of the flower are sepals; there are no petals.

I.   *Genera with both sepals and petals.*
     Here we place six genera, of which two have bilaterally symmetric petals, the others radially symmetric petals.

     A. Genera with bilateral symmetry of petals: *Delphinium* (petals small, forming a "bee" in the center; upper sepal with a hollow tube extending backwards – spur); *Aconitum* (petals mostly two, concealed by the upper, helmet-shaped sepal).

     B. Genera with radial symmetry of petals: *Ranunculus* (green sepals, white or yellow petals, many pistils which form achenes); *Actaea* (white sepals which soon fall; small white petals; one pistil which forms a berry); *Myosurus* (very long head of pistils; very small sepals and petals; narrow leaves); *Aquilegia* (flowers hanging; petals mostly red, prolonged upward into hollow tubes – spurs; five pistils).

II. *Genera that lack petals; the sepals are generally petal-like but may fall as the flower opens so that apparently no perianth is present.* Myosurus *is said to lack petals sometimes; see under IB above.*
     From these genera we first separate Clematis, *with paired, mostly pinnately divided leaves, and generally four sepals; most species are vines.*
     We group the rest by the manner in which their flowers are borne.

A. Genera (with no petals) having flowers in racemes or large clusters (compare B and C): *Cimicifuga* (a very tall, narrow raceme); *Xanthorhiza* (a branched raceme of brown-purple flowers); *Trautvetteria* (a flattish flower-cluster); *Thalictrum* (a much-branched flower-cluster; sepals soon falling; leaves divided into very many small segments).

B. Genera (with no petals) having one or several flowers at the tip of a leafy stem. Of these the first two have yellow or yellowish flowers, the rest white, pink, or lavender flowers.

1.   Yellow or yellowish flowers: *Caltha* (leaves not divided or cleft); *Trollius* (leaves divided or cleft).

2.   White, pink, or lavender flowers: *Anemone* (leaves palmately lobed, cleft, or divided); *Anemonella* (leaves on wiry stalks, divided in threes, the segments small); *Isopyrum* (leaves divided in threes, the segments small and generally three-lobed); *Hydrastis* (one leaf at the base, two on the stem, all palmately lobed; one flower; three sepals which soon fall).

C. Genera with single flowers on stems that have no leaves or only very small ones (bracts): *Coptis* (leaf-blades divided into three small segments); *Hepatica* (leaf-blades three-lobed but not divided).

THE LARKSPURS (DELPHINIUM)

The larkspurs are easily distinguished by the "spur" or hollow tube which extends back from the base of the uppermost sepal: presumably the lark's spur. The other four sepals have the form usual for petals, and all five are colored alike, generally some shade of blue or purple, sometimes white. The two upper petals also have spurs which extend backwards within the spur of the upper sepal. The small blades are clustered in the center of the flower; in some species they wear a "beard," a tuft of hairs. There are mostly three pistils (in our native species) which develop into pods (follicles); and numerous stamens. The leaf-blades of the larkspurs are divided or cleft into narrow segments which radiate — palmately — from the tip of the stalk.

The botanical name of the genus dates from ancient times, having been used by the Greek physician Dioscorides in the first century of our era. It is derived by some from the Greek word for "dolphin," on account of some fancied resemblance. Gardeners distinguish between annual and perennial species, reserving the name delphinium (as a common name) for the latter; but botanically they are all species of the genus *Delphinium*.

The seeds yield poisonous alkaloids. All parts of the plant are poisonous and (especially in the West) have caused the death of many cattle.

THREE-HORNED LARKSPUR, D. TRICORNE, is the smallest of our native species, reaching generally about 2 feet in height. The few leaves are near the base of the stem. The flowers are a purplish or deep blue. There are relatively few flowers in the raceme. The three pods, their ends curling outwards, form the "three horns" of the name.

April to June: in woods and on rocky slopes from Pennsylvania to Minnesota and Nebraska and southward to Georgia, Alabama, Arkansas, and Oklahoma. *Plate 30.*

D. EXALTATUM is our tallest species, growing to over 6 feet. The segments of the numerous leaves are wider than in other species, with more curved outlines, and rather shallowly cut into pointed lobes. The raceme contains many flowers; the color is blue or white.

July to September: in woods and thickets and on rocky slopes, often high in the mountains, from Pennsylvania to Ohio and south to North Carolina and Alabama. *Plate 30.*

D. VIRESCENS reaches a height of 5 feet. The stem is finely downy. The flowers are white, often with a greenish tinge (*virescens* means "becoming green"), sometimes pale blue.

May to July: in prairies and open woodlands from Minnesota to Manitoba and southward to Illinois, Louisiana, Texas, and New Mexico. *Plate 30.*

D. CAROLINIANUM resembles *D. virescens* in stature and in having a downy stem. It is not quite so tall — to about 4 feet. The flowers are deep blue or purple. The spur is proportionally longer than that of *D. virescens* — up to $\frac{3}{5}$ inch. Technically it is distinguished by having projecting wings on the seeds.

May and June: in open woods, on sand-hills, and in fields from Ohio to Missouri and southward to Florida and Texas.

Besides these four species, *D. treleasei* is found in southwestern Missouri. It is much like *D. tricorne* but has sepals spotted with yellow and petals with yellow "beard." Cultivated larkspurs, natives of the Old World, are sometimes found growing wild; especially *D. ajacis*, with flowers of various colors and leaves divided and cleft into very narrow segments.

PLATE 30

Aconitum uncinatum   *Justice*

Brasenia schreberi   *Johnson*

Aconitum reclinatum   *Justice*

Delphinium tricorne   *Elbert*

Delphinium virescens   *Johnson*

Delphinium exaltatum   *D. Richards*

MONKSHOODS (ACONITUM)

The plants known as monkshood get that name from the peculiar upper sepal, called the helmet, which has a high hollow crown and in front a small beak. Two small petals are hidden under this hood; there may be vestiges of other petals, not so hidden. There are many stamens and from three to five pistils which form as many pods (follicles). The flowers are in a raceme.

The leaf-blades are palmately cleft or divided usually into five or seven lobes which in turn are cut into many irregular teeth. The stem grows from an underground tuber, which also sends out from its summit a slender horizontal branch (rhizome) under the surface; this forms a new tuber.

The plants are very poisonous, especially the underground parts and the seeds. The deadly alkaloids are of great value — of course properly diluted — medicinally, both internally and in liniments.

Monkshoods are not common in our range. The three species mentioned below are quite similar but easily distinguished.

A. UNCINATUM has a smooth stem up to 3 feet long, weak and often leaning against other plants.

August to October: in woods in Maryland and Virginia; from Pennsylvania to Indiana and southward to Georgia and Alabama. *Plate 30.*

A. NOVEBORACENSE has an erect stem, 2 or 3 feet tall, which is hairy towards the top, among the flowers.

June and July: in moist woods in the Catskill Mountains of New York; in northeastern Ohio, Wisconsin, and Iowa.

A. RECLINATUM has a trailing stem said to reach a length of 10 feet, or sometimes standing erect to a height of 3 feet; it is finely hairy in the flowering portion. The helmet-shaped sepal differs from that of other species in tapering upward into a narrow extension, a "spur."

June to September: in mountain woods from Virginia and West Virginia to Georgia. *Plate 30.*

THE BUTTERCUPS (RANUNCULUS)

The buttercups are familiar wild flowers around the world in the North Temperate Zone and farther north, and may be seen by mountain-climbers at high altitudes. One very common species carpets English fields with gold and has invaded North America. Some grow submerged in lakes or in swift-running mountain streams; others prefer swampy meadows; and in general many species are addicted to wet places. From this comes the Latin name, which means "little frog"; the plants are found in the same places as the amphibians. Almost all flower in spring and early summer. Many species are also called crowfoot, from the shape of their leaves. Like other members of this family, the plants are often poisonous to grazing animals.

The flowers have generally five green sepals and five yellow or white petals; but the number varies. The yellow petals have a curious waxy patina which is due to a peculiar layer of cells just beneath the surface. There are numerous stamens and pistils, the pistils on a hump (receptacle) in the middle; this may become longer in fruit. Each flower grows singly at the end of a stalk which rises from among the leaves. Frequently a second stem grows from the same point, bearing more leaves and then a new flower-stalk; and this pattern may continue. The pistils develop into small seedlike fruits — achenes.

The species are so numerous that they offer some

difficulty in identification. Some may hybridize, yielding intermediate forms. The characteristics of the achenes are most useful, but these, of course, are not always present when the flowers are seen. The manner of growth is often helpful. All the leaves from the ground up should be observed, and such minor features as the hairs or down on the stem.

We first separate the aquatic species which grow submerged in water (only their flowers emerging) or with their leaves floating on the surface (not including species that grow with their "feet" in shallow water and most of their stems and leaves in the air).

I. *Aquatic species. Some of these have white flowers, others yellow.*

A. White-flowered aquatic species. (Compare B.)

WHITE WATER CROWFOOT, R. AQUATILIS, is common all around the northern hemisphere. The leaves are all submerged, their blades cut into innumerable hairlike parts which mat together when taken from the water. The leaf has a short stalk.

May to September: in ponds and streams throughout Canada and southward to New Jersey, Pennsylvania, Michigan, Minnesota, South Dakota, New Mexico, and California; also in northern Europe and Asia. *Plate 31.* The species has been divided into several varieties, sometimes considered separate species, with some resulting confusion.

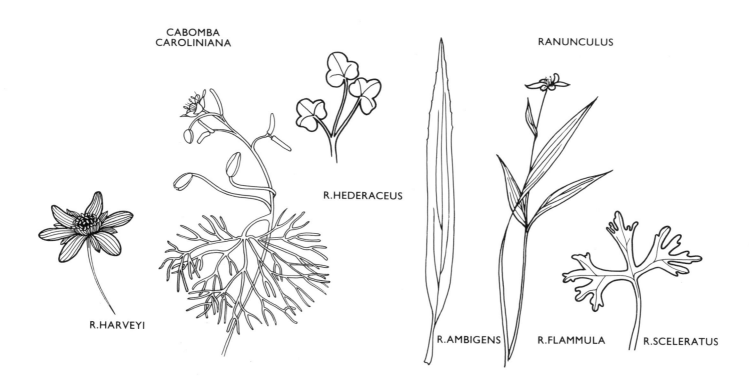

CABOMBA
CAROLINIANA

RANUNCULUS

R.HEDERACEUS

R.HARVEYI

R.AMBIGENS   R.FLAMMULA   R.SCELERATUS

R. CIRCINATUS is very similar to *R. aquatilis*, but the
leaves lack the short stalks of the latter species,
and their divisions are more rigid, not collapsing so
much when taken from the water.

June to September: in ponds and streams from
Newfoundland and Quebec to Alberta and Washing-
ton and southward to Delaware, Tennessee, Kansas,
Texas, and Arizona; also in Europe and Asia.

This species has received various names. Some
botanists, considering our plants a species distinct
from the Old-World plants, have named it *R. longi-
rostris*.

R. HEDERACEUS has long-stalked leaves with roundish blades which float on the surface; they are
lobed but not deeply.

April to August: in shallow ponds, small streams,
and wet shores in Newfoundland; from southeastern
Pennsylvania and Maryland to South Carolina, mostly near the coast; also in Europe.

B. Yellow-flowered aquatic species.

YELLOW WATER CROWFOOT, R. FLABELLARIS, has
submerged leaves finely divided into many very
narrow, limp segments. The stem is stout and hollow.
Occasionally plants are stranded on wet shores, and
there form long-stalked leaves with roundish blades
cleft into from three to five lobes.

April to June: in quiet waters and on muddy
shores from Maine to British Columbia and southward to North Carolina, Louisiana, Kansas, Utah,
and California. *Plate 31*.

R. gmelini, with less finely divided leaves, and petals only $\frac{1}{8}$
inch long, is northern and western, just entering our range in Maine,
Michigan, Minnesota, and Iowa.

II. *Species growing on dry land, or in shallow water,
swamps, etc., with stem and leaves in the air. The
flowers are yellow. These terrestrial species may be
grouped according to their leaf-blades — whether
lobed, cleft, or divided.*

A. Terrestrial species with no leaves lobed, cleft,
or divided (they may be notched or scalloped).
The first four of these have long narrow leaves,
only those at the base perhaps with small ovate
blades. In the last two practically all leaves have
more or less round blades on distinct stalks.
(Compare B and C.)

1. Species with long narrow leaves. (Compare 2.)

SPEARWORT, R. FLAMMULA, has a slender creeping
stem, from which grow erect flowering branches
to a height of about 6 inches. The leaves are mostly
in tufts at the base of these branches; they are threadlike or grasslike. The stamens are few for a buttercup,
not more than twenty.

June to August: on damp shores across Canada and southward to New York, Michigan, Minnesota, Colorado, and Oregon; also in Europe and Asia. A form with distinct blades to the leaves is reported as far south as New Jersey and Pennsylvania. The American plants of this species form a variety distinct from the Old-World plants. They are sometimes even treated as a separate species, *R. reptans*.

SPEARWORT or WATER-PLANTAIN, R. AMBIGENS, has a stem that more or less lies on the ground, the tip finally growing upward; it also forms runners. The leaves have lanceolate blades on short stalks which sheathe the stem. There may be a few small teeth at the margins of the blades.

June to September: in ditches and other wet and muddy places from Maine to Ontario and Minnesota and southward to Georgia, Tennessee, and Louisiana.

R. LAXICAULIS has a weak stem (*caulis*) about 2 feet tall, much branched and bearing many small flowers. The basal leaves have small ovate blades on long stalks. The leaves on the stem are lanceolate or very narrow. All have small marginal teeth. The petals are about twice as long as the sepals.

April to June: in wet places from Connecticut to Florida on the coastal plain, thence west to Texas; inland from Indiana to Kansas and southward.

R. PUSILLUS is similar in general aspect to *R. laxicaulis* but the petals are tiny, only ⅛ inch long or less, shorter than the sepals.

April to June: in shallow water, swamps, etc., mostly on the coastal plain from New York to Florida and westward to Texas; inland from Ohio to Missouri and southward; in California.

2. Terrestrial species all of whose leaves have undivided and unlobed, roundish blades.

LESSER-CELANDINE, R. FICARIA, grows at most a foot tall, forming a cluster of scalloped round blades on fairly long stalks. The flowers are distinctive, with up to a dozen petals.

April to June: in waste places, open woodlands, etc. in the Atlantic states; an European plant escaped from cultivation. *Plate 31*.

The real celandine is a plant of the poppy family, no relation to this species and not even anything like it. Why this buttercup was placed in the same genus by the early botanists is not all clear. "Celandine" is derived from the Greek name of the true celandine, in English characters written *Chelidonium*; this in turn was derived from the Greek word for swallow, since the flowers (said Dioscorides) appear with the swallows. *Ranunculus ficaria* gets the second half of its

name from its supposed usefulness in the treatment of the disease called "fig"; figwort is another name for the species, also pilewort; and, in various parts of England, legwort, fogwort, golden-guineas, cream-and-butter, crazy-bet, and gentleman's-cap-and-frills.

SEASIDE CROWFOOT, R. CYMBALARIA, has slender runners from which rise erect, leafless, flowering stems up to 10 inches tall. The leaves are in tufts at the base of the erect stems. They are long-stalked, with roundish, scalloped or toothed blades. There are from one to ten flowers on the stem, each with five sepals and five petals.

May to October: on muddy shores, chiefly salt or brackish, across Canada and southward to New Jersey, Illinois, Arkansas, Kansas, and Mexico; also in South America, Europe, and Asia. *Plate 31*. This range obviously makes the English name rather inappropriate.

The authorities say nothing of a red color of mature fruits; but there is the photograph.

B. A second group of terrestrial species has some leaves, on the stem, lobed, cleft, or divided; the basal leaves mostly having roundish blades on long stalks. The petals are small in this group.

1. In three of these species the petals are shorter than the sepals. (Compare 2.)

SMALL-FLOWERED CROWFOOT, R. ABORTIVUS, is a very variable and common weed. The stems may reach a height of 3 feet, but are commonly about 18 inches tall. The basal leaves have blades often indented where they join their stalks, and scalloped or toothed; some may have divided blades. The leaves on the stem are divided mostly into narrow, blunt segments.

March to August: in woodlands and open places from Maine to Saskatchewan and southward to Florida, Oklahoma, and Colorado. *Plate 31*. This is sometimes a nuisance in gardens.

R. MICRANTHUS resembles *R. abortivus* but is hairy. Some of the roots are tuberous.

March to May: from Massachusetts to Missouri and southward to Georgia, Alabama, and Arkansas.

R. ALLEGHENIENSIS also is like *R. abortivus* and is difficult to distinguish from it without the achenes. These have a hook at the end instead of the microscopic short beak of *R. abortivus*.

April to July: in woods and on rocky slopes from Massachusetts and Vermont to Ohio and southward in the mountains to South Carolina and Tennessee; not common.

PLATE 31

Ranunculus flabellaris   *Johnson*

Ranunculus cymbalaria   *Johnson*

Ranunculus ficaria   *Rickett*

Ranunculus aquatilis   *Rickett*

Ranunculus recurvatus   *Rickett*

Ranunculus abortivus   *Rickett*

Ranunculus acris   *Rickett*

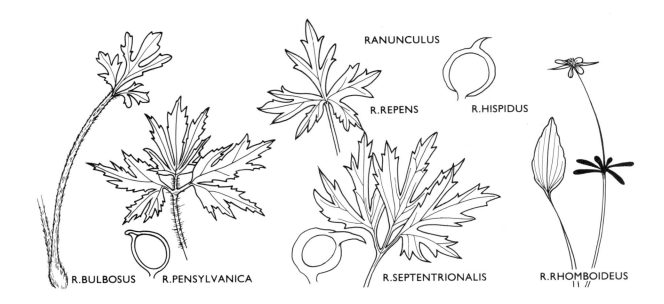

2.   Two other species of group B also have small petals but they are longer than the sepals.

R. HARVEYI, a midwestern species, resembles *R. abortivus* or *R. micranthus* except in the flowers: the petals are about twice as long as the sepals. The stem may be hairy or smooth.

April and May: in rocky woods from Maine to Alabama and Arkansas.

R. RHOMBOIDEUS has basal leaves with blades that mostly taper into the stalks instead of being round and indented. The sepals are hairy, and shorter than the petals but not half their length.

April and May: on open wooded slopes and in prairies from Ontario to British Columbia and southward to Michigan, Illinois, and Nebraska; formerly abundant, now uncommon.

   C. The remaining terrestrial species have all their leaves lobed, cleft, or divided. Some of these have small petals, $\frac{1}{4}$ inch long or less, as short as or shorter than the sepals. The rest have petals $\frac{1}{2}$ inch long or longer, exceeding the sepals.

1.   Terrestrial species with all leaves lobed, cleft, or divided and petals $\frac{1}{4}$ inch long or less. (Compare 2.)

CURSED CROWFOOT, R. SCELERATUS, is distinguished by the tall "receptacle" on which the pistils are seated. The lobes and divisions of the rather succulent leaves are mostly narrow and blunt.

May to August: in marshes, pools, springs, etc. across Canada and southward to Florida, Louisiana, New Mexico, and California; also in Europe and Asia. *Plate 32.* The name (*sceleratus* means "cursed") may refer to its poisonous qualities. The juice is extremely acrid and may cause blisters on the skin.

BRISTLY CROWFOOT, R. PENSYLVANICUS, has its pistils (and the achenes into which they develop) in a cylindrical mass, like those of *R. sceleratus*. It is easily distinguished from that species by its hairy stem and by the sharper points to the lobes and divisions of the leaves.

July to September: in marshes, ditches, and wet meadows across Canada and southward to Delaware, Ohio, Illinois, Iowa, Nebraska, Colorado, and perhaps Arizona; also in Asia.

R. RECURVATUS has scattered or sparse hairs on the stem. The leaves have broad blades which are cleft into three lobes but not divided; like the stems they are sparsely hairy. The conspicuous characteristic which gives the species its name is the hook ("recurved") on the achene.

May to July: in moist woodlands and on banks from Newfoundland and Quebec to Manitoba and southward to Florida and Texas. *Plate 31.*

Besides these the very small, northern *R. pygmaeus*, with leaves cleft into three, may be found on some of our high mountains.

2.   Terrestrial species with all leaves lobed, cleft, or divided and petals $\frac{1}{2}$ inch long or longer.

TALL BUTTERCUP, R. ACRIS, has an erect stem up to 5 feet tall. The leaves are cleft and divided into many narrow, sharp-pointed lobes, teeth, and segments. Stem and leaves are more or less hairy. This is the common buttercup that makes fields of gold in England and is now conspicuous in eastern North America. Unfortunately it is probably, because of its abundance in fields, the most frequent cause of poisoning of cattle by buttercups. The poison is transmitted to the milk, which it renders unpalatable.

PLATE 32

Ranunculus fascicularis *Johnson*

Ranunculus sceleratus *Elbert*

Ranunculus septentrionalis *Gottscho*

Actaea rubra *Elbert*

Ranunculus repens *Elbert*

Actaea rubra *Johnson*

Actaea rubra *Johnson*

May to August: in fields and meadows, on roadsides, etc. from Labrador to Alaska and southward to Virginia, Ohio, Illinois, Kansas, and Oregon. *Plate 31.*

BULBOUS BUTTERCUP, R. BULBOSUS, is another immigrant from Europe. It is recognized by the thick base of the stem which, with the enveloping broad leaf-bases, forms a sort of bulb. It grows up to 3 feet tall. The lobes and teeth of the leaves are rather blunt.

March to July: in fields and open woodlands and on roadsides from Newfoundland to Ontario and southward to Georgia and Louisiana; also in the West.

SWAMP BUTTERCUP, R. SEPTENTRIONALIS, has a long creeping stem, the flowering branches growing upward. It is usually hairy. The larger leaves are mostly divided into three ovate segments on short stalks. The achenes are distinctive with a wide flange and a swordlike beak.

April to July: in bottomlands, on stream-banks, in wet meadows, etc. from Labrador and Quebec to Manitoba and southward to Maryland, Kentucky, Arkansas, and Texas. *Plate 32.*

R. HISPIDUS is difficult to distinguish from *R. septentrionalis* without the achenes. Both species are very variable. It is more or less hairy and generally erect, up to a foot tall or taller. The leaves are divided into three ovate segments of which only the one at the end is stalked. The achenes have a very narrow flange and a very inconspicuous beak.

March to June: in moist and dry woods and rocky places from Massachusetts to Wisconsin and North Dakota and southward to South Carolina, Alabama, and Arkansas.

EARLY BUTTERCUP, R. FASCICULARIS, is a low plant, the stems growing to a height of about a foot. They are silky. The roots are often tuberous. The petals are a rather pale yellow. The lobes of the leaves are narrow and blunt.

March to May: in dry soil in open woods and rocky slopes from New Hampshire to Ontario and Minnesota and southward to Georgia, Tennessee, Louisiana, and Texas. *Plate 32.*

CREEPING BUTTERCUP, R. REPENS, has long trailing stems which send up flowering branches. The leaves are mostly divided into three stalked segments. There are from five to nine petals. This is a variable species, some forms having numerous petals. These "double-flowered" forms are cultivated.

May to September: in ditches and wet ground from Labrador to Ontario, Michigan, and Minnesota and southward to North Carolina, Kentucky, and Missouri, and in the West; naturalized from Europe. *Plate 32.*

Besides all these, *R. macounii* may be found in the extreme northwestern part of our range. It resembles *R. pensylvanicus*, but it is more apt to trail on the ground and to form runners.

BANEBERRIES (ACTAEA)

The baneberries are small, unbranched plants, 2 or 3 feet tall, with a few large leaves which are much divided into small, ovate, sharp-toothed segments on long stalks, and a dense raceme of small white flowers terminating the stem. The short, broad sepals fall as the flower opens, and the narrow petals do not last long; the flower may be misjudged to have only one circle of perianth-parts, or no perianth at all. The flowers are followed by white or red berries; the English name refers to their poison, which can cause serious illness or even death.

WHITE BANEBERRY, A. PACHYPODA, is easy to distinguish from the following species, not by the color of its berries but by the thickness of the stalks which bear them (*pachypoda* means "thick-footed"). This feature is visible, under magnification, even in the flowering stage; the stalks are as thick as the pistil. They may bear minute hairs. The berries are unreliable for identification since, though they are usually white, there is a form of the species that has red berries (with the same thick flower-stalks). The white berries are conspicuously marked with a dark dot (where the broad stigma was; there is almost no style); this has earned them the name doll's-eyes. The segments of the leaves are usually quite smooth.

July to October: in woods, wet thickets, etc. from Quebec to Manitoba and southward to Georgia, Louisiana, and Oklahoma. *Plate 33.*

RED BANEBERRY, A. RUBRA, bears its flowers and fruits on slender stalks which are generally quite downy in the flowering stage. The berries are red or — to further add to the confusion — ivory-white. (These species provide a lesson in the futility of many English names of plants!) The segments of the leaves of *A. rubra* are generally downy along the veins on the lower side.

August to October: in woods and thickets across Canada and southward to New Jersey, West Virginia, Indiana, Iowa, South Dakota, Arizona, and Oregon. *Plate 32.*

PLATE 33

Myosurus minimus   *Rickett*

Aquilegia canadensis   *Rickett*

Clematis viorna   *Aborn*

Actaea pachypoda   *Gottscho*

Clematis pitcheri   *Dobbs*

Actaea pachypoda   *Johnson*

Clematis virginiana   *Rickett*

Clematis virginiana   *Johnson*

MYOSURUS

We have only one species of *Myosurus* in North America. Others are found in Central and South America and in Australia and New Zealand. They are distinguished by the very long column covered with pistils, that rises in the center of the flower; this is the "mouse-tail." The leaves are all at the base of the flower-stalk; they are narrow, grasslike.

MOUSE-TAIL, M. MINIMUS, grows not more than 6

inches tall. The sepals seem to be attached by their middle; the lower part is a hollow tube, a "spur." The petals are very narrow, about the same length as the upper part of the sepals; they may be missing.

March to June: in fields and rocky or sandy places in Virginia and from Ontario to British Columbia and southward to Florida, Texas, and California; also in Europe and Asia. *Plate 33.*

COLUMBINES (AQUILEGIA)

The columbines are familiar and beautiful garden flowers of many colors. Their distinctive feature is the hanging or horizontal flower whose five petals have long tubes – "spurs" – extending upwards or backwards. The sepals are brightly colored, like the petals or of a contrasting color. There are many stamens and five pistils. The ovaries become pods (follicles) which open along their inner sides. The leaves are much divided into small, stalked segments which are usually roundish and notched.

The name columbine comes from the Latin *columba*, dove; the five spurred petals were apparently thought to resemble as many doves, clustered perhaps around a fountain. The Latin name is likewise of doubtful origin; it is sometimes derived from *aquila*, "eagle"; but why?

WILD COLUMBINE, ROCK-BELLS, or HONEY-SUCKLE, A. CANADENSIS, grows to a height of 3 feet or more. The leaves are divided in threes, the divisions again in threes, and so on until the ultimate segments are reached. These are generally three-lobed. The petals are generally red with yellow blade, the sepals red; but various color-forms are known.

April to July: in rocky wooded places from Newfoundland and Quebec to Ontario and Manitoba and southward to Florida, Alabama, Arkansas, and Texas. *Plate 33.* To call this plant honeysuckle is an example of the confusion in English names.

EUROPEAN COLUMBINE, A. VULGARIS, is cultivated and occasionally found growing wild. The flowers are blue, purple, pink, or white.

VIRGIN'S-BOWER AND LEATHER-FLOWERS (CLEMATIS)

Clematis is unique among our genera of the buttercup family in having its leaves in pairs on the stem. They are mostly pinnately divided; undivided in a few species. Many of the species are vines. The leaf-stalks coil around any support, becoming what the botanist knows as tendrils. (Some of these vines scarcely belong in this book, being more or less woody; but it is hard to draw a sharp line.) In most species each flower has four sepals; some have more. There are many stamens and pistils. The pistils become seedlike fruits – achenes – crowned with a long, usually feathery "tail."

The species are easily separated into two groups.

I. *Plants with many white flowers in an inflorescence.*

VIRGIN'S-BOWER, C. VIRGINIANA, is the commonest species, climbing over other plants often to a height of 10 feet or even more. The leaf-blades are generally divided into three toothed segments. The feathery-tailed fruits are conspicuous in late summer.

July to September: in moist places, on roadsides, etc. from Quebec to Manitoba and southward to Georgia, Alabama, Mississippi, Louisiana, and Kansas. *Plate 33.*

C. DIOSCOREIFOLIA differs from *C. virginiana* in having leaf-segments that are not toothed. It is a native of Japan, escaped from cultivation, to roadsides and thickets, from Massachusetts to Florida and Tennessee.

II. *Plants with a single flower terminating each long stalk. The stalks may end the stem or come from axils of leaves. The flowers are purple, blue, or yellowish.*

LEATHER-FLOWER, C. VIORNA, is a climbing plant, with leaf-blades divided into from three to seven segments. The flowers are an inch long or less, with four purplish, joined sepals which curve outwards at the tips.

May to August: in woods from Pennsylvania to Illinois and Iowa and southward to Georgia and Texas. *Plate 33*.

LEATHER-FLOWER, C. PITCHERI, is a climbing plant with leaf-blades divided into from three to nine segments which show a prominent network of veins on the lower surface. The purplish or red sepals have their upper halves curved outwards.

June to August: in borders of woods from Indiana to Nebraska and southward to Tennessee and Texas. *Plate 33*.

CURLY-HEADS or LEATHER-FLOWER, C. OCHROLEUCA, is an erect, silky-haired plant, not climb-ing, with undivided leaf-blades. The sepals are less than an inch long, silky on the outside, dull yellow or purplish.

April to June: in woods and on rocky slopes from New York to Pennsylvania and southward to Georgia.

PURPLE or MOUNTAIN CLEMATIS, C. VERTICILLARIS, is a rather woody climber, with leaf-blades divided into three segments. The four sepals are more than an inch long, blue or mauve, mostly hairy. Many of the stamens resemble narrow petals.

May and June; on rocky slopes and in woods from Quebec to Manitoba and southward to North Carolina, Ohio, Michigan, and Iowa.

CIMICIFUGA

One species of *Cimicifuga* is widespread in our range. Other species grow in the South and West, and in Asia.

BLACK SNAKEROOT, BLACK COHOSH, or BUGBANE, C. RACEMOSA, is an extraordinary plant, with enormous leaves divided usually into three parts and the parts divided pinnately into toothed blades or again divided into three and the three parts divided pinnately; the whole seems like a branch bearing many leaves. From among them rises a narrow raceme of small flowers which may reach a height of 8 feet. The sepals fall as the flower opens. There are several tiny petal-like stamens besides those of the normal form, which are numerous. There is only one pistil, which becomes a small pod (follicle). These make a curious rattling when dry, whence the plant is sometimes called rattletop.

June to September: in moist woods from Massachusetts to Ontario and southward and southwestward to Georgia, Tennessee, and Missouri. *Plate 34*. The name *Cimicifuga* is derived from two Latin words meaning "bug" and "to put to flight." The unpleasant smell of the flowers was supposed to have this effect.

Another species C. *americana*, occurs in the mountains of Pennsylvania and West Virginia and southward. It differs in having several pistils in each flower. It does not grow so tall as C. *racemosa*.

XANTHORHIZA

There is only one species in this genus.

YELLOW-ROOT, X. SIMPLICISSIMA, has slender, rather woody stems up to 2 feet tall bearing pinnately divided leaves. The flowers are on long drooping branches. They are small, the sepals about ⅛ inch long and brown-purple. There are no real petals, but five minute sterile stamens that take their place. There are only from five to ten functional stamens, and five or more pistils. The pistils become small follicles.

The Latin and English names of the genus mean the same, referring to the roots, which are yellow; the bark also is yellow.

April and May: in damp woods from New York to Kentucky and southward to Florida and Alabama. *Plate 34*. *Simplicissima* means "very simple," which as applied to plants refers not to mental characteristics but to a lack of branches!

TRAUTVETTERIA

Two or three species compose this genus; one occurs in the northeastern United States.

FALSE BUGBANE or TASSEL-RUE, T. CAROLINIENSIS, has a stem 4 or 5 feet tall, crowned with numerous white flowers in a rather flat cluster. The leaves are broad and palmately lobed. There are usually four sepals which fall as the flower opens, and no petals. The stamens are numerous. The several pistils become small pods (follicles).

June to August: along streams, in woods, and on prairies and bluffs from Pennsylvania to Missouri and southward to Florida and Kentucky. *Plate 34*. For the name bugbane see *Cimicifuga* above.

MEADOW-RUES (THALICTRUM)

The meadow-rues are graceful plants, mostly 2 or 3 feet tall, with leaves (much like those of a columbine) divided into many small segments, and a crown of numerous small white or yellow or purple flowers. The color of the flowers is mostly the color of the many stamens, for the sepals fall as they open, and there are no petals. There are several pistils, in most species on different plants from the stamens. They become achenes.

The English name refers to the resemblance between the leaves and those of the herb rue (*Ruta*).

The genus is easily recognized, but to identify all the species a hand magnifier is necessary.

LADY-RUE, T. CLAVATUM, is distinguished by having stamens and pistils in the same flower. The stalks of the stamens are conspicuous; they are broad and white like small petals.

May to July: in moist woods in the mountains of Virginia, West Virginia, and Kentucky and southward to Georgia and Alabama.

TALL MEADOW-RUE, T. POLYGAMUM, may reach 7 feet or more in height. The stamens in staminate flowers stand erect, making a fine show with their broad white stalks. There are usually a few stamens in pistillate flowers. ("Polygamous" in the language of botany means having some flowers with both stamens and pistils, others with only stamens or pistils.)

June to August: in meadows, swamps, roadside ditches, etc. from Labrador and Newfoundland to Ontario and southward to Georgia and Tennessee. *Plate 34.* A common and variable species.

PURPLE MEADOW-RUE, T. DASYCARPUM, grows tall — up to 6 feet — with an often purple stem. The leaf-segments are usually covered with a fine down on the lower surface. A variety with a whitish bloom on stem and leaves occurs.

May to July: in meadows and swamps and on stream-banks from Ontario to Alberta and southward to Ohio, Oklahoma, New Mexico, and Arizona. *Plate 34.* This is the western counterpart of *T. polygamum*, but the two overlap in the Midwest.

PURPLE or WAXY MEADOW-RUE, T. REVOLUTUM, may be distinguished by the small glands (round, waxy bodies) on the under surface of the leaf-segments. The stamens have thin stalks and droop from the flower-stalks.

May to July: in dry woodlands and prairies from Massachusetts to Ontario and southward to Florida, Alabama, and Arkansas. In the southern parts of this range the leaves may lack glands, and the plants closely resemble *T. polygamum*; it is then necessary to measure the stamen-heads, which are more than $\frac{3}{8}$ inch long; in *T. polygamum* they are generally shorter than $\frac{3}{8}$ inch.

EARLY MEADOW-RUE, T. DIOICUM, is usually only 2 or 3 feet tall, with small leaf-segments, and yellow stamens that hang from the ends of the flower-stalks. The leaves have long main stalks (below the point of division).

April and May: in woods from Quebec to Manitoba and southward to Georgia, Alabama, and Missouri. *Plate 34. Dioicum* means "two houses," and refers to the segregation of pistils and stamens on distinct plants.

T. CONFINE is a far-northern plant, growing to about 3 feet in height. The upper leaves have no stalk or a very short one: the three main divisions of a leaf may be mistaken for three leaves growing from one point, but the single pair of small scales at the base — the stipules — shows that it is all one leaf. The stamens are pendent from the flower-stalks.

June and July: on rocky shores from Labrador and Quebec to Manitoba and southward to northern New York, Wisconsin, and Minnesota. *Plate 34.*

Besides all these, several other species are known from restricted ranges or just touch on our borders. *T. venulosum* is a smaller edition of *T. confine* growing in western Canada and found in Wisconsin and Minnesota. *T. coriaceum* and *T. steeleanum* are found in the southeastern mountains, including southern Pennsylvania and western Maryland, Virginia, and West Virginia. *T. macrostylum* grows in southern Virginia and southward.

CALTHA

There are several species of *Caltha*, the marsh-marigolds, in the colder parts of the globe, but only one is at all common in our range.

MARSH-MARIGOLD, C. PALUSTRIS, has a branched, hollow stem that bears a mound of foliage 2 feet tall or taller, covered with flowers. The five or more sepals are bright yellow and petal-like; there are no petals. Stamens are numerous. The pistils make a cluster of pods (follicles).

April to June: in swamps, wet meadows, and shallow water (*palustris* means "of swamps") across Canada to Alaska and southward to South Carolina, Tennessee, Iowa, and Nebraska. *Plate 178.*

PLATE 34

Scribner

Cimicifuga racemosa

Thalictrum polygamum

Smith

Thalictrum dasycarpum

Johnson

Thalictrum dioicum

Johnson

Thalictrum confine

Elbert

Trautvetteria carolinensis

Elbert

Xanthorhiza simplicissima

Justice

A yellow dye may be obtained from the petals. The young foliage is palatable when cooked as greens, and has been much used in this way in New England. It should not be eaten raw, for it is highly poisonous until boiled. The flower-buds are made into pickles.

Caltha was the Latin name of the true marigold, in the daisy family, misapplied to this relative of the buttercups. "Marigold" seems to have nothing to do with "Mary" or "gold," but is probably a corruption of an Anglo-Saxon word meaning "horse-blister"; the common name of the plant in parts of England is "horse-blob" ("blob" being dialect for "blister"). A few other English names of this common plant are bachelor's-buttons, bulldogs, carlicups, crazy-Betty, goldilocks, kingcup, marybuds, may-bubbles, may-flower, monkey-bells. In America it is also called cowslip (or cowslop) — i.e. a plant that grows where cows have dropped their dung; but in England that name is applied to a primrose. Grigson writes: "In Ireland . . . the May-flower keeps its importance on May Day. On this fertility festival, witches and fairies are about and are unusually active, . . . May Day bunches [of *Caltha*] are picked and hung over the doors, and the fertility of the cattle is protected."

GLOBE-FLOWERS (TROLLIUS)

The globe-flowers grow in many parts of the Northern Hemisphere, and at least one is familiar in gardens. There are two species in North America, one in the northeastern states; and one cultivated. The general aspect of the plants is that of a large buttercup. The English name describes the shape of the flowers. The botanical name is from the German, *Troll-blume*; but what the connection is with trolls — goblins — I do not know.

T. LAXUS grows a foot or two tall. There are long-stalked basal leaves and several leaves without stalks on the stem, all with palmately cleft or divided blades. There are no petals. The large yellow sepals, from five to fifteen, are petal-like.

April and May: in wet places from Connecticut to Michigan and southward to Delaware and Ohio. *Plate 35.* A rare plant; formerly reported from Maine and New Hampshire.

ANEMONES, WINDFLOWERS (ANEMONE)

There are about 100 species of *Anemone* scattered around the world in the North Temperate Zone and farther north. They are mostly plants of woodlands and meadows. The name is commonly derived from the Greek word for wind and is connected with a myth which relates that a nymph beloved of Zephyr, the southwest wind, was changed to a flower by a jealous deity. The names, botanical and English, are appropriate for many species, since their stems and leaves are delicate and tremble in the wind. But a perhaps more authentic derivation is from a Semitic name for Adonis, who, dying, was changed into the crimson *Anemone* of the near East. This and other species, including one from Japan, have yielded handsome garden varieties.

Some local English names for the common European species are granny's-nightcap, lady's-shimmy, Moll-o'-the-woods, and shamefaced-maiden.

Our species have white or greenish (occasionally reddish) sepals; there are no petals (in one species some sterile stamens that might be called petals). The principal leaves are at the base of the flowering stem; long-stalked with palmately lobed or divided blades. On the stem there are usually three or more leaves in a circle, forming what the botanist calls an involucre; these aid in identification. The flowers are arranged much as in the buttercups: one flower on a long stalk without leaves, rising from the involucre; then, from the same point, another stalk bearing a new involucre and another flower; and so on. The pistils become achenes.

I.   *A species covered with silky hairs and with large sepals which may be blue, purple, or white.*

PASQUE-FLOWER or PRAIRIE-SMOKE, A. PATENS, is a rather low plant, about a foot tall, silky all over with long whitish hairs. At the time of flowering many of the leaves are immature and form a close cluster. Their blades are divided and deeply cleft into many narrow lobes. The leaves on the stem (the involucre) lack stalks, and are rather close to the flower. The sepals may exceed an inch in length. As the pistils mature into achenes, the long styles become longer and form a feathery "tail" to each fruit; the head of fruit is very distinctive.

April to June: in prairies and other open places from Wisconsin to Alaska and southward to Illinois, Texas, New Mexico, and Washington; in Europe and Asia. *Plate 35.* The species has been divided into several varieties, labeled as distinct species by some botanists.

II. *Species with a circle of* stalked *leaves on the stem (the involucre), and not silky-hairy.*

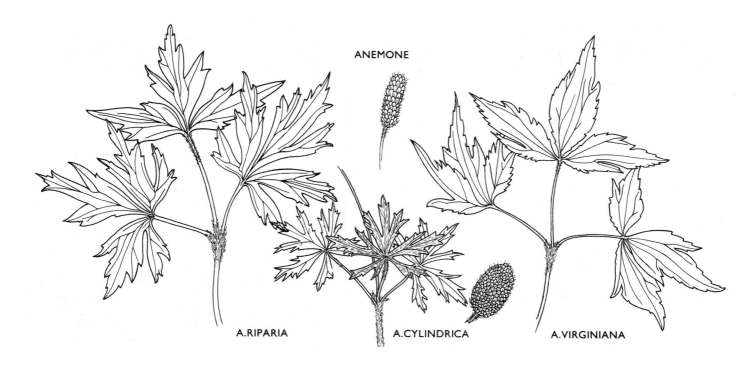

ANEMONE

A.RIPARIA   A.CYLINDRICA   A.VIRGINIANA

WOOD ANEMONE, A. QUINQUEFOLIA, is the earliest
    of our windflowers, a plant not more than a foot
tall and usually less. There is commonly one basal
leaf, the blade divided into three, and the side segments often so deeply cleft that there are in effect five
segments. In western plants the stem may be hairy.

    April to June: in open, moist woods, on stream-
banks, and in wet meadows from Quebec to Manitoba and southward to New Jersey, in the mountains
to Georgia, Kentucky, and Iowa. *Plate 35*.

A. VIRGINIANA and the following two species are
    called thimbleweeds: the receptacle in the center
of the flower, upon which the pistils are seated, is
quite tall and becomes taller when the pistils have become seedlike fruits (achenes); this is the "thimble."
The three species are alike in this respect and not
very different in their other characteristics. *A. virginiana* is the least in size, not reaching 3 feet. It is
more or less hairy. It may be distinguished from the
other thimbleweeds by the shape of the segments of
the leaf-blades: they *curve* towards the base (see the
drawings). The "thimble" has a curved, almost ovate
outline.

    June to August: in rocky places in woodlands
from Quebec to North Dakota and southward to
Georgia, Alabama, Arkansas, and Kansas. *Plate 35*.

A. CYLINDRICA may be over 3 feet tall. Its stem and
    the lower surface of its leaves are covered with a
grey down. The segments of the leaf-blades have
straight margins towards the base (see the drawings).

They are deeply cleft into sharp-pointed and toothed
lobes. The "thimble" is cylindric, with parallel sides.

    May to July: in dry open soil from Maine to
British Columbia and southward to New Jersey,
Ohio, Missouri, Kansas, New Mexico, and Arizona.
Plate 35.

A. RIPARIA is the tallest thimbleweed, reaching a
    height of 4 feet or more. The stem may have
scattered hairs but is often smooth. The end segment
of each leaf-blade generally has straight sides towards
the base (see the drawings). The outline of the
"thimble" is oval.

    May to July: on rock ledges and stream-banks
across Canada and southward to western New England and New York, the mountains of western Maryland, Illinois, and Minnesota. A form with reddish
flowers is reported from eastern Quebec.

III. *The remaining species have a circle of leaves* with-
    out stalks *on the stem below the flowers.*

A. CANADENSIS seems a coarse plant for this genus,
    though not 3 feet tall. The leaf-blades are broad
and deeply cleft into toothed segments. The five sepals are white, and up to an inch long.

    May to July: in moist prairies and meadows and
on stream-banks across Canada and southward to
Maryland, West Virginia, Indiana, Kansas, and New
Mexico. *Plate 35*. It is cultivated and sometimes
"goes wild" outside of the above range.

A. CAROLINIANA is a smaller, rather bushy plant (about a foot tall) with leaf-blades cut into many narrow and rather blunt segments. The most distinctive feature is the number of sepals, which is not less than ten and may run to twenty.

April and May: in prairies and sandy places from Indiana to Minnesota and South Dakota and southward to Florida and Texas. *Plate 178.*

ANEMONELLA

There is but one species of *Anemonella.*

RUE-ANEMONE, A. THALICTROIDES, is a delicate flower of early spring. From its cluster of root-tubers spring several leaves with black, wiry, stalks bearing blades divided into three and each segment again divided into three. The final small, round segments are notched at the outer margin (as shown in the drawing). Among the leaves rise the slender black flowering stems, each with an involucre (see the introduction to *Anemone*) below the single flower. The involucre is composed of two leaves, each divided into three; but since there is no main stalk to either leaf, they appear like six leaves each with a thin stalk. The sepals are white or pink. There are usually from five to ten, but "double" flowers with many more are not uncommon. The pistils form a cluster of achenes.

April to June: in woods, from Maine to Minnesota and southward to Florida and Oklahoma. *Plate 35.* The small notched segments of the leaves recall those of meadow-rue, *Thalictrum,* whence the second half of the botanical name; also those of rue (*Ruta*). *Anemonella* means "little anemone." The species was placed in *Anemone* by Linnaeus, the "father of botany." It has sometimes been confused with the following species, but the differences are clear.

ISOPYRUM

There are many species of *Isopyrum;* four are found in North America, one in our range.

FALSE RUE-ANEMONE, I. BITERNATUM, has something of the aspect of rue-anemone, the basal leaves having three segments on a long stalk, the segments again divided into three, and the ultimate segments small and round. A glance at the drawing will show that these are distinctly lobed, not merely notched. Moreover, there are similar leaves singly on the stem, the upper with very short stalks, but not gathered together to form an involucre. The roots bear scattered small tubers, not a cluster as in *Anemonella.* The stems and leaf-stalks are green. The usually five sepals are white. The numerous stamens have flat, white stalks. The pistils form a cluster of small follicles.

April and May: in woods from Ontario to Minnesota and southward to Florida and Texas. *Plate 35.* This small plant, commonest in the less populous areas of the country, actually has no common name; the one given above has been made up by an editor!

HYDRASTIS

We have one species of *Hydrastis;* another grows in Asia.

GOLDEN-SEAL, H. CANADENSIS, is a plant less than 2 feet tall with broad leaf-blades cleft into usually five lobes. There is one fairly long-stalked leaf at the base and two, shorter-stalked, at two points on the stem. At the tip of the stem is the single greenish flower. The three sepals fall as the flower opens, leaving only the numerous stamens and pistils. The pistils become dark red berries. The stem and basal leaf grow from a yellow underground stem (rhizome), which is used in medicine. Because of its having been collected for this purpose, the species has become rare.

April and May: in woods from Vermont to Minnesota and Nebraska and southward to Georgia, Alabama, and Arkansas. *Plate 36.*

PLATE 35

Anemone patens *Lee*

Anemone virginiana *Johnson*

Anemonella thalictroides *Rickett*

Isopyrum biternatum *Johnson*

Trollius laxus *Elbert*

Anemone cylindrica *Johnson*

Anemone quinquefolia *Johnson*

Anemone canadensis *Johnson*

COPTIS

There are several species of *Coptis*, four in North America, but only one in the northeastern states.

GOLDTHREAD, C. GROENLANDICA, is a small plant, not 6 inches tall, with all its leaves growing from the thin yellow underground stem (rhizome), and several leafless stems bearing small white flowers. The leaves are evergreen. The leaf-blades are divided into three. There are from five to seven sepals, no petals, numerous stamens, and several pistils.

May to July: in mossy woods, bogs, and swamps across Canada and southward to New Jersey, the mountains of North Carolina and Tennessee, Indiana, and Iowa; also in Asia. *Plate 36*.

LIVERLEAF (HEPATICA)

We have two very similar species of *Hepatica*. The genus is characterized by its lobed leaves, all at the base, and the circle of three small, unlobed leaves just below the flower. This is an involucre; it may be mistaken for sepals, but careful examination will show that it is separated from the flower by a short length of stem. The actual sepals are the white or colored parts of the flower. There are numerous stamens and pistils; the latter become achenes. Both our species have white, pink, or lavender flowers, growing singly on hairy leafless stems. The leaves last through the winter, lying on the ground, usually rather flaccid and brown, at flowering time. New leaves appear just after the flowers.

Our two species have been considered two varieties of one; even merely varieties of the European *H. nobilis*; but in their extreme forms they are very distinct.

This genus is one of the classic examples of the "doctrine of signatures," which taught that each plant was "signed" for healing some afflicted part of the human body. The three-lobed leaf indicated the liver, for diseases of which the plant was (falsely) thought to be sovereign.

ROUND-LOBED LIVERLEAF, H. AMERICANA, has leaves averaging about 3 inches across the blades, on shaggy stalks. *H. acutiloba* differs, as the name suggests, in having leaf-blades with pointed lobes; they are also larger, about 4 inches across, and of a different green. The hairs on this species are longer and are directed backward along the stems and leaf-stalks. There are other, more technical differences. The two species undoubtedly hybridize, yielding plants which cannot be definitely assigned to either. They both occupy much the same range, but *H. americana* is more likely to be found in acid soils, *H. acutiloba* in limy soils. Both grow commonly in woods.

H. americana: March to June, from Nova Scotia to Manitoba and southward to Florida, Alabama, and Missouri. *Plate 36*.

H. acutiloba: March to June, from Maine to Minnesota and southward to Georgia, Alabama, and Missouri. *Plate 36*.

THE POPPY FAMILY (PAPAVERACEAE)

Poppies of various kinds are familiar in the wild and in gardens, in both Old and New Worlds. The family, however, is not large. It is characterized by a milky or colored juice. The species native in our range have two sepals, which fall as the flower opens. There are four or more petals, numerous stamens, and one pistil. The leaf-blades of our species are divided or deeply cleft.

The most celebrated member of the family is an Old-World poppy, *Papaver somniferum*, from whose milky juice opium and its derivatives are obtained. The name means "sleep-bringing."

SANGUINARIA

There is but one species of *Sanguinaria*.

BLOODROOT or PUCCOON, S. CANADENSIS, is a familiar and beautiful flower of spring. The single flower appears on a leafless stem but enfolded by a round, veiny, deeply lobed leaf-blade; both leaf-stalk and flower-stalk spring from an underground, horizontal stem (rhizome). This has orange-red juice, the "blood," and is the "root" referred to in the name. The flower in its most symmetric form has eight

PLATE 36

Hepatica americana *Johnson*

Sanguinaria canadensis *Gottscho*

Coptis groenlandica *Johnson*

Hepatica acutiloba *Johnson*

Hydrastis canadensis *D. Richards*

Stylophorum diphyllum *Gottscho*

Chelidonium majus *Rickett*

white petals, four narrow ones alternating with four wider ones; but they are very variable, sometimes numerous. The two sepals are rarely seen except on the bud. The leaf expands after flowering; several varieties have been named for its differing forms. Its blade may become 8 inches wide, and it overtops the slim seed-pod (capsule).

March to May: in woods, often on dry rocky slopes, or along streams in the open from Quebec to Manitoba and southward to Florida, Alabama, and Oklahoma. *Plate 36.* The red sap of the rhizome has been used as a dye. Puccoon is a name given by the Indians to several plants that yield a dye. *Sanguinaria* may be distinguished as red puccoon. Yellow puccoon is *Lithospermum canescens.*

CELANDINE (CHELIDONIUM)

There is but one species of *Chelidonium,* a native of the Old World now well established in the New.

GREATER CELANDINE, C. MAJUS, has stalked leaves
borne singly on the stem. Their blades are divided pinnately into segments which are themselves variously notched and lobed. The lower surface is whitish and smooth. The flower has, besides the two sepals which fall, four yellow petals, numerous stamens, and a slim pistil. It is about an inch across.

April to September: in moist soil from Quebec to Iowa and southward to Georgia and Missouri. *Plate 36.* Dioscorides wrote that the name Chelidonion, which means "swallow," was given to this plant because the swallows used the orange-yellow juice to restore the sight of their blinded nestlings. It was recommended at least as late as the seventeenth century as a cure for sore eyes. It has also been used, more recently, to remove warts, and is called wartweed in many parts of England. An alternative but less convincing explanation of the name was that it bloomed when the swallows returned.

STYLOPHORUM

Only one species of this genus inhabits North America. The others are Asian.

CELANDINE-POPPY, S. DIPHYLLUM, somewhat resembles the greater celandine, but is quickly distinguished by its two *paired* leaves on the stem (there are also leaves at the base of the stem). Each leaf-blade is deeply cleft or divided pinnately. The four yellow petals make a flower about 2 inches across.

March to May: in moist woods from western Pennsylvania to Wisconsin and southward to Virginia, Tennessee, and Missouri. *Plate 36.*

GLAUCIUM

This is a genus of the Old World, abundant in the Mediterranean lands. One species has become naturalized in North America.

HORNED-POPPY or SEA-POPPY, G. FLAVUM, is most abundant near the coast. Its stem grows as much as 3 feet tall, bearing a single yellow flower and several leaves without stalks whose blades seem almost to surround the stem. At or near the base of the stem there are leaves with stalks. All the blades are more or less pinnately lobed or cleft. As in other species of this family, the juice is yellowish.

June to August: in waste places, chiefly sandy, from Massachusetts to Virginia; also inland to Michigan and West Virginia. *Plate 37.*

Besides the above species, species of poppies (*Papaver*) may escape from cultivation and become established; the petals are most commonly red. (There are native species of *Papaver* in Alaska.) Also a cultivated species of prickly poppy (*Argemone mexicana*), native in the Southwest, may be found escaped in our range. A southern species of the same genus (*A. intermedia*) reaches northward into southern Illinois and Missouri. Both have prickle-edged leaves, two or three sepals, white petals, and many yellow stamens.

THE PITCHER-PLANT FAMILY (SARRACENIACEAE)

The English name identifies the distinguishing peculiarity of this family. There are two other genera in widely separated parts of the Americas, also fitted for catching insects.

PITCHER-PLANTS (SARRACENIA)

This genus includes the only pitcher-plant commonly found in the northeastern United States. A second species, *S. flava*, the yellow-flowered trumpets of the South, extends northward to southeastern Virginia.

PITCHER-PLANT, S. PURPUREA, is known by its characteristic pitcher-shaped or vase-shaped leaves, in the cavities of which water collects. Small insects drown in this water, and the products of their decomposition are absorbed by the plant and form part of its nutrition. The species has been divided into two varieties according as its pitchers are smooth or hairy on the outside; their proportions also vary. The single flower hangs from the end of a leafless stem. It has five sepals (with three small bracts below them), five red-purple petals, many stamens, and a curious pistil: the style spreads into a sort of umbrella with five small stigmas on the concealed surface. There is also a form with yellow petals.

May to August: in bogs and peaty places from Labrador throughout Canada and southward to Maryland, Ohio, Indiana, and Minnesota. *Plate 37*.

THE ROSE FAMILY (ROSACEAE)

The *Rosaceae* form a large and quite easily recognizable family. Its species are familiar on our tables as well as in our gardens and in the wild: strawberries, raspberries, cherries, plums, peaches, almonds, apples, pears, and quinces are all in the rose family. In the garden we value our roses, but possibly do not realize that spiraea, Japanese quince, hawthorns, and crabapples belong to the same family. In the wild there are many wild roses, wild blackberries, hawthorns, wild crabs, wild cherries, and other trees and shrubs not here included. But there are also many herbaceous plants well known to the enthusiast for wild flowers.

These may be recognized, as a group, by their generally numerous stamens and several or many pistils, surrounded by usually five petals and five sepals. The "receptacle" or base of the flower generally forms a sort of cup or saucer, on or near the margins of which stand the perianth and stamens. In several genera the pistils are on a hump or dome in the center (as in the buttercups). The fruits of the herbaceous wild species are small pods (follicles) or seedlike achenes. The leaves are borne singly on the stem, generally with a quite conspicuous pair of appendages (stipules) at the point of attachment. The blades of many species are divided, pinnately or palmately.

I. *We separate first two genera that lack petals; they have four sepals to a flower, and usually one pistil:* Sanguisorba (*leaves pinnately divided*); Alchemilla (*leaves palmately lobed*).

II. *Among the remaining herbaceous genera we have some with yellow petals, some with white, pink, or purple.*

A. Genera with yellow petals: *Potentilla* (most species; small bracts alternate with the sepals, like an extra calyx; leaves divided palmately or pinnately); *Geum* (most species; leaves mostly divided pinnately with the end segment the largest; styles of pistils sharply bent in the middle and still present on the seedlike fruits – achenes); *Agrimonia* (leaves pinnately divided with small segments between larger ones; receptacle which bears perianth cup-shaped and provided with hooked bristles; this forms a "bur" around the seedlike fruits – achenes); *Waldsteinia* (long-stalked leaves, the blade divided palmately into three; flowers in small clusters on leafless stems); *Duchesnea* (like *Waldsteinia*, but flowers with large bracts alternating with sepals, and fruit looking like a strawberry but tasteless).

B. Genera with white, pink, or purple petals.

1. Here we may notice first two genera with leaves not divided: *Spiraea* (somewhat woody stems bearing lanceolate or ovate leaves without stalks and without stipules); *Dalibarda* (leaves from the ground, with long stalks and roundish blades). See also *Gillenia*, below.

2. Genera with white, pink or purple flowers and palmately or pinnately divided leaves: *Potentilla* (three species; see under A); *Geum* (four species; see under A); *Fragaria* (leaf blades divided palmately into three; characteristic strawberry fruit); *Rubus* (leaf-blades

divided into three on a stalk from a creeping stem; characteristic blackberry fruit); *Gillenia* (leaves without stalks, the palmately arranged segments appearing like separate, undivided leaves all at one point; narrow petals); *Filipendula* (tall, much-branched inflorescence of many small pink flowers); *Aruncus* (stamens and pistils in separate flowers on different plants; small white flowers in branched racemes).

BURNET (SANGUISORBA)

These are mostly tall plants with pinnately divided leaves. Their distinctive features are their lack of petals and the number of sepals, which is four instead of the usual five of this family. The botanical name is derived from two Latin words signifying "blood absorber," the red-flowered European species being thought to have this power. The English name is apparently a corruption of "brunette," from the red-brown color of the flowers of this European species.

AMERICAN BURNET, S. CANADENSIS, may reach a
     height of 6 feet. The segments of the leaves are stalked with lanceolate, toothed blades. The numerous white flowers are massed in a thick spike at the summit of the stem, the filaments projecting and giving a fuzzy appearance to the whole.
     June to October: in boggy and marshy places from Labrador to Manitoba and southward to Delaware, to Georgia in the mountains, and to Ohio and Illinois. *Plate 37.*

Another species, the European *S. minor*, is cultivated, and occasionally escapes to the wild. It has green or brown sepals. It is called salad burnet. Though little used now in our present neglect of the art of salads, it was once popular. John Evelyn wrote of its "so chearing and exhilarating . . . quality" and said that "a fresh sprig in Wine, recommends it to us. . . ." This should be worth trying.

ALCHEMILLA

The genus *Alchemilla* is represented in many parts of the Old World and South America, but only two or three naturalized species occur in the United States. They are characterized by palmately lobed leaves and small green flowers with four sepals, no petals, and four stamens. There is commonly a single pistil, becoming an achene in fruit.

LADY'S-MANTLE, A. VULGARIS, grows up to 2 feet
     tall, bearing leaves with blades about 4 inches wide. The leaf-blades are not only lobed but sharply toothed. The flower consists largely of a green cup (the receptacle) bearing the four green sepals on its rim.
     June to October: a weed in waste places in Nova Scotia and in scattered places in New England and New York. *Plate 37.* In olden times this species was credited with magical powers because of the "dew" on its leaves (probably exuded water). This reputation was responsible for the name *Alchemilla*, according to the herbalist Bock: it was associated with alchemy, which was considered a sort of magic. Others derive the name directly from Arabic; but the Arabs probably got the word where *they* got "alchemy" — from the Greek.

A. MICROCARPA is bushy and much smaller, its stems
     not more than 4 inches long. The flowers are in small clusters along the stems. This European plant has become naturalized in the South and reaches northward to Delaware, growing in lawns, fields, and waste places.

CINQUEFOILS, FIVE-FINGERS, AND SILVERWEEDS (POTENTILLA)

The genus *Potentilla* is a large one and some of its species are difficult to distinguish. As a genus, however, it is fairly easy to recognize. There are five sepals, and, alternating with them and below them, five bracts which seem like an extra calyx. There are five petals, yellow in most species. The stamens and pistils are generally numerous, the pistils on a hump in the center of the flower. Because of the five yellow petals and numerous stamens and pistils, the cinquefoils may be mistaken for buttercups; but the five bracts, the "extra calyx," are sufficient distinction.

The pistils become achenes.
     The name means "the little potent one" because of the reputedly potent medicinal powers of one species, *P. anserina*, which was also cultivated for food in ancient times.
     Although cinquefoil means "five leaves," this name is conveniently used for the whole genus, regardless of the number of leaf-segments.
     To identify the species, the plants are first classified by the way in which their leaves are divided, palmately or pinnately.

PLATE 37

Sarracenia purpurea   *Gottscho*

Glaucium flavum   *V. Richard*

Potentilla canadensis   *Rickett*

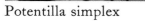
Potentilla simplex   *Johnson*

Potentilla recta   *Rickett*

Alchemilla vulgaris   *Roche*

Sanguisorba canadensis   *Gottscho*

POTENTILLA

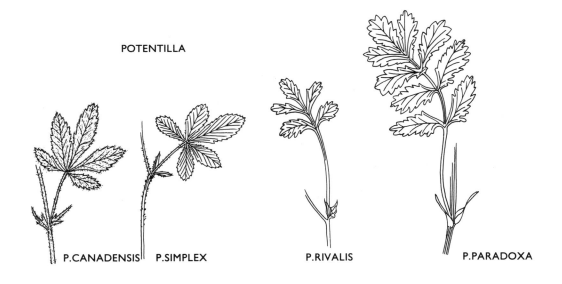

P.CANADENSIS P.SIMPLEX   P.RIVALIS   P.PARADOXA

I. *Plants with leaves divided palmately into from three to seven segments. (Compare II.)*

These plants may in turn be classified by the disposition of their flowers, whether single flowers are borne on stalks that grow from the axils of leaves, or a number of flowers make up an inflorescence.

A. Cinquefoils with leaves divided palmately and single flowers on stalks from the axils of leaves. These species have creeping stems and yellow petals. (Compare B.)

P. CANADENSIS and P. SIMPLEX are very similar.

Both have stems at first erect, then arching and lying on the ground. Both have leaf-blades divided into five segments. They may be more or less easily distinguished by the shape of these segments. In *P. canadensis* they have straight sides converging to the leaf-stalk, and teeth only towards the end (see the drawings). In *P. simplex* the sides are curved and toothed nearly to the base. The flowers are little more than $\frac{1}{2}$ inch across.

March and April to June: in dry soil from Nova Scotia to Ontario, *P. simplex* to Minnesota, and southward to Georgia, Tennessee, and Missouri, *P. simplex* to Oklahoma. *Plate 37.*

P. REPTANS has five or seven leaf-segments and larger flowers, up to an inch across.

May to August: a native of the Old World, now found in lawns and waste places from Nova Scotia to Ontario and Virginia.

B. Cinquefoils with leaves divided palmately and flowers in an inflorescence. These species have more or less erect stems. The first four species have yellow flowers, the fifth has white flowers; the first three have at least some leaves divided into five or more segments, the fourth and fifth have three leaf-segments.

P. RECTA has hairy stems (to 2 feet tall) and leaves, the lower leaves with five or seven segments which are blunt at the end. The petals are pale yellow and notched. The flower is about an inch across. This pretty European species makes a bright show in many eastern meadows.

May to August: in fields and roadsides from Newfoundland to Minnesota and southward to Virginia, Tennessee, Arkansas, and Kansas; a rapidly spreading weed. *Plate 37.*

P. RIVALIS has softly hairy stems to 2 feet tall. There are three or five leaf-segments, narrow and sharp-pointed. The flowers are very small, less than $\frac{1}{4}$ inch wide. There may be only a few stamens.

May to August: in prairies, bottomlands, and moist soil from Minnesota westward to British Columbia and southward to Illinois, Kansas, Mexico, and California. A rather perplexing, widespread group of plants. Some botanists consider these plants as belonging to three distinct species: *P. rivalis*, with some leaves pinnately divided; *P. pentandra*, with five leaf-segments palmately arranged; and *P. millegrana*, with three leaf-segments and very finely downy. The flowers are much alike in all.

SILVERY CINQUEFOIL, P. ARGENTEA, is an invader from the Old World. The branching stems may grow nearly 2 feet tall. The five leaf-segments are narrow, deeply toothed (almost lobed), and silvery underneath. The flowers are less than $\frac{1}{2}$ inch across.

June to September: in dry open ground from Newfoundland to Montana and southward to Virginia, Ohio, and Illinois. *Plate 38.*

PLATE 38

Potentilla argentea *Uttal*

Potentilla tridentata *Johnson*

Potentilla fruticosa *Johnson*

Geum canadense *Rickett*

Geum canadense *Rickett*

Potentilla norvegica *Scribner*

Potentilla anserina *Scribner*

Potentilla palustris *Johnson*

P. NORVEGICA is a stout bushy plant up to 3 feet
tall, usually hairy. The leaves have three rather
broad, coarsely toothed segments. The flowers are
nearly ½ inch across, the petals slightly shorter than
sepals and bracts.

June to October: in waste places, thickets, etc.
from Greenland and Labrador to Alaska and southward to North Carolina, Texas, and Arizona; a common, very variable weed. *Plate 38*.

P. TRIDENTATA is easily distinguished from the
foregoing species by its white petals. There are
creeping woody stems from which erect branches
grow. These have leaves mostly near the base, each
divided into three segments which are three-toothed
(tridentate) at the end (which is broad).

May to October: in dry, rocky places throughout northern Canada and southward to Connecticut,
the mountains of Georgia, Michigan, Iowa, and
North Dakota. *Plate 38*.

II. *Cinquefoils with pinnately divided leaves. (See also
P. rivalis under I.) Most have yellow flowers.*

A. Cinquefoils with pinnately divided leaves and
yellow petals. (Compare B.)

P. PARADOXA grows up to 20 inches tall. The leaf-
segments number from seven to eleven. They are
generally broader towards the tip and rather bluntly
toothed. The flowers are about ¼ inch across.

May to September: in prairies and bottomlands
and damp places generally from Ontario to British
Columbia and southward to New York, Ohio, Louisiana, Kansas, and New Mexico.

P. PENSYLVANICA is distinguished by the whitish
wool on the under surface of its leaf-segments.
These are from five to eleven, and deeply toothed or
almost cleft. The flowers are about ½ inch across.

June to August: in dry soil of prairies and shores
from Newfoundland and Labrador to Alaska and
southward to Ontario, Michigan, Nebraska, New
Mexico, and California; a complex assortment of
plants sometimes considered several species.

SILVERWEED, P. ANSERINA, the original "little potent one," is a spreading plant with runners
which root and produce clusters of erect leaves. The
leaves have numerous segments, very small ones often
interposed between the larger ones, all silky beneath
with long silvery hairs.

May to September: in moist sandy or rocky
places across Canada and southward to New York,
Indiana, Iowa, New Mexico, and California; also in
the Old World. *Plate 38*.

P. PACIFICA resembles *P. anserina*, the leaves being
more woolly than silky. It is mostly a western
species, but occurs from Labrador to Long Island
near the coast.

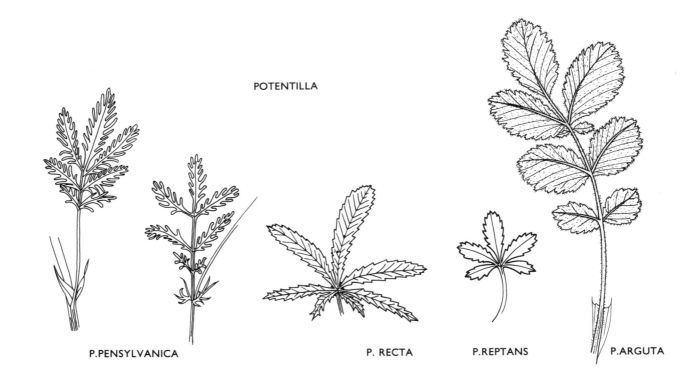

POTENTILLA

P.PENSYLVANICA   P. RECTA   P.REPTANS   P.ARGUTA

P. FRUTICOSA is a shrub, but is included here because
of its similarity to other species of *Potentilla*. The
leaf-segments are narrow and without teeth, generally silky. The flowers are commonly about an inch
across.

June to October: in meadows and on open hillsides across Canada and southward to New Jersey,
Ohio, Iowa, New Mexico, and California. *Plate 38*.

B. Cinquefoils with pinnately divided leaves and
petals not yellow.

P. ARGUTA has white (or cream-colored) flowers. The
leaves are divided into from five to eleven segments. The flowers are crowded, about $\frac{3}{4}$ inch across.
The plant is rather clammy with brownish, glandular
hairs.

June to August: in dry woods and prairies from
Quebec to British Columbia and southward to the
District of Columbia, Indiana, Oklahoma, Colorado,
and New Mexico.

P. PALUSTRIS has red-purple flowers nearly an inch
across. The five or seven leaf-segments are lanceolate or elliptic, either smooth or silky; the upper
three segments are close together, as if palmate.

June to August: in swamps, marshy meadows,
and other wet places from Greenland to Alaska and
southward to New Jersey, Ohio, Iowa, Wyoming,
and California. *Plate 38*.

Besides all these several Canadian species touch our northern
borders and inhabit the high mountains of New England. *P. robbin-
siana* is a dwarf species only about 2 inches tall; with three leaf-segments. Several other European species have established themselves in
scattered places. *P. intermedia* somewhat resembles *P. norvegica* but
has five leaf-segments. *P. nicolletii* resembles *P. paradoxa* but has
fewer leaf-segments (from five to eleven); it ranges from Minnesota to North Dakota and south to Missouri and Kansas.

AVENS (GEUM)

Most of the plants of *Geum* have pinnately divided leaves with the segment at the end larger than
those at the sides. A surer way to recognize the genus
is to use a hand lens on the styles of the pistils: in
most species there is a sharp crook near the tip. The
two species that lack this have styles that are hairy at
the base or throughout (these have often been placed
in a separate genus). In all the styles are not shed
after fertilization but form "tails" on the numerous
seedlike fruits (achenes). The petals are white, yellow, or purplish. There are small bracts alternating
with the sepals, like an extra calyx.

The English name is from the old French name
for *G. urbanum*, a European species rarely seen in the
United States. This is also called herb-bennet, a corruption of the Latin *herba benedicta*, "blessed plant";
the pleasant fragrance of its root was said to keep the
Devil away.

I. *Species with white flowers. (See also under II; some
species have cream-colored or greenish-yellow petals.)*

G. CANADENSE is a rather straggling, branching plant
up to 4 feet tall, smooth or slightly hairy. The
principal leaves have three segments, but the lower
ones have five, the three at the end larger.

May to August: in woods and thickets and along
roadsides from Nova Scotia and Quebec to North Dakota and southward to Georgia and Texas. *Plate 38*.

G. LACINIATUM is a bigger and hairier plant, up to 3
feet tall. The upper leaves are divided into three,
the lower often into more than three, the segments on
all being generally sharply and prominently toothed
or jaggedly cut ("laciniate"). The petals are smaller
than the sepals.

May to July: in damp places in woods and along
roadsides from Nova Scotia to Michigan and southward to Maryland, Illinois, and Kansas.

II. *Species with yellow, cream-colored, or orange flowers (see also under III).*

G. VERNUM is a slender plant not more than 2 feet
tall, with yellow flowers. Some of the lower leaves
have undivided but lobed leaves. Some leaves are pinnately divided with deeply toothed or even lobed segments. The flowers are only about $\frac{1}{4}$ inch across.

April to June: in woods from New York and
Ontario to Michigan and southward to Maryland,
Tennessee, Arkansas, and Kansas. *Plate 39*.

G. ALEPPICUM is a hairy plant which may reach 5
feet in height. The leaves vary greatly, but have
a general tendency to mix small segments with large
ones, all sharply toothed. The yellow petals are as
long as or slightly longer than the sepals.

May to August: in thickets and meadows from
Quebec to British Columbia and southward to New
Jersey, Indiana, Iowa, New Mexico, and Mexico.
Plate 39. The name comes from a town in Syria,
where the species also grows. Our plants are a variety,
formerly considered a distinct species under the name
G. strictum.

G. MACROPHYLLUM grows up to 3 feet tall. The
leaves have a round segment at the end with
much smaller segments along the sides. The plant is

somewhat bristly. The yellow petals are as long as or longer than the sepals.

May to August: in moist woods and on wet ledges from Labrador to Alaska and southward to New York, Michigan, Idaho, and California. *Plate 39.*

G. VIRGINIANUM has a hairy stem (at least the lower part) and hairy leaves. The leaf-segments are rather blunt and shallowly toothed. The petals are cream-colored or greenish-yellow, smaller than the sepals.

June to August: in dry woods and rocky places from Massachusetts to Indiana and southward to North Carolina and Tennessee.

G. PECKII is a small plant of the high mountains, growing only about a foot tall. The leaves have a round, sharp-toothed segment at the end, with one or more pairs of very small segments on the sides (or sometimes none). The yellow petals are longer than the sepals.

June to September: in damp rocky and peaty places in the mountains of Maine and New Hampshire; also in Nova Scotia. *Plate 39.*

III. *Species with purplish flowers, or yellowish with a purple tinge.*

PURPLE AVENS, G. RIVALE, may be known by its drooping flowers. The leaves on the stem generally have only three segments; those at the base have five or more. The bracts outside the sepals are longer than the sepals themselves.

May to August: in wet meadows and bogs from Labrador to British Columbia and southward to New Jersey, West Virginia, Illinois, Minnesota, New Mexico, and California; also in Europe and Asia. *Plate 39.* It is called water avens in England; also Billy's-buttons, granny's-nightcap, and various other things.

G. TRIFLORUM is remarkable for the very long, hairy "tails" on its achenes; a head of fruits resembles a sort of feather-duster. The tails are often 2 inches long. The plant differs from other species of *Geum* also in the numerous small and rather jagged segments of which its pinnately divided leaves are composed. The whole plant is softly hairy. It is not tall, little more than a foot.

April to June: in woods and on prairies from western New York to Ontario and British Columbia and southward to Illinois, Iowa, New Mexico, and California. *Plate 39.* In many books this will be found under the name *Sieversia triflora*, the striking fruits being thought sufficient to separate the plant from *Geum*.

THE AGRIMONIES (AGRIMONIA)

Agrimonies may at first sight suggest a *Geum*, with their leaves divided pinnately into large and small segments. The end segment of a leaf, however, is not much if any larger than the others. The small yellow flowers are in a long narrow spike. Botanically the genus is distinguished by the presence of hooked bristles on the cup-shaped end of the flower stalk, all forming a sort of small, top-shaped bur around two seedlike fruits (achenes). The flowers are only about ¼ inch across, or less.

Agrimony or *Agrimonia* is from an old Greek name for a wound in the eye, to heal which some plant — perhaps an agrimony — was used. The small burs stick to clothing, and those of the European *A. eupatoria* have been called harvest-lice and sweethearts. They appear in July and August.

A. GRYPOSEPALA is a tall species, sometimes reaching 6 feet in height. The stem and the veins on the lower surface of the leaves are hairy. The hand lens will reveal glands especially on the lower surfaces. There are from five to nine large segments.

In woods from Quebec to North Dakota and southward to North Carolina, Tennessee, and Kansas; British Columbia to California. *Plate 40.*

A. STRIATA is like *A. gryposepala* and even taller. The stem that bears the flowers is densely hairy, with no glands; there are numerous glands on the lower surface of the leaves. There are up to eleven large segments, with long-pointed tips.

In woods from Quebec to British Columbia and southward to New Jersey, West Virginia, Iowa, New Mexico, and Arizona.

A. ROSTELLATA reaches 3 feet in height. It is nearly smooth, but glandular. There are five or seven leaf-segments with very large, blunt teeth. The name, which means "small-beaked," comes from the sepals which stand erect in the fruiting stage and form a small beak or dome which projects above the hooked bristles (but this is true also of other species).

In woods from Massachusetts to Kansas and southward to Georgia, Louisiana, and Oklahoma.

A. PUBESCENS will reach 5 feet in height, with from five to nine large leaf-segments. Stem and leaves bear long, usually curly hairs.

In moist woods from Maine to Minnesota and Nebraska and southward to Georgia, Tennessee, and Oklahoma. *Plate 40.*

PLATE 39

Geum aleppicum *Johnson*

Geum triflorum *Johnson*

Geum peckii *Rhein*

Waldsteinia fragarioides *Elbert*

Geum vernum *Pollock*

Geum macrophyllum *Scribner*

Geum rivale *Johnson*

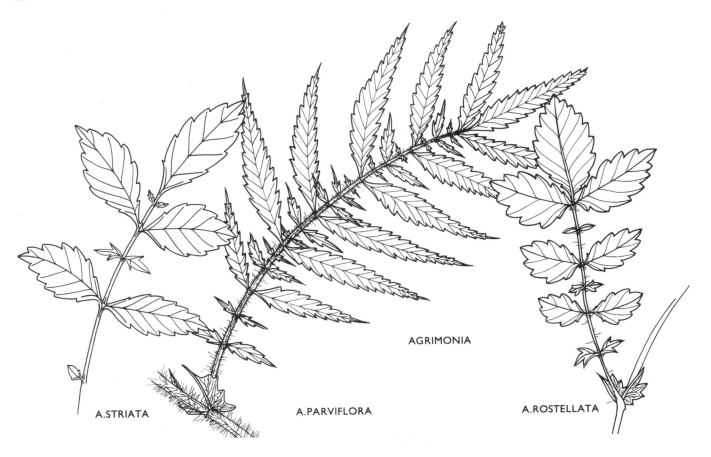

A.STRIATA   A.PARVIFLORA   AGRIMONIA   A.ROSTELLATA

A. PARVIFLORA may be 6 feet tall or taller. The stem is densely covered with long hairs. There are from eleven to twenty-three of the larger leaf-segments which bear many glands (seen through a hand lens) on their lower surface.

In moist woods and thickets from Connecticut to Nebraska and southward to Florida and Texas; also in Mexico and Hispaniola.

A. microcarpa resembles *A. rostellata*, but is hairy. It has usually only three large leaf-segments. It is essentially southern, reaching northward to Pennsylvania.

WALDSTEINIA

This small genus is represented in our range by one northern and mountain species with a southern variety. The plants have leaves that suggest those of a strawberry, but no succulent and edible fruit. Instead, the seedlike achenes into which the pistils develop are contained within the cup-shaped end of the flower-stalk. The petals are yellow.

BARREN-STRAWBERRY, W. FRAGARIOIDES, forms several leaves at the tip of its short underground stem (rhizome), each having a blade divided into three broad, toothed segments on a long (8-inch) stalk. In the midst of these rises a leafless stem bearing a cluster of flowers, each up to an inch across. The southern variety differs in having shorter petals.

April to June: in woods from New Brunswick and Quebec to Minnesota and southward to Georgia, Tennessee (the variety), and Missouri. *Plate 39.*

DUCHESNEA

Our one species of this small genus looks much like a *Potentilla* with a fruit like a strawberry.

INDIAN STRAWBERRY, D. INDICA, has creeping stems from which rise, at intervals, leaves and flowers. The leaf somewhat resembles that of a strawberry, having a blade divided into three segments. The flowers are distinguished from those of *Potentilla* by the

PLATE 40

Duchesnea indica   *Elbert*

Spiraea latifolia   *Rickett*

Spiraea tomentosa   *Rickett*

Spiraea corymbosa   *D. Richards*

Rickett

Agrimonia gryposepala

Spiraea alba   *Elbert*

Agrimonia pubescens   *Elbert*

Agrimonia gryposepala   *Rickett*

bracts that alternate with the sepals; these are longer and broader than the sepals and three-toothed at the broad outer end.

April to August: a native of Asia naturalized in moist waste ground from Connecticut to Iowa and southward to Florida and Oklahoma. *Plate 40*.

MEADOW-SWEETS AND HARDHACK (SPIRAEA)

The meadow-sweets and their kin are really shrubs and as such perhaps have no place in this book. However, their woody stems are not conspicuous — and their spires of bright flowers are. Since they are not quite in the same class as roses and brambles, the common native species are included here.

The flowers are small but numerous. Each has a shallow cup at the tip of its stalk, in which are seated the (usually) five pistils, and around the margin of which stand numerous stamens, five pink or white petals, and five sepals. The leaves are almost unique in our native *Rosaceae* in being without stipules. They are also undivided, toothed but not lobed or cleft. Our species flower – somewhere in their range – from June to September.

The botanical name was given to some plant by the Greeks, and is apparently derived from the word for a wreath. Some of our cultivated species (from Asia, or hybrids of such species) are commonly known as bridal-wreath. A species of this genus grows in England; but the lovely English meadow-sweet is *Filipendula*.

MEADOW-SWEET, S. LATIFOLIA, grows up to 4 feet tall, with purplish brown branches. The leaves are coarsely and sharply toothed. The flowers are in a tapering inflorescence or rather cluster of inflorescences, the lower ones springing from the axils of the uppermost leaves. The branches of the inflorescence are smooth. The flowers are white or tinged with pink.

Mostly in low, moist meadows, but also on rocky slopes from Newfoundland and Quebec to Michigan and southward to southern New York and North Carolina. *Plate 40*.

S. ALBA, another meadow-sweet, is similar to *S. latifolia*. The stem and its branches are yellowish, the leaves more finely toothed. The branches of the inflorescence are downy or closely woolly. The flowers are white.

Mostly in damp meadows and other moist places from Quebec to Alberta and southward to Delaware, western North Carolina, Ohio, Illinois, northern Missouri, and South Dakota. *Plate 40*.

S. CORYMBOSA is a more southern species, distinguished by its flat or domed inflorescence. The leaves are oval with large, sharp teeth. Branches and leaves are either smooth or downy. The flowers are white or pink.

In mountain woods from New Jersey to Pennsylvania and West Virginia and southward to Georgia and Kentucky. *Plate 40*.

S. VIRGINIANA, another species with flat inflorescence, its leaves nearly or quite without teeth, is found in rocky places in the mountains from West Virginia to Tennessee and North Carolina.

S. TOMENTOSA, hardhack, has leaves that have dense wool on the lower surface, coloring it white or yellowish. The flowers, in a branched, spire-shaped inflorescence, are bright pink (but there is a white-flowered form).

In rocky meadows, hillsides, and other generally moist places from Quebec to Manitoba and southward to Georgia, Tennessee, and Arkansas. *Plate 40*.

DALIBARDA

There is only one species of this genus.

DEWDROP, D. REPENS, is a curious little plant of the northern forests and the mountains. It has slim creeping stems from which arise the stalked leaves and the leafless flowering stems. The leaf-blades are heart-shaped and shallowly scalloped, on stalks up to 4 inches long. The flowers are borne singly on their

stems about the same height above the ground. They have five white petals and numerous stamens. However, these flowers usually form no fruit; other flowers, without petals and on shorter stalks, are fertile.

June to September: in woods from Quebec to southern Ontario and Minnesota and southward to New Jersey, the mountains of North Carolina, Ohio, and Michigan. *Plate 41*.

PLATE 41

Rubus chamaemorus *Scribner*

Gillenia trifoliata *Rickett*

Filipendula rubra *Johnson*

Fragaria vesca *D. Richards*

Aruncus dioicus *Gottscho*

Fragaria virginiana *Smith*

Dalibarda repens *Elbert*

STRAWBERRIES (FRAGARIA)

Strawberries scarcely need description; but it is perhaps necessary to point out that the edible "berry" is not a berry at all in the usual sense of the botanist — a succulent fruit developed from an ovary — but the central part of the stem tip, the receptacle of the flower, enormously enlarged. The "seeds" on its surface are seedlike fruits, achenes, each developed from a pistil and each containing one seed. The flowers are much like those of *Potentilla*, with the same circle of small bracts below the sepals and alternating with them. The short stem sends up long-stalked leaves, with blades divided palmately into three segments, and flowers in clusters on stems that have no ordinary leaves but do have bracts.

The cultivated strawberries of our tables are all hybrids. One of their ancestors was a species of the Pacific coast of North and South America. *F. virginiana* has been used in some crosses.

The botanical name refers to the fragrance of the fruit.

WILD STRAWBERRY, F. VIRGINIANA, is the most widely distributed species. It is characterized by the sinking of the achenes ("seeds") in small pits on the surface of the fruit. The flower-cluster is flattish and usually beneath the leaf-blades.

April to July: in fields and open woods and slopes, from Labrador and Newfoundland to Alberta and southward to Georgia, Alabama, and Oklahoma. *Plate 41*. Most Americans who grew up in the country know the delicious flavor of these little fruits — worth the labor of gathering enough for a mouthful.

WOOD STRAWBERRY, F. VESCA, differs from *F. virginiana* in having its achenes ("seeds") on the surface of the fruit, not sunken in it. The flowers form a taller cluster which may rise above the leaves.

April to August: in rocky woods and open places from Newfoundland to Alberta and southward to Virginia, Indiana, Missouri, Nebraska, and New Mexico; also in Europe. *Plate 41*.

BLACKBERRIES, RASPBERRIES, AND BRAMBLES (RUBUS)

The vast and complex genus to which the blackberries and their relatives belong are obviously shrubs and to be excluded from wild flowers as we have limited them. However, a few species creep on the ground, with erect leaves and flower-stalks which are not noticeably woody; these are briefly treated here.

The leaves are generally divided, palmately or pinnately or in a combination of the two. The flowers are much like those of a strawberry but without the circle of bracts below the sepals — the "extra calyx." Pistils are borne on a dome-shaped extension of the flower-stem, the receptacle; they become small succulent stone-fruits which adhere together to form the "berry."

DWARF BLACKBERRY, R. PUBESCENS, has creeping stems from which rise erect herbaceous, generally spineless branches up to 20 inches tall, bearing from two to five long-stalked leaves with blades divided into three segments. There may be a single flower at the end, or this may be accompanied by one or two others on stems from the axils of leaves. The fruit is dark red.

May to July: in damp woods, bogs, shores, etc.

from Labrador to British Columbia and southward to New Jersey, Indiana, Iowa, Colorado, and Washington.

CLOUDBERRY or BAKED-APPLE-BERRY, R. CHAMAEMORUS, has a creeping stem (rhizome) underground which sends up erect herbaceous, spineless branches not more than a foot tall. These bear usually two or three palmately lobed leaves and a single flower. The fruit is yellow when ripe, and edible.

June to August: in bogs and on moist mountain-tops throughout Canada and southward along the coast of Maine, in the mountains of New England, and on Long Island; also in northern parts of Europe and Asia, a distribution called circumpolar. *Plate 41*.

DEWBERRY, R. HISPIDUS, has trailing, usually prickly canes from which rise leaves with blades divided into three segments, and erect flowering branches a few inches tall bearing several similar leaves, and flowers in a small raceme. The fruit is seedy, not tasty.

June to September: in open soil, damp or dry, from Quebec to Wisconsin and southward to Maryland, North Carolina, Ohio, and Illinois.

GILLENIA

These plants are easily recognized by their five narrow, white or pale pink petals, which project, ribbonlike, in a somewhat untidy fashion. There are many stamens and five pistils which become small

pods (follicles) splitting open along one side. The leaves are divided into three palmately, and have no stalk, so that the three segments of one leaf may be mistaken for a circle of three undivided leaves. Their

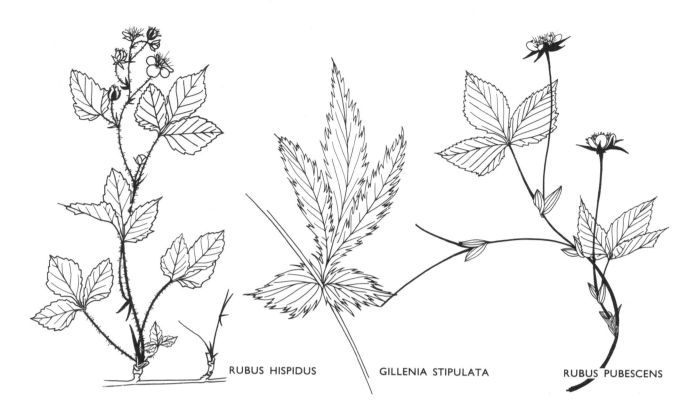

RUBUS HISPIDUS   GILLENIA STIPULATA   RUBUS PUBESCENS

true nature is revealed by the stipules, which in one species are so large as to look like two more leaf-segments, while in the other species they are mere hairs. Both grow 3 feet tall or taller.

INDIAN PHYSIC or AMERICAN IPECAC, G. STIPULA-TA, has large stipules and very sharply toothed – almost jagged – leaf margins. The petals are at most ½ inch long.

   May to July: in woods from western New York to Kansas and southward to Georgia and Texas. Both

this and the following species contain a bitter substance (obtained from the root) with emetic properties. It was used medicinally by Indians and colonists.

BOWMAN'S-ROOT, G. TRIFOLIATA, has tiny stipules and more finely toothed leaf-margins. The petals are from ½ to 1 inch long.

   May to July: in woods from New York to southern Ontario and Michigan and southward to Georgia and Alabama. *Plate 41*. See the note under the preceding species.

FILIPENDULA

   The species of *Filipendula* are tall plants with pinnately divided leaf-blades, the stems topped with ample clusters of small pink or white flowers. Petals and sepals number five each (with some variation), and there are numerous stamens and several pistils which become achenes. Only one species is native in the eastern United States.

QUEEN-OF-THE-PRAIRIE, F. RUBRA, grows up to 8 feet tall. The end segment of the leaf is large, lobed or cleft and jagged with uneven, sharp teeth. The segments at the side are much smaller, but also deeply lobed or cleft. The flowers are pink.

   June to August: on meadows and prairies from Pennsylvania to Minnesota and southward to Geor-

gia and Kentucky; escaped from cultivation in New England and New York. *Plate 41*.

F. ULMARIA is an immigrant from Europe and Asia, called in England meadow-sweet (the name we apply to species of *Spiraea*) or queen-of-the-meadows; but it was apparently not originally named for the meadows but for the fermented beverage called mead, which it was used to flavor. It also had medicinal virtues, and was strewn on floors to make "the hart merrie." It has white petals, a less jagged end-leaf-segment, and white down on the under surface of the leaves. It has escaped from cultivation from Newfoundland and Quebec to New Jersey, West Virginia, and Ohio.

ARUNCUS

We have one species of this small genus; another is found in the West.

GOAT'S-BEARD, A. DIOICUS, has stamens and pistils in different flowers and on different plants (*dioicus* means "in two households"). Both kinds of flowers are white, in long clusters on stems up to 7 feet tall. The leaves are pinnately divided into several pairs of narrow, pointed, toothed segments, the lower segments themselves pinnately divided. There are five each of sepals and petals, numerous stamens in the male flowers, usually three pistils in the female; they become pods (follicles) which split open along one side.

May to July: in woods from Pennsylvania to Iowa and southward to Georgia, Alabama, and Oklahoma. *Plate 41.* A familiar adornment of roadsides in the southern mountains.

THE MALLOW FAMILY (MALVACEAE)

The mallows and their relatives are easily recognized by one peculiarity of their flowers: the numerous stamens are joined to make a cylinder around the style. From this structure the many pollen-bearing heads of the stamens project on slender stalks. The pistil also is characteristic, with an ovary composed of five or more parts, in most of our species forming a ring of nutlike fruits that separate at maturity – together often looking something like the segments of a peeled tangerine. The leaves are borne singly. The leaf-blades tend to have a round outline and are generally palmately lobed, cleft, or divided.

The best-known cultivated species are hollyhock, okra, several species of hibiscus, and the various kinds of cotton. It is not a large family but has contributed what is certainly one of the world's most important crops.

The genera that grow wild in the northeastern United States can be distinguished as follows:

I. *Genera with pollen-bearing heads of stamens extending from the sides of the column of stamens throughout its length, usually in clusters at intervals; through the opening of the column extend the five branches of the style tipped with round stigmas:* Hibiscus (*flowers either pink or white and 6 inches across, or yellow and smaller*); Kosteletzkya (*flowers pink, about 3 inches across*).

II. *Genera with pollen-bearing heads extending in a dense cluster from the upper half of the column of stamens; stigmas either threadlike or round:* Callirhoë (*flowers rose, purple, or white, more than an inch across*); Malva (*petals pink, purple or white, indented at the outer edge*); Althaea (*with six or more bracts just beneath the calyx; flowers pink, about an inch across*); Sphaeralcea (*flowers red or yellow*); Napaea (*flowers white, less than an inch across, in a tall branched inflorescence*); Sida (*flowers less than an inch across, either yellow and in the axils of leaves or white in a large, branching inflorescence*); Abutilon (*flowers from ¼ to 1 inch across, yellow; leaves velvety*).

THE ROSE-MALLOWS (HIBISCUS)

The genus *Hibiscus* contributes some of our loveliest wild flowers, with large, delicate, pink, white, or yellow petals forming a flaring corolla. In the center is the stamen-column with the pollen-heads emerging from its sides. The summit of the column is toothed and bare of pollen-forming heads, and through its opening emerges the style, divided into five short branches, each branch bearing a round stigma. There are about twelve narrow bracts beneath the calyx. The fruit is a capsule with several seeds in each of its five chambers. Most of our species grow in wet places, flowering from July to September or October.

ROSE-MALLOW, SEA-HOLLYHOCK, or SWAMP-ROSE, H. PALUSTRIS, has ovate leaf-blades which are sometimes lobed, tapering to a sharp point. It often grows to about 8 feet in height. The upper part of the stem and the lower surface of the leaves are whitened by a fine down. The flowers are generally pink, sometimes purple or white; the individual petals exceed 2 inches in length, the whole flower being sometimes 6 inches across. Dr Fernald called it "mousy-smelling."

In marshes and on wet banks of streams from Massachusetts southward to North Carolina; and from western New York to Ontario, Michigan, and

Hibiscus palustris

Gottscho

Illinois; elsewhere it may be found as an escape from cultivation. *Plate A.*

ROSE-MALLOW or SWAMP-ROSE, H. MOSCHEUTOS, is very like *H. palustris* – indeed it has been suggested that they are races of one species. The leaves of *H. moscheutos* are narrower, sometimes with three points. The flowers are even larger, to 8 inches across. They tend to be cream-colored with a red center.

In coastal and inland marshes and shallow water from Maryland to Indiana and southward to Florida and Alabama. *Plate 42.*

H. LASIOCARPUS differs from the preceding species in having leaves that are softly downy on both surfaces. The flowers are pink or white with a crimson center.

In marshes from southern Indiana to Missouri and southward to Florida and Texas. This has also been by some botanists joined to *H. palustris.*

H. MILITARIS gets its name from the leaves which suggest, with their two sharp lobes at the base, the old weapon called a halberd. It is a smooth plant, about 6 feet tall. The flowers are about 6 inches across, pale pink with a darker center.

In swamps and on wet banks from Pennsylvania to Illinois, Minnesota, and Nebraska and southward to Florida and Texas. *Plate 42.*

FLOWER-OF-AN-HOUR, H. TRIONUM, is quite distinct from the preceding four species. It reaches a height of only 2 feet. The leaves are long-stalked and the blades divided or deeply cleft into three narrow segments or lobes which are bluntly toothed or lobed along the sides. The flowers are yellow with a purplish-black center ("eye") about 3 inches across, and open only for a few hours.

A native of Europe, now a weed in waste places, roadsides, and fields from Nova Scotia to Minnesota and southward to Florida and Texas. *Plate 42.*

KOSTELETZKYA

Most species of this genus are tropical, only one reaching northward into our range.

SEASHORE-MALLOW, K. VIRGINICA, closely resembles *Hibiscus*, the technical distinction being that it has but one seed in each chamber of the fruit. It grows to about 3 feet in height. The leaves are gray-green, with a fine but slightly rough down, their blades ovate or angled, often with an indented base. The flowers are pink, about 3 inches across.

July to September: in marshes and on shores of ponds from Long Island along the coast to Florida, thence to Texas; also in Bermuda and the West Indies. *Plate 43.*

THE POPPY-MALLOWS (CALLIRHOË)

The poppy-mallows are westerners which have invaded our midwestern states. They are plants of dry places – even roadsides and railroad tracks – with bright rose or purple 2-inch flowers. Five slender styles emerge from the column of stamens, the stigmas being on their inner sides.

C. INVOLUCRATA has roughly hairy stems which tend to spread horizontally. (Under a lens the hairs may often be seen to have a bulbous base.) The leaf-blades are palmately lobed or cleft, the lobes themselves lobed and bluntly toothed. There are three narrow bracts just beneath the calyx.

June to August: on prairies and in waste places from North Dakota to Wyoming and southward to Arkansas, Texas, and New Mexico; occasionally straying eastward as far as Ohio. *Plate 42.*

C. DIGITATA is smooth or nearly so. The leaf-blades are cleft or divided into very narrow lobes or segments. The flowers are on long slender stalks. There are no bracts under the flowers of this species.

April to July: on dry prairies and in sandy places from Missouri and Kansas to Arkansas and Texas; reported also from Indiana and Illinois. *Plate 42.*

C. ALCAEOIDES closely resembles *C. digitata* but is hairy with stiff hairs which may be "stellate," that is, star-shaped, with radiating prongs. The flowers vary in color from rose to white. There are no bracts.

May to August: in dry soil from Illinois to Nebraska and southward to Tennessee and Texas.

C. TRIANGULATA differs from all our other species in having unlobed leaf-blades; they are generally triangular, with deeply indented base, and notched rather than toothed along the edges. The flowers are in clusters on stems from the axils of the leaves. There are three bracts just below the calyx.

May to August: on sandy prairies and in dry woods from Wisconsin to Nebraska and southward to Alabama and Texas; North Carolina to Georgia. *Plate 42.*

PLATE 42

Hibiscus moscheutos *Rhein*

Malva sylvestris *Rickett*

Hibiscus trionum *Johnson*

Hibiscus militaris *Rickett*

Callirhoë involucrata *Johnson*

Callirhoë triangulata *Lee*

Callirhoë digitata *Johnson*

THE MALLOWS (MALVA)

The true mallows are all immigrants from abroad, and like so many plant wanderers have become weeds around dwellings and in waste places. They may be recognized by their petals, which are shallowly or deeply indented at the outer edge. The leaves have roundish blades, more or less lobed or cleft palmately. There are three bracts just beneath the calyx. The flowers grow singly or in clusters from the axils of leaves.

MUSK-MALLOW, M. MOSCHATA, is a handsome species, with pink, lavender, or white flowers about 2 inches across. The leaves have generally deeply cleft blades, the lobes themselves cleft or toothed. The bracts of the flower are narrow. The species is named for the faint musky odor of the flowers.

June to September: in fields, old gardens, waste places, and along roadsides from Newfoundland and Quebec to British Columbia and southward to Maryland, Tennessee, Missouri, and Nebraska. *Plate 43.*

HIGH MALLOW, M. SYLVESTRIS, attains a height of about 3 feet. The stem is more or less hairy.

The leaf-blades are not deeply cleft but lobed. The flowers, clustered in the axils, are about 2 inches across, red-purple with dark veins.

May to August: in waste places from Quebec to North Dakota and southward. *Plate 42.*

COMMON MALLOW or CHEESES, M. NEGLECTA, is a familiar weed, lying nearly flat on the ground. The leaves have round blades on long stalks, shallowly lobed and scalloped at the edges. The small flowers (about an inch across) are clustered in the axils; the petals are pale lavender or white, about twice as long as the sepals. The fruit consists of a flattish ring of segments together simulating a Cheddar cheese—and often eaten by children.

April to October: in waste places and around dwellings throughout the country. *Plate 43.*

Two other weedy species are commoner in the West but are found in places in our range. They resemble *M. neglecta*, and have often been confused with it. They are best distinguished by their small petals, scarcely longer than the sepals. Those of *M. rotundifolia* are hairy near the base, those of *M. parviflora* smooth. There are also technical differences in the fruits.

ALTHAEA

This is an Old-World genus, of which one species has become established in this country. *A. rosea*, the hollyhock, is also sometimes found growing wild.

MARSH-MALLOW, A. OFFICINALIS, is a tall plant, up to 4 feet in height, with velvety leaves. The blades are ovate, sharply toothed at the margins, often slightly lobed. The pale pink flowers are clustered in

the axils of leaves; they are about an inch across.

July to October: at the edges of marshes, salt or fresh, from Quebec to Virginia; and in scattered places inland as far as Michigan and Arkansas. It was formerly cultivated for its mucilaginous roots, from which "marshmallow" was obtained; this natural material has been replaced by the synthetic product made mostly from various sugars and gelatine.

SPHAERALCEA

The species of *Sphaeralcea* grow in Africa and America, but only one is established in our range. The western *S. coccinea* (*Plate 43*) just touches western Iowa.

GLOBE-MALLOW, S. ANGUSTA, is a small plant, about

a foot tall, with narrow pointed leaves. Stem and leaves are beset with branched hairs that lie flat against the surface. The flowers are yellow, only about ⅓ inch across. Plants are found on dry ground from Illinois to Nebraska and Kansas, and southward to Alabama, flowering in June.

NAPAEA

There is one species of *Napaea*.

GLADE-MALLOW, N. DIOICA, may be 10 feet tall. The leaves have broad blades cleft into sharp lobes,

the edges of which are sharply toothed and may be again lobed. The flowers are small but numerous, in a large, branched cluster at the summit of the stem. Stamens and pistils are in separate flowers on different

PLATE 43

Napaea dioica   *Johnson*

Malva moschata   *Elbert*

Malva neglecta   *Johnson*

Sphaeralcea coccinea   *Scribner*

Abutilon theophrasti   *D. Richards*

Sida spinosa   *D. Richards*

Kosteletzkya virginica   *Allen*

Sida hermaphrodita   *Rhein*

plants (*dioica* means "in two households"). The petals are white, about ¼ inch long.

June to August: in moist soil in scattered places from Pennsylvania to Minnesota and southward to Virginia, Ohio, Illinois, and Iowa; reported in Vermont; a rare species. *Plate 43*.

SIDA

Sida is a tropical genus, one tropical species reaching the United States, and one being native in our northeastern range. These two are so different in aspect that they might — for the purposes of this book — be considered separate genera.

PRICKLY-MALLOW, S. SPINOSA, is a small, branching plant 2 or 3 feet tall, with lanceolate or elliptic leaf-blades on short stalks, unlobed but with toothed edges. It is softly downy. A short spine at the base of each leaf gives the species its names. The flowers are small (about ½ inch across), yellow, on short stalks in bunches in the axils of leaves.

June to October: in fields and waste places from Massachusetts to Michigan and Nebraska and southward to Florida and Texas. *Plate 43*. The Latin name is scarcely distinctive.

VIRGINIA-MALLOW, S. HERMAPHRODITA, grows up to 10 feet tall and has broad, palmately lobed leaf-blades; the lobes taper into very sharp points. The flowers are about an inch across, white, in a branched cluster at the summit of the stem.

July to October: in moist soil from Pennsylvania to southern Michigan and southward to Maryland and Tennessee; not common. *Plate 43*.

ABUTILON

There are many species of *Abutilon* in the warmer parts of the world, including our southwestern states; but the species described below is the only one found in our range — and it is a native of Asia.

VELVET-LEAF, A. THEOPHRASTI, is a stout weed up to 5 feet tall, with large, heart-shaped leaf-blades. The whole plant is velvety; the hairs under a lens are seen to be branched, starlike ("stellate"). The flowers are relatively small, not more than an inch across, with yellow petals, growing on short stalks in the axils of leaves. The fruit is the usual ring of segments, in this species ridged and with outward-curving horns, and opening across the flat top while still attached.

July to October: in fields and waste places practically throughout the country but commoner in the southern parts. *Plate 43*. The species is named for Theophrastus, a botanist of ancient Greece.

THE ST.-JOHN'S-WORT FAMILY (HYPERICACEAE)

One peculiarity of the *Hypericaceae* is that in the leaves are glands which contain oil and sometimes a pigment; these appear as translucent spots when held against a source of light, or as black dots on the surface. The black dots are also characteristic of the petals of some species.

The leaves are mostly without stalks and without teeth, and in most of our species in pairs (in the others, in circles). The flowers of most species are yellow, with five petals, many stamens, and a pistil with several styles; the ovary becomes a small pod (capsule), generally with one or more beaks at the tip.

Our three genera are easily distinguished: *Hypericum* has five yellow petals; *Triadenum* has pink flowers; *Asycrum* has four yellow petals.

THE ST.-JOHN'S-WORTS (HYPERICUM)

The numerous species of *Hypericum* are much alike, except for a group with very small flowers and almost no leaves. Most are herbaceous, but several are shrubby. The stamens are typically numerous except in the small-flowered group. In some species they are arranged in several bunches. The pistils have from three to five styles. Most of the species are native, but the commonest is a weed from the Old World.

The inflorescences of some species provide good illustrations of the cyme: a terminal flower or fruit with the stem forking just below it and the forks rising above it to repeat the process.

It is not always easy to identify the species, and one must be prepared to use a hand lens and a small ruler with fine divisions. We may first group them according to the length of their petals and leaves.

I.   *Species with petals ¼ inch long or longer. The leaves of these plants, though very variable, are in general an inch long or longer. They have generally one main vein with branch veins departing from it in pinnate arrangement. (Compare II.)*
     These plants may be further subdivided into those that have black dots in the flowers and those that have none.

A. Species with black-dotted sepals or petals.

H. PERFORATUM (to 3 feet) is the Old-World species mentioned above that has so thoroughly established itself in North America. It is a branching plant with narrowly elliptic leaves, those on the branches usually much shorter than those on the main stem (½ inch as against 1 inch long). The flowers are numerous. The petals are black-dotted especially at the margin on one side; they are slightly asymmetric and the dots tend to run down the shorter side. The petals are about ½ inch long.

June to September: on roadsides and in fields from Newfoundland and Quebec across Canada and southward to North Carolina, Tennessee, Missouri, and California. *Plate 44.* This is one of the most magical of all herbs, potent in warding off all sorts of evil spirits and sickness. The potency was increased by smoking it in fires kindled on the eve of St. John's day, June 24, in rites that go far back in antiquity. The species has given its name to the whole genus.

H. PUNCTATUM (to 4 feet) has elliptic leaves from 1 to 2 inches long, round at the ends. The leaves as well as the petals are copiously marked with black lines and dots (they are "punctate"). The petals are about ⅖ inches long.

June to September: in fields and woods from Quebec to Minnesota and southward to Florida and Texas. *Plate 44.*

H. PSEUDOMACULATUM is sometimes treated as a variety of the foregoing species. The leaves are more ovate – that is, broadest between the base and the middle – and larger, up to 2 inches long. Both sepals and petals, besides the leaves, are copiously marked with black lines and dots.

June to August: in various situations from Illinois to Missouri and southward to Tennessee, Florida, and Texas.

B. Species with no black dots on the flowers.

H. PYRAMIDATUM (to 6 feet), great St.-John's-wort, has the largest flowers and fruit of any of our species. It may grow 6 feet tall, and has ovate or elliptic leaves up to 4 inches long. The flowers grow mostly singly on stems from the axils of leaves. The petals are an inch or more long, and the capsules about the same. The flowers expand in the morning and close in the afternoon.

July to September: on river-banks, in moist meadows, etc. from Quebec to Manitoba and southward to Maryland, Indiana, and Kansas.

H. ELLIPTICUM (to 20 inches) has smaller flowers, with petals ⅓ inch long and rather short and broad elliptic leaves mostly from ¾ inch to 1 inch long. The sepals are widest near their tips.

June to August: in moist places from Newfoundland and southern Quebec to Manitoba and southward to Maryland, West Virginia, Illinois, Iowa, and North Dakota.

H. ADPRESSUM (to 30 inches) has erect stems from a horizontal stem (rhizome) with numerous narrow leaves, those on the branches shorter than those on the main stem (1 inch as against 2 inches or more). Many flowers are crowded in the inflorescence. The petals are not more than ⅓ inch long. The sepals are widest near their base, and rather blunt at the tip.

July to September: at the margins of ponds and in wet meadows and bogs from Massachusetts to Illinois and southward to Georgia and Alabama. *Plate 44.*

H. kalmianum and *H. prolificum* are two shrubby species which may be mentioned here.

H. KALMIANUM (named for Pehr Kalm, a pupil of Linnaeus, who explored North America) is only about 2 feet tall, with crowded narrow leaves an inch or two long. The flowers are in small clusters at the tips of the branches. It grows in rocky and sandy soil mostly near the Great Lakes from New York to Ohio, Indiana, and Wisconsin; also in Quebec; flowering in July and August. *Plate 44.*

H. PROLIFICUM is taller, up to 7 feet, and more branched, with longer and wider leaves that are narrow – almost stalked – at the base. The flowers are in several clusters at and near the top. It is found mostly in dry rocky soil from New York to Minnesota and southward to Georgia and Louisiana, and escaped from cultivation elsewhere; it flowers from July to September. *Plate 44.* Both of these bushes make a fine show with their crown of many golden stamens.

Besides these species, several southerners intrude into our range: *H. densiflorum*, well named for its crowded inflorescence, with very narrow leaves (*Plate 44*); *H. sphaerocarpum*, with small round capsules and narrow leaves; *H. dolabriforme*, with narrow, sharp-pointed leaves up to 2 inches long; *H. frondosum*, with broadly elliptic leaves up to 3 inches long, often cultivated and escaped in various places; *H. denticulatum*, with leaves nearly as broad as long and petals small for this group, only $\frac{1}{3}$ inch long, and toothed ("denticulate") on the edges. These species are best treated with the plants of the southeastern states, where St.-John's-worts are numerous.

II. *Species with inconspicuous petals less than $\frac{1}{4}$ inch long, mostly about $\frac{1}{8}$ inch. The leaves of some species are an inch long, but those of most are $\frac{1}{2}$ inch or less, in some species nothing but minute scales. Except the smallest, the leaves have several main veins spreading from the base of the blade.*

H. MAJUS (to 2 feet) has blunt, lanceolate leaves an inch long or longer, with five or seven main veins; the petals are about $\frac{1}{5}$ inch long.

July to September: in open, moist ground from Quebec across Canada and southward to Delaware, Pennsylvania, Illinois, Iowa, Nebraska, Colorado, and Washington. *Majus* means "greater."

H. CANADENSE has nearly the same stature and form as *H. majus*. Its leaves are narrow, sharp pointed, mostly not exceeding an inch in length, with generally three main veins. The petals are about $\frac{1}{8}$ inch long.

July to September: in sandy and muddy places and wet meadows from Quebec and Newfoundland to Manitoba and southward to Georgia, Alabama, Illinois, and Iowa.

H. dissimulatum resembles the foregoing two species and may be a hybrid between *H. canadense* and *H. mutilum*, but we have no definite evidence. It grows in bogs and wet sand in the coastal plain from Nova Scotia to North Carolina and inland to New Hampshire and West Virginia.

H. MUTILUM (to 3 feet) has broadly elliptic or ovate, blunt leaves an inch long or longer, with three or five main veins. The petals are minute, scarcely $\frac{1}{8}$ inch long.

July to September: in moist ground from Newfoundland to Minnesota and southward to Florida

and Texas; a common, widespread, and variable species. *Plate 44*.

H. BOREALE (to 16 inches) is a small plant with stems that tend to lie on the ground, the tips curving up. The small leaves are elliptic, mostly about $\frac{1}{2}$ inch long, with three or five main veins. The petals are minute, $\frac{1}{12}$ inch long.

July to September: in wet and peaty soil and even in shallow water from Newfoundland and Quebec to Minnesota and southward to Virginia, Ohio, Illinois, and Iowa. *Plate 44*.

H. GYMNANTHUM (to 3 feet) is recognized by its nearly triangular leaves with a base that partly encircles the stem; they are mostly about $\frac{1}{2}$ inch long, with three or five main veins. The inflorescence rises nakedly (*gymn-*) above the leaves, the branches ending in minute flowers with petals only $\frac{1}{12}$ inch long.

June to September: in moist sandy or peaty ground from Long Island and New Jersey to Missouri and southward to Florida and Texas.

ORANGE-GRASS or PINEWEED, H. GENTIANOIDES (to 2 feet), would scarcely be taken for an *Hypericum* or even for a flowering plant. The leaves are minute narrow scales. The wiry green stem is repeatedly forked, bearing numerous small flowers at the ends of branches and along their sides.

June to October: in sandy or rocky places, often exposed to full sun, from Maine to Minnesota and southward to Florida. *Plate 45*. Linnaeus placed this and the following species in a separate genus which he named *Sarothra*.

NITS-AND-LICE, H. DRUMMONDII, resembles the foregoing but is less bushy and has longer, very narrow leaves (to $\frac{1}{2}$ inch long). The flowers hug the sides of erect branches, which form the type of cyme in which only one branch develops below each terminal flower.

July to September: in sandy or rocky places from Maryland to Iowa and Kansas and southward to Florida and Texas.

MARSH-ST.-JOHN'S-WORTS (TRIADENUM)

The marsh-St.-John's-worts differ from *Hypericum* in little more than the color of the flowers, and some technical details. (For this reason the more exacting botanists have placed these species in *Hypericum*.) There are generally only nine stamens, in three bunches alternating with three large orange glands (this is the meaning of the botanical name of the genus, *aden-* signifying "gland").

T. VIRGINICUM grows 2 feet tall or more. The leaves are ovate or elliptic and blunt; at the base they are broad and embrace the stem. The flowers are clustered at the end of branches from the axils of leaves, or in the axils of the uppermost leaves.

July and August: in wet sandy and boggy places from Nova Scotia to Illinois and southward, mostly along the coast to Florida and Mississippi. *Plate 45*.

PLATE 44

Hypericum prolificum

Hypericum kalmianum

Johnson

Hypericum perforatum   *Johnson*

Hypericum adpressum   *Allen*

Hypericum mutilum   *Scribner*

Hypericum densiflorum   *Allen*

Hypericum punctatum   *Elbert*

Hypericum boreale   *Elbert*

A variety with smaller flowers is found farther north, from Labrador to Manitoba and southward to Pennsylvania and Nebraska.

T. TUBULOSUM (to 3 feet) has longer leaves which taper to a narrow base. The flower-clusters are less dense.

July to September: in wooded swamps from Virginia to Missouri and southward to Florida and Louisiana. There is a variety with stalked leaves.

ASCYRUM

These yellow-flowered plants are distinguished from *Hypericum* by having four sepals and four petals instead of five. The sepals are of two sizes, two large outer ones enclosing two small inner ones. These sepals remain attached in the fruiting stage, enclosing the capsule.

ST.-PETER'S-WORT, A. STANS, stands 3 feet tall or more. The leaves are elliptic or ovate often with indented base. The flowers are at the tip of the stem and in the axils of leaves. The petals are ½ inch long or longer.

July to September: in sandy soil from Long Island and New Jersey to Kentucky and southern Missouri and southward to Florida and Texas; chiefly on the coastal plain. *Plate 45.* St. Peter's day is June 29. It marked the close of magical rites associated with St.-John's-wort. The name St.-Peter's-wort was somehow transferred to our plant from some English species of *Hypericum.*

ST.-ANDREW'S-CROSS, A. HYPERICOIDES, is a variable species, bushy-branched, growing 2 feet tall or taller. The leaves are narrow, often widest towards the tip, tapering at the base. The petals are somewhat less than ½ inch long.

July to September: in sandy soil on rocks, and in thickets from Massachusetts to Kansas and southward to Florida, Texas, and Mexico; in the West Indies. *Plate 45.*

THE ROCKROSE FAMILY (CISTACEAE)

Most species of *Cistaceae* are European. Ours have five petals, usually numerous stamens, and a pistil which forms a pod (capsule). This fruit is enclosed by the calyx. When mature it splits into three parts. The two outer sepals are generally much smaller than the three inner ones.

ROCKROSES or FROSTWEEDS (HELIANTHEMUM)

These plants have narrow, pointed leaves borne singly and comparatively large flowers (an inch across) with yellow petals. Flowers produced later in the season have no petals and do not open, but form capsules nevertheless. Several species are cultivated.

FROSTWEED, H. CANADENSE, grows a foot or two tall. Its stems and leaves are covered with branched ("stellate") hairs. The flowers are soon overtopped by branches, so that they appear to grow from the side of the stem.

May to July: in dry soil from Nova Scotia and Quebec to Minnesota and southward to North Carolina, Tennessee, Mississippi, and Missouri. *Plate 45.* Late in the season the bark is cracked and through the cracks strings of ice crystals may emerge; whence the English name.

H. BICKNELLII is similar to the foregoing species but has more numerous flowers in a branched inflorescence atop the stem. It also is a "frostweed."

June and July: in dry soil from Maine to Minnesota, South Dakota, and Colorado and southward to North Carolina and Texas. *Plate 45.*

HUDSONIA

Our two species of *Hudsonia* are characteristic heatherlike plants of beaches, dunes, and other sandy places, with bushy stems sprawling on the ground, small scale-like or needle-like leaves, and many yellow flowers borne singly at the ends of short branches. Both flower from May to July.

PLATE 45

Ascyrum hypericoides   *D. Richards*

Triadenum virginicum   *Gottscho*

Ascyrum stans   *Allen*

Helianthemum bicknellii   *Horne*

Hypericum gentianoides   *Ryker*

Hypericum gentianoides   *Johnson*

Helianthemum canadense   *Rickett*

BEACH-HEATHER or POVERTY-GRASS, H. TOMEN-
TOSA, has scale-like leaves up to $\frac{1}{6}$ inch long. It
grows from Quebec to Alberta and southward to
North Carolina, Indiana, Illinois, and North Dakota.
Plate 46.

FALSE HEATHER, H. ERICOIDES, has needle-like
leaves about $\frac{1}{4}$ inch long. It is found in Newfoundland to Delaware along the coast (and perhaps
farther south). *Plate 46.*

The genus *Lechea* of this family has minute red flowers on
branching stems that bear many small leaves.

THE LOASA FAMILY (LOASACEAE)

There are several species of *Loasaceae* in the western states, but only one in the northeastern part
of the country.

MENTZELIA

We have a single species of *Mentzelia.*

STICKLEAF, M. OLIGOSPERMA, is a plant that can
grow 3 feet tall but may form bushy masses on
rocky bluffs. The leaves, borne singly, are sharply
toothed, with short stalks or none; they are covered
with short sticky hairs. The flowers are deep yellow,
the five petals about $\frac{1}{2}$ inch long. There are about
twenty stamens, and a pistil which becomes a small
pod (capsule).

June to August: on rocky bluffs and in dry soil
from Illinois to South Dakota and Colorado and southward to Louisiana, Texas, and Mexico.

M. decapetala, the blazing-star of the western states, is found
in northwestern Iowa.

THE CACTUS FAMILY (CACTACEAE)

The cactus family is characteristic of the hot,
dry regions of our western states and of Mexico
and other southern countries (it is a New-World
family). Only a few species have made themselves
at home in the Northeast.

The family is characterized by having thick,

MENTZELIA OLIGOSPERMA   DIPHYLLEIA CYMOSA

PLATE 46

Jeffersonia diphylla *Aborn*

Opuntia compressa *V. Richard*

Caulophyllum thalictroides *Johnson*

Podophyllum peltatum *Gottscho*

Hudsonia tomentosa *V. Richard*

Hudsonia ericoides *Allen*

succulent stems of various shapes, mostly prickly, and generally no leaves (except small ones that drop off immediately). The sepals and petals are numerous, with no sharp distinction between them. At their base they pass into a cup-shaped or funnel-shaped receptacle, the inner surface of which is lined with the many stamens. The ovary is inferior.

PRICKLY-PEARS (OPUNTIA)

This is a large genus in the West, but in our range is represented by only four or five species.

O. COMPRESSA consists of thick oval sections joined end to end, the surface marked by small spots containing minute reddish-brown barbed hairs, but generally no spines. The minute hairs are much more dangerous than spines would be, for when they come in contact with skin they become detached and work into the tissues, causing painful inflammation.

The flowers are yellow, often with a red center. They are seen from May to July.

On rocky bluffs, sand dunes, etc. from Massachusetts to Ontario and Minnesota and southward to Georgia and Oklahoma. *Plate 46.* In early summer the end joints bear small, narrow, thick leaves.

O. TORTISPINA resembles the foregoing species but is armed with stiff spines, three or more of which project from each of the small spots on the surface.

On prairies from Ohio and Wisconsin to Colorado and southward to Kentucky and New Mexico.

O. FRAGILIS differs from the foregoing species in having segments which are not flattish but round – like potatoes; they are only about 2 inches long. The plant is much branched and covered with spines. The flower is about 2 inches across.

In dry open places from Michigan to British Columbia and southward to Illinois, Kansas, Texas, and Arizona.

Two other species of *Opuntia* have been reported in Wisconsin and Missouri, and a species of *Mammillaria* in Minnesota.

GROUP VI

SEPALS two, four, or six; petals four, six, or eight; petals separate and radially or bilaterally symmetric. Stamens six, eight, twelve, or eighteen but not twice the number of petals. Exception: *Podophyllum* has twice as many stamens as petals.

I. *Petals and stamens of the same number:* barberry family (*except* Podophyllum).

II. *Petals fewer than the stamens.*

    A. Four similar petals; six stamens of equal length: caper family.

    B. Four petals; six stamens, two shorter than the other four: mustard family.

    C. Four petals in two pairs, two outside, two inside, adhering at the tips; six stamens, joined: bleeding-heart family.

THE BARBERRY FAMILY (BERBERIDACEAE)

The barberries are well known in cultivation and in the wild as thorny shrubs with red berries. They have herbaceous relatives which do not in the least resemble them except in certain floral characteristics – those by which the botanist classifies plants. In the herbaceous species here described, there are four or six sepals, six or eight petals or in one species up to nine, and as many stamens as there are petals, or twice as many in one species. Several species are poisonous.

CAULOPHYLLUM

The only other species of *Caulophyllum* is Asiatic.

BLUE COHOSH or PAPOOSE-ROOT, C. THALICTROIDES, is a stout plant which may be 4 feet tall, but is often much less in the northern part of its range. The stem bears a single leaf, but this is so large and so divided into segments which are themselves divided and redivided that it gives the impression of many leaves. The ultimate segments are small, roundish and notched blades, somewhat resembling those of meadow-rue (*Thalictrum*, whence the botanical name). The flowers are in a large, branched inflorescence. Individually they are small, greenish-yellow, with six pointed petals. The "berries" are most curious, for they are not berries. They are simply the seeds, which split the ovary (the true fruit) as they develop, and form a blue, fleshy outer layer. There are two such seeds from each flower. The ovary disappears entirely as the seeds develop.

April to June: in moist deep woods from New Brunswick to Manitoba and southward to South Carolina, Alabama, and Missouri. *Plate 46.*

JEFFERSONIA

The only other species of *Jeffersonia* is Asiatic. The name commemorates Thomas Jefferson, a patron of science as well as a President of the United States.

TWINLEAF or RHEUMATISM-ROOT, J. DIPHYLLA, is recognizable by the leaves, each divided or deeply cleft into two segments so that there are apparently two blades on one stalk. The flowers grow singly on leafless stems. There are four sepals which soon fall. The eight petals are white, the flower about an inch across. There are eight stamens. The fruit is a small pod, the top part of which comes off like a lid. The leaves are small at flowering time, reaching their full size when the fruit is mature.

April and May: in woods from New York and southern Ontario to Wisconsin and Iowa and southward to Maryland and Alabama. *Plate 46.*

DIPHYLLEIA

The only other species of *Diphylleia* is Japanese.

UMBRELLA-LEAF, D. CYMOSA, has a stout erect stem up to 3 feet tall, growing from an underground stem, a rhizome, and bearing two leaves, each roundish in outline and cleft into two halves with jagged margins. The flowers are in a cluster at the summit. They are white, each little more than $\frac{1}{2}$ inch across. They are followed by blue berries about $\frac{1}{2}$ inch in diameter. The rhizome may send up, instead of a flowering stem, a single leaf with a round blade attached near its middle to the long stalk.

May to August: in woods by mountain streams from Virginia to Georgia.

PODOPHYLLUM

Our species of this family all have Asiatic counterparts, and our May-apple is no exception. We have one species of *Podophyllum*; the others are in Asia.

MAY-APPLE or MANDRAKE, P. PELTATUM, lives from year to year as a horizontal underground stem, a rhizome. This sends up either a single leaf having a round, toothed blade on a long stem; or a flowering stem with two such leaves and a single flower at the junction of the two leaves. The flower has from six to nine large petals, twice as many stamens, and a large pistil with no style, the stigma sitting on the ovary. The flower has a too-sweet fragrance. The ovary becomes a yellowish berry, which is edible when ripe, sweetish and mildly acid; it is sometimes made into a preserve. Other parts of the plant are reputedly poisonous.

April to June: in open woods and on hillsides and in meadows from Quebec to Minnesota and southward to Florida and Texas. *Plate 46.* This is no relation to the European mandrake, a species of *Mandragora* in the potato family. This has a root, often forked, supposed to take the form of a human being, and associated with numerous superstitions in medieval plant lore. Our mandrake differs in the numbers of floral parts from other members of its family, and has sometimes been separated from them and placed in a family of its own.

THE CAPER FAMILY (CAPPARACEAE*)

The caper family is chiefly tropical; only a few species occur in the United States. The capers used in cooking are the flower-buds of a species of *Capparis* native in southern Europe. The family is characterized by four sepals, four petals, six or more stamens, and a narrow pistil. In most of these characteristics they resemble the mustard family, and the species likely to be found growing wild in the northeastern United States may be mistaken for members of that family; but there are not two sizes of stamens as there are in the mustards.

SPIDERFLOWERS (CLEOME)

The spiderflowers (not to be confused with spiderworts), are so named for their stalked petals and pistil, which, with the six stamens, give the flower a leggy look. The petals, though all alike, generally stand on one side of the flower. The leaves are pal-

_____
* Usually through a mistaken etymology spelled *Capparidaceae*.

mately divided. Several species are well known, rather old-fashioned garden flowers. One of these may be found established as a wild flower: *C. spinosa*, native of tropical America, with sticky stems and leaf-blades divided into five or seven segments, and often a pair of prickles at the base of each leaf-stalk. Other species are native in the West.

PLATE 47

Cleome serrulata *Elbert*

Polanisia dodecandra *Johnson*

Barbarea vulgaris *Johnson*

Brassica nigra *Roche*

Dentaria heterophylla *Uttal*

Barbarea verna *Murray*

SPIDERFLOWER or STINKING-CLOVER, C. SERRU-
LATA, grows on prairies from Indiana westward
to Saskatchewan, Washington, and Arizona. The leaf-
blades are divided into three segments. Stem and leaves are smooth. The petals, with rather short stalks, are pink or white; appearing from May to September. This species also is sometimes cultivated. *Plate 47*.

CRISTATELLA

There are only two species of this genus, both western; but one reaches as far eastward as Illinois.

C. JAMESII is a small plant, usually branched, little
more than a foot tall, sticky-downy all over. The
flowers are small, only about $\frac{1}{4}$ inch across, in small racemes. The petals are yellowish or white, two larger than the other two. There may be up to nine stamens.
June to August: in sandy and gravelly places in Illinois and Wisconsin, and westward and southward to South Dakota, Louisiana, and Texas.

POLANISIA

The species of *Polanisia* differ from others of the family in having numerous stamens. The petals are shallowly indented at the end, almost heart-shaped.

CLAMMY-WEED, P. TRACHYSPERMA, is sticky-
downy. The leaf-blades are divided into three
elliptic segments. The white or pink petals may reach
$\frac{1}{2}$ inch in length, and at least some of the stamens
project beyond the petals.
June to September: on prairies and in sandy soil
from Indiana to Minnesota and thence westward to British Columbia; southward to Missouri, Texas, and California; a western species which wanders east-ward.

P. DODECANDRA is very similar to the foregoing (the
two are sometimes placed in one species). The
flowers are smaller and the stamens scarcely project. It
grows in dry soil from Quebec to Manitoba and south-ward to Maryland, Tennessee, Arkansas, and Okla-homa; probably escaped from cultivation in the east-ern states. *Plate 47*.

THE MUSTARD FAMILY (CRUCIFERAE)

The mustard family is among the easiest of all plant families to recognize. There are four sepals and four petals; the petals generally spread out to form a cross – "crucifer" means "cross-bearer." There are in almost all species six stamens, two shorter than the other four and placed on opposite sides of the pistil. Linnaeus described this curious condition, fancifully, as "tetradynamous," which means "four-powerful"; the term has stuck. Aside from such terminology, a hand magnifier used on a four-petaled, radially symmetric flower will quickly determine whether or not the mustard family is indicated.

Most of the genera share with the mustards themselves (*Brassica*) some pungent-tasting substance. Several species, besides black mustard, are cultivated for this property: radish, horse-radish, and water cress come to mind. Other species lack the pungent principle or have it to a slighter ex-tent, but are cultivated as vegetables: various species of *Brassica* furnish our cabbages, Brussels sprouts, and turnips. Other species are grown for the oil in their seeds. Many species of other genera are cultivated in borders and rock gardens: stocks, aubrieta, wallflowers, candytuft, alyssum, and the rock cresses.

The family is represented all over the world, but is most abundant in temperate zones and in the drier parts. Many species are found in our mountainous and arid western states. Throughout North America a number of weeds, largely immigrants from the Old World, are crucifers.

While the family is easy to recognize, the genera in it are difficult to determine by easily visible characteristics. The guide to genera below *may* lead the reader to the genus of the plant he wishes to identify; frequent recourse to the illustrations is suggested.

In most families of flowering plants the fruits cannot be used for identification by one who has a flowering specimen only in hand. In the *Cruciferae*, fortunately, the flowers are generally in the elongated clusters called racemes, the lower and older ones already fruiting while buds are still opening at the tip. Except for very young plants, therefore, characteristics of both flowers and fruits can be seen at the same time. The guide to genera is based on this; a simple guide is scarcely possible without it.

The fruits are seed-pods of various shapes, generally but not always divided into two chambers by a lengthwise partition. At maturity the two halves split apart, leaving the partition standing in the middle.

A further aid to identification, but one that requires the careful use of a hand magnifier, is the character of the hairs, if any are present. They may be all simple – that is, unbranched; or some or all may be branched, with two or more prongs.

We first separate the genera by the color of their flowers. However, several genera straddle the two groups, having species in both.

I.   *Plants with yellow petals.*
These may be further divided by their seed-pods.

A. Plants with yellow petals and seed-pods longer than thick; the length twice the thickness or more. In most of the species in these genera (but not all) the leaves are pinnately lobed, cleft, or divided. The first five genera have simple hairs (if any), the last three branched hairs: *Brassica* (pod with prominent beak); *Barbarea* (very smooth; leaves with "ears" at the base); *Rorippa* (most species; pods not very long, curved in some); *Erucastrum* (like *Brassica*; beak less prominent on pod); *Diplotaxis* (like *Brassica*; pod ten times as long as thick); *Raphanus* (pod $\frac{1}{4}$ inch thick, with prominent beak); *Erysimum* (leaves not divided nor lobed nor cleft); *Descurainia* (petals very small; leaves divided into numerous fine segments); *Sisymbrium* (pods very narrow, $\frac{1}{16}$ inch thick or even less).

B. Plants with yellow petals and seed-pods nearly or quite as thick as they are long. All these bear branched hairs, some a very dense covering of them: *Lesquerella* (pod nearly a sphere); *Camelina* (pod pear-shaped; leaves undivided, unlobed, not cleft, with "ears" at the base); *Alyssum* (pod nearly circular, flat).

Besides these, some species of *Rorippa* (see under A above) have very short pods, hardly longer than thick; one species of *Draba* (see under II) has pale yellow flowers; its leaves are in a rosette at the base; and *Eruca* (see under II) may have petals slightly yellowish; its pods have prominent *flat* beaks.

II.   *Plants with white, pink, lavender, or purple petals. These also may be further divided by the shape of their seed-pods into three groups.*

A. Seed-pods very narrow with parallel sides, their length ten times their width or even more. (Compare B and C.)

1.   Of these, one genus has leaves palmately cleft or divided: *Dentaria*.

2.   Four genera of IIA have leaves that are pinnately lobed, cleft, or divided: *Cardamine* (four species, one with petals $\frac{1}{2}$ inch long, three with very narrow pods tending to stand erect); *Sibara* (leaves mostly near the base; stem more or less hairy); *Arabis* (basal leaves only of some species pinnately lobed); *Leavenworthia* (stalks of individual flowers much longer than the common stem from which they grow); *Iodanthus* (lower leaves pinnately cleft near base only).

3.   Five genera have leaves not lobed, cleft, or divided (some are toothed): *Cardamine* (six species with roundish blades on stalks); *Arabis* (mostly with "ears" at the base of the leaves); *Arabidopsis* (leaves mostly at the base); *Hesperis* (petals about an inch long); *Alliaria* (broad triangular, toothed leaves; onion odor).

B. Seed-pods with curved sides (elliptic, spherical, egg-shaped, etc.), their length not more than six times their width: *Draba* (small plants with leaves with few teeth and no lobes and mostly at the base; at least some hairs branched); *Berteroa* (similar to *Draba* but no leaves at the base; petals deeply notched); *Nasturtium* (growing in water; leaves pinnately divided); *Raphanus* (pods thick, beaked; leaves pinnately cleft); *Eruca* (pods with broad, flat beak; leaves pinnately cleft); *Armoracia* (pods football-shaped; one tall species on land, one small one in water); *Cakile* (succulent seaside plant; pods in two unlike sections); *Capsella* (pods heart-shaped); *Thlaspi* (pods flat, circular; two seeds in each chamber); *Lepidium* (pods flat, circular; one seed in each chamber).

THE MUSTARDS (BRASSICA)

In the genus *Brassica* we cultivate the cabbages, cauliflower, Brussels sprouts, broccoli, kohlrabi, turnips, rutabaga, mustard, and rape; and the Chinese have several other edible kinds. Some of these have escaped from cultivation and grow wild in this country; and several other species, also from the Old World, have become weeds in America. They are scarcely attractive wild flowers, but are sufficiently conspicuous that their identity is often sought.

They all have yellow petals about $\frac{1}{2}$ inch long, and are distinguished from other yellow-flowered crucifers by the stout beak on the pod, and by the characteristic leaves. The leaves (at least the lower ones) are pinnately cleft or lobed with the end lobe larger than the side lobes. (This is the shape named by botanists lyre-shaped or lyrate, for no reason known to the present author.)

CHARLOCK, B. KABER, may be known by its very prominent, angled beak, about a third of the whole pod, and usually containing one or two seeds. The stem may be nearly 3 feet tall; it is apt to be bristly.

May to July: a common weed in cultivated and waste land throughout the country.

BLACK MUSTARD, B. NIGRA, has a hairy stem which may reach 5 feet in height. The leaves have definite slender stalks. The beak on the pod is not angled and does not contain a seed. The mature pods, less than an inch long, stand erect, close against the stem.

June to October: this is the source of the condiment mustard; it is now naturalized in cultivated and waste land throughout the country. *Plate 47*.

CHINESE or INDIAN MUSTARD or BROWN or LEAF MUSTARD, B. JUNCEA, is nearly smooth and somewhat whitened with a waxy bloom. It grows 3 feet tall or taller. The mature pods reach a length of $1\frac{1}{2}$ to $1\frac{3}{4}$ inches.

June to September: common in fields.

B. CAMPESTRIS, also known as B. RAPA, is easily distinguished by its upper leaves, which have no stalks, the blades "clasping" the stem with a pair of "ears" at the base (see the drawing). The plant is smooth and whitish with a bloom. The pods may be 2 or even 3 inches long, with a slender beak.

June to October: naturalized as a weed in fields, etc. throughout the country.

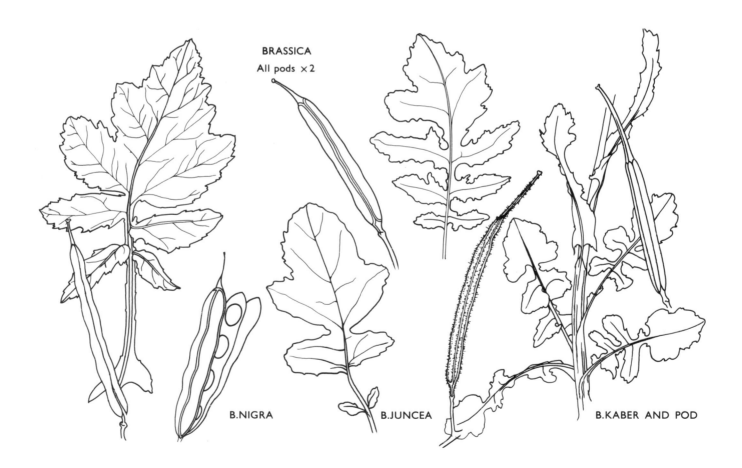

BRASSICA
All pods ×2

B.NIGRA   B.JUNCEA   B.KABER AND POD

WHITE MUSTARD, B. HIRTA, is established in some places as a weed. It may be known by the bristly pods which end in a flat beak as long as the seed-bearing part or longer.

WINTER CRESSES (BARBAREA)

The winter cresses may be mistaken for mustards of the genus *Brassica*, but are easily distinguished by the minuteness of the beak on the pod. They are all smooth or nearly so. At least the upper leaves "clasp" the stem, a basal finger or lobe projecting beyond the stem on either side (see the drawing).

YELLOW ROCKET, B. VULGARIS, is best recognized
by the upper leaves, which are deeply cleft and somewhat fan-shaped. The basal leaves have up to four pairs of lobes beside the large end lobe; but sometimes they are not lobed. The branching stems are often 3 feet tall. The mature pods may slightly exceed an inch in length.

April to August: a very abundant weed, sometimes coloring entire fields bright yellow, from Newfoundland to Kansas and southward to Virginia and Kentucky. *Plate 47*. For the name see under *Eruca*.

EARLY WINTER CRESS, B. VERNA, differs from *B. vulgaris* chiefly in having from four to ten pairs of side lobes on the basal leaves, and a number of lobes on the upper leaves. The mature pods may be 3 inches long.

March to May: naturalized in fields practically throughout the country. *Plate 47*.

B. ORTHOCERAS, a northern species found along our
borders, has basal leaves nearly or quite unlobed (the side lobes when present being very small). The petals are pale yellow. The pod is from 1 to $1\frac{1}{2}$ inches long.

June to September: in swamps and other wet places from Labrador to Alaska and southward to Maine, Ontario, Michigan, Wisconsin, Colorado, and California.

THE YELLOW CRESSES (RORIPPA)

The yellow cresses are small plants with leaves mostly very deeply cleft pinnately. Most of them grow in damp places, and are smooth. The petals are yellow and very small. They are most easily recognized by their pods, which are generally short, barely twice as long as thick, in some species not even that long, and more or less oval in outline. The curious Latin name is derived from the old Saxon name of these plants — several species being from the Old World.

R. SYLVESTRIS sends up erect branches, to 2 feet tall,
from a creeping underground stem (rhizome). The pods are about $\frac{1}{2}$ inch long and narrow.

May to September: naturalized in wet places from Newfoundland to North Dakota and southward to North Carolina and Louisiana; a common weed.

R. ISLANDICA is a very variable species, growing up to
4 feet tall, smooth or hairy. The pods are elliptic or almost circular in outline, from $\frac{1}{12}$ to $\frac{2}{5}$ inch long.

May to October: on shores and in waste places from Labrador to British Columbia and southward to Florida, Texas, and California; a "circumpolar" plant, occurring all around the globe in the far north. *Plate 48*.

R. SINUATA grows from a rhizome underground, its
erect stems reaching a height of a foot or more.

Sinuata means "wavy" in outline, describing a common form of its leaves, which are less jagged than those of some other species. However, the best means of identification is by the pods, which are about $\frac{1}{2}$ inch long and curved (see the drawings).

April to July: in sandy and rocky fields, bottomlands, etc. from Ontario to Washington and southward to Michigan, Illinois, Arkansas, Texas, Arizona, and California. *Plate 48*.

R. SESSILIFLORA is a branching plant often exceeding
a foot in height. The flowers are minute, with almost no stalks (which is the meaning of *sessiliflora*; *sessili-* means "sitting"); they may lack petals, and the stamens depart from the usual crucifer pattern in being only four. The pods are about $\frac{1}{2}$ inch long.

April to October: in mud, shallow water, and wet bottomlands from Indiana to Nebraska and southward to Florida and Texas; also in Virginia and District of Columbia.

R. OBTUSA is quite similar to *R. sessiliflora*, with similarly minute flowers, but with six stamens.

May to September: in muddy or sandy places from Ohio to Missouri, southward to West Virginia and Texas; in the Pacific States.

R. AMPHIBIA, as its name indicates, grows either on

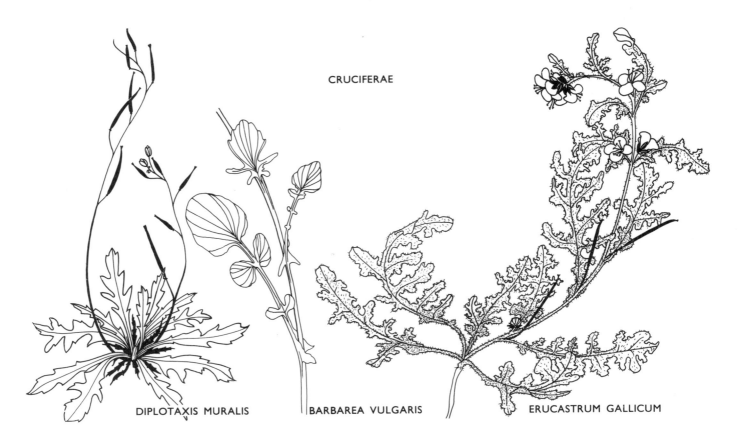

CRUCIFERAE

DIPLOTAXIS MURALIS   BARBAREA VULGARIS   ERUCASTRUM GALLICUM

land or in water, its stems often being 3 feet long, the submerged leaves pinnately cleft into narrow lobes, the leaves in the air lanceolate and toothed but not cleft. The pods are long-stalked, about $\frac{1}{4}$ inch long.

June and July: in shallow water and on shores

from Quebec to Connecticut and New York; reported from Iowa.

Other Old-World species have been reported as established in scattered places: *R. austriaca*, *R. prostrata*, *R. heterophylla*.

ERUCASTRUM

Only one species of *Erucastrum*, an European genus, has become naturalized in North America. The name indicates that it is like *Eruca* – which it is not, at least so far as our species is concerned.

E. GALLICUM might easily be taken for a *Brassica*, but the beak is less evident on the pod. The leaves are pinnately cleft (the end lobe not larger), and are

found even in the lower part of the raceme – the lower flowers thus being in the axils of leaves (see the drawing). The stem and leaves are downy; the plant grows 2 or 3 feet tall. The petals are pale yellow.

May to October: in waste places and fields, not common, from Newfoundland to British Columbia and southward to Pennsylvania, Kentucky, and Texas. It is said to be rapidly spreading.

DIPLOTAXIS

This is a genus of Europe and Asia, of which a few species have strayed into the United States. They are very like *Brassica*, except that some of them have white flowers, and the beak on the pod is short. The pods are very long and narrow. Our species have pinnately cleft leaves mostly near the base. Both the following species are naturalized in waste places, flowering from May to September.

WALL ROCKET D. MURALIS, (*mura* means "wall";
in the damp climate of northern Europe many species thrive on old walls), grows up to 20 inches tall, with nearly all the leaves at the base. The petals are yellow, about $\frac{1}{3}$ inch long; the pods $1\frac{1}{2}$ inches.

Abundant in places, mostly near the coast, from Quebec and Ontario to Minnesota and southward to New Jersey, Illinois, and Iowa.

PLATE 48

Dentaria laciniata *Gottscho*

Dentaria diphylla *Johnson*

Erysimum asperum *Rollins*

Raphanus raphanistrum *Johnson*

Rorippa islandica *Rickett*

Rorippa sinuata *Rollins*

SAND ROCKET, D. TENUIFOLIA, is rather larger than the preceding species, up to 3 feet tall. There are more leaves on the stem, as well as at the base. The petals may reach a length of an inch.

From New Brunswick to Ontario and southward to Virginia and Michigan; also in the West.

RADISHES (RAPHANUS)

Radishes are familiar in our gardens and our salads. These are the roots (or, anatomically, the transition from root to stem); perhaps the flowers are less known. The leaves are pinnately cleft. The petals are large for this family ($\frac{1}{2}$ inch long); the blades stand on a stalk. The pod is bulged by the seeds within, narrower between them, and has a conspicuous beak.

WILD-RADISH or JOINTED-CHARLOCK, R. RAPHA-
NISTRUM, may grow more than 2 feet tall, with coarse leaves, the lower ones up to 8 inches long, the lobes near the tip larger than those near the base. The plants are more or less bristly-hairy. The petals are yellow. The pods, including the beaks, are nearly 3 inches long. This is a weed from Europe, now found in waste places and grainfields practically throughout North America, flowering all summer and into autumn. Grigson calls it a "rattish and world-conquering farmer's weed." *Plate 48*.

The cultivated radish is *R. sativus*. It is occasionally found in waste places and near gardens. It is distinguished by pale purple petals.

ERYSIMUM

The genus *Erysimum* has species nearly around the world. Our native species are unique among our yellow-flowered and narrow-fruited crucifers in having unlobed, undivided leaves; a European species naturalized here may have some pinnately cleft leaves. The pods are long and narrow, with four angles, about the same width throughout their length, and tipped by the flat stigma instead of a beak. The petals are yellow or orange and have a stalk-like base. They are more or less hairy, with branched hairs (as seen with a magnifier). "Treacle" is derived from a Greek word meaning a remedy for a venomous bite; so treacle-mustard is a plant used in this way. The name was first applied to *Thlaspi arvense*, later to the first species below.

TREACLE-MUSTARD or WORMSEED-MUSTARD, E.
CHEIRANTHOIDES, has few or no branches, the stem rising to a height of 4 feet or more. The leaves are narrow, tending to be lanceolate, perhaps with a few teeth on the edges, and bearing three-forked hairs. The flowers are small, the petals only $\frac{1}{5}$ inch long. The stalks of the fruits extend out almost at right angles to the main stem, but the pods (about an inch long) are more or less erect at the ends of the stalks.

June to September: in fields, meadows and waste places across Canada and southward to North Carolina, Tennessee, Arkansas, Colorado, and Oregon; also in Europe and Asia; by some considered native in North America, by others an introduced weed.

E. REPANDUM is a smaller plant than the preceding, up to 2 feet tall, with larger, pale yellow petals.

The larger leaves may have wavy margins, or they may be pinnately cleft. The hairs on them are two-pronged. The pods may be 4 inches long, extending out in all directions.

May to July: naturalized from the Old World in waste places from Massachusetts to Oregon and southward to Alabama and Texas and elsewhere in the West.

WESTERN-WALLFLOWER, E. ASPERUM, is a stiff
plant up to 3 feet tall, with narrow leaves which are generally whitish-downy. The blade of the showy yellow or orange petals is nearly $\frac{1}{2}$ inch long. The pods are downy, about 4 inches long.

May and June: on prairies and bluffs and in open woods from Ohio to Minnesota and Washington and southward to Missouri, Oklahoma, and California; typically a plant of the drier West. *Plate 48*.

The true wallflower, a popular garden plant, is in the genus *Cheiranthus*. Another western-wallflower, *E. arkansanum*, with broader leaves and petals, is known from Illinois and Missouri and westward.

E. INCONSPICUUM grows up to 2 feet tall or taller,
with few or no branches. The leaves are very narrow. The petals are pale yellow, very small. The pods may be 2 inches long or longer, standing nearly erect on their stalks.

May to August: in prairies and dry woodlands from Ontario to Alaska and southward to Missouri, Nevada, and British Columbia; and occasionally straying eastward to Nova Scotia and New England.

TANSY-MUSTARDS (DESCURAINIA)

The plants called tansy-mustards are frankly weeds rather than wild flowers; they are briefly mentioned here only for the sake of rounding out this weedy family. The English name likens them to tansy (a composite), which they somewhat resemble in their leaves. These are divided pinnately into numerous segments, these again divided, the final segments being very narrow. The flowers are small, bright or pale yellow. The pods are narrow, with no beak.

The species are *D. pinnata*, usually glandular and sticky; *D. sophia*, with pods spreading outwards and about an inch long; and *D. richardsonii*, with pods more erect and not more than $\frac{1}{2}$ inch long. All are widespread weeds, flowering in summer.

TUMBLE- AND HEDGE-MUSTARDS (SISYMBRIUM)

These unattractive plants are the weediest of a weedy family, deserving only scant notice here. They have pinnately cleft leaves, small yellow flowers, and extremely narrow pods without beaks. The hairs are unbranched.

The common species are *S. officinale*, hedge mustard, a barnyard and roadside weed from Europe, with long skinny racemes, the pods pressed close against the stem, and the basal lobes of the leaves pointing backwards (*Plate 48*); and *S. altissimum*, tumble mustard, with pods sometimes 4 inches long, not close against the stem, pale yellow flowers, and long narrow leaf-segments. Many weeds are called tumbleweeds, especially in the West; the name signifies that the whole plant breaks off when it is dead and dry and rolls with the wind, often forming dense masses against fences. Both the above species are from the Old World, now widely established as weeds in the New. They flower in summer, *S. officinale* with the longest season. Several other species are occasionally found.

LESQUERELLA

Lesquerella is distinguished by its pods which are spherical or nearly so. The petals are yellow. The leaves are narrow and not lobed or divided. The plants are more or less whitened with branched hairs, or with scales. It is chiefly a western genus.

L. LUDOVICIANA grows to a height of a foot or more.

The leaves are lanceolate, the broadest part towards the tip. The pods as well as the leaves are whitened with branched, scale-like hairs. The stalks of the flowers and fruits are curved downwards. The fruit is about $\frac{1}{4}$ inch in diameter or less, with the style forming a beak.

May to July: on prairies and in sandy and gravelly places from Minnesota to Montana and southward to Kansas and Arizona; also in Illinois.

L. GLOBOSA has stems up to 20 inches tall, with long leaves not much more than an inch long, all whitened by branched hairs. The fruit is about an inch in diameter. Their stalks are not curved but extend outwards and upwards.

April to June: on limestone bluffs from Ohio to Tennessee.

Two western species occur in western Missouri.

FALSE FLAX (CAMELINA)

Two species of Old-World herbs of this genus are found in our range. They have pear-shaped pods (standing erect on their small end), yellow petals, and mostly lanceolate leaves which "clasp" the stem by their two basal lobes or "ears."

C. SATIVA was formerly cultivated for its oily seeds.

The stem, which may reach a height of 3 feet, is smooth or nearly so. The pods are about $\frac{1}{3}$ inch long.

April to August: in waste places from Quebec to British Columbia and southward to South Carolina, Missouri, Colorado, and California.

C. MICROCARPA is a smaller plant than *C. sativa*, rough-hairy with both branched and unbranched hairs. The pods are about $\frac{1}{5}$ inch long (*microcarpa* means "small-fruited").

April to September: in waste places from Newfoundland to British Columbia and southward to Virginia, Missouri, Texas, and California.

ALYSSUM

This Old-World genus is not the genus of the sweet alyssum of our gardens (*Lobularia*), but does include the common rock-garden basket-of-gold, *A. saxatile*. One species of *Alyssum* has become naturalized in North America.

A. ALYSSOIDES is about a foot tall, whitened all over with starlike hairs. The leaves are narrow and only about ½ inch long. The petals are pale yellow or whitish. The pods are discs only about ⅙ inch across.

April to June: in waste places and grasslands across Canada and southward to New Jersey, Ohio, Minnesota, Utah, and California.

The name *Alyssum* is from Greek words meaning "not" and "madness"; it was formerly reputed to cure rabies.

TOOTHWORTS (DENTARIA)

The toothworts are distinguished by having their leaves palmately cleft or divided. There may be long-stalked leaves at the base and one or two short-stalked leaves on the stem below the flowers. The flowers are white or pale purple, the petals large for this family. The pod is long, narrow, and flat. These are all woodland plants, flowering in spring (March to June). The flowering stems, a foot or more tall, grow from succulent white or yellowish rhizomes which are toothed (these are presumably the "teeth" of the name); they are edible and palatable.

TOOTHWORT, D. LACINIATA, has three leaves each cleft or divided into generally five narrow lobes or segments. Basal leaves are usually lacking. The lobes or segments vary in the extent to which they are toothed, lobed, or jagged. It grows from Quebec to Minnesota and Nebraska and southward to Florida, Louisiana, and Kansas. *Plate 48*.

CRINKLEROOT, D. DIPHYLLA, has two leaves nearly at the same level on the stem, each divided into three broad, toothed segments. It occurs from Quebec to Minnesota and southward to Georgia and Alabama. *Plate 48*.

D. MAXIMA usually has three leaves on the stem at different levels, each divided into three broad, toothed, stalked segments. It is found from Maine to Wisconsin and southward to West Virginia and Tennessee.

D. MULTIFIDA has two leaves on the stem, at the same level, each divided into threadlike segments. It occurs from Ohio and Indiana southward to Georgia and Alabama.

D. HETEROPHYLLA has basal leaves (*-phylla*) different (*hetero-*) from those on the stem. The basal leaves have three ovate segments, variously toothed or lobed. The two or three leaves on the stem (usually at the same level) are divided into lanceolate segments which may or may not be toothed. This species grows from New Jersey to Indiana and southward to Georgia and Alabama. *Plate 47*.

Two other species, *D. anomala* and *D. incisifolia*, are listed in manuals. *D. anomala*, found in Connecticut with *D. laciniata* and *D. diphylla*, may be a hybrid between these two. *D. incisifolia*, also from Connecticut, is thought to be a hybrid between *D. laciniata* and *D. maxima*.

THE BITTER CRESSES (CARDAMINE)

It is difficult to characterize the genus *Cardamine*, which includes a group of very various plants. The leaves of some are pinnately divided; those of others are round-bladed and undivided. Some have minute flowers; others have comparatively large ones. Most, but not all, are found in wet places. They are held in one genus on the basis of certain details of fruit and seed. None have yellow petals. They are most likely to be confused with *Arabis*, but the species of *Arabis* more frequently have branched hairs.

I. *Bitter cresses with leaves undivided or with only very small segments at the side and comparatively a very large end segment.*

SPRING CRESS, C. BULBOSA, is a smooth plant up to 2 feet tall. The basal leaves have long stalks bearing round blades. The leaves on the stem are narrow and without stalks, sometimes with a few teeth. The petals are white, about ½ inch long. The species takes its botanical name from the cluster of small round

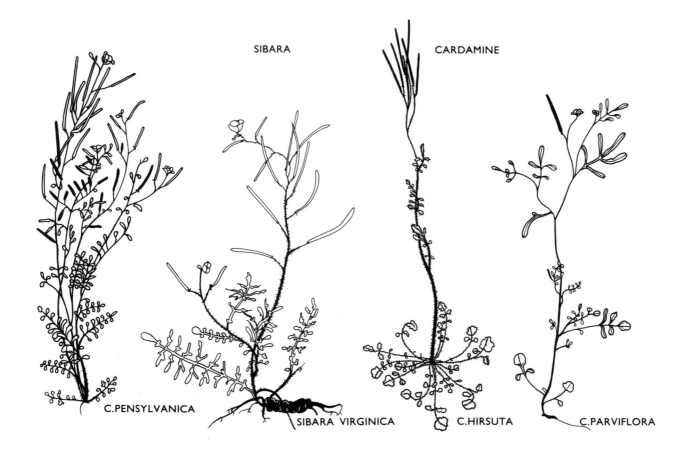

SIBARA   CARDAMINE

C.PENSYLVANICA   SIBARA VIRGINICA   C.HIRSUTA   C.PARVIFLORA

corms (not bulbs) at the base of the stem. *Plate 49*.

March to June: in shallow water and wet places from Quebec to Minnesota and South Dakota and southward to Florida and Texas.

C. DOUGLASII is about a foot tall, with a hairy stem.

The petals are purple or pink. Otherwise it is much like *C. bulbosa*.

March to May: in wet bottomlands and woods from Connecticut to Wisconsin and southward to Virginia, Tennessee, and Missouri. *Plate 49*.

MOUNTAIN-WATER-CRESS, C. ROTUNDIFOLIA, has all its leaves much alike, with roundish blades on short stalks (sometimes with a pair of very small segments on the stalk). The stems are weak, growing from long slim creeping stems (rhizome and runners). The petals are white, from $\frac{1}{4}$ to $\frac{2}{5}$ inch long.

May and June: in swamps, running water, brooksides, etc. from New York to Ohio and southward to New Jersey, in the mountains to North Carolina, and Kentucky.

C. LONGII is much like *C. rotundifolia* in its round-bladed leaves, and has a similarly weak stem only about a foot tall. Petals are lacking.

June to September: along tidal estuaries in Maine, Maryland, and Virginia.

C. BELLIDIFOLIA is a small plant only about 4 inches tall. The leaves have ovate blades on slender stalks. The few flowers are white, the petals only $\frac{1}{5}$ inch long or less.

June to September: in cool wet places throughout Canada and southward in the high mountains of Maine, New Hampshire, and Oregon.

II. *Bitter cresses with at least some leaves distinctly divided pinnately, the side segments not minute in comparison with the end segment.*

CUCKOO-FLOWER or LADY'S-SMOCK, C. PRATENSIS, grows 2 feet tall or taller. The slender, generally unbranched stem bears many pinnately divided leaves, the segments varying from very narrow to round. The flowers are pink or white, the petals about $\frac{1}{2}$ inch long.

April to July: in meadows, swamps, and shallow water throughout Canada and southward to Virginia, Indiana, and Minnesota; also in Europe and Asia. *Plate 49*. This is a very variable species, our plants often differing from those of the Old World. Pods are often not formed, the plants reproducing by short branches which spring from the base.

C. PENSYLVANICA may reach 2 feet in height. It is rather like a small edition of *C. pratensis*, with pinnately deeply cleft or divided leaves, the end lobe or segment the largest. The pods are very narrow, and the flowers only about $\frac{1}{6}$ inch across.

March to August: in springs and on wet soil across Canada and southward to Florida, Texas, and California. A common and very variable species. It is said to be "an excellent substitute for watercress."

C. PARVIFLORA is a low plant, usually not more than a foot tall. The leaves are pinnately divided into very short, narrow segments (including the end one). The petals are only $\frac{1}{8}$ inch long or less; the pods are only about an inch long and less than $\frac{1}{25}$ inch wide.

April to August: in dry soil, open or shaded, from Quebec to Minnesota and southward to Florida and Texas; and in the Old World.

C. HIRSUTA grows only a foot tall at most, with pinnately divided leaves, those at the base with round segments, those on the stem with narrow segments. The stalks of the leaves have stiff hairs (they are "hirsute").

March and April: an immigrant from the Old World, now naturalized in moist soil from New York to Missouri and southward to Georgia and Alabama. *Plate 49.*

SIBARA

One species occurs in northeastern America.

S. VIRGINICA is a small weed of early spring, usually about a foot tall or less, with hairs at least on the lower part of the stem. The leaves are all deeply pinnately cleft (the end lobe a little broader than the numerous side lobes); most of the leaves spread close to the ground. The petals are white, sometimes tinged with pink, very small (less than $\frac{1}{8}$ inch long). The pods

are only about an inch long, about $\frac{1}{12}$ inch wide, rather flat, spreading outwards and upwards from the stem.

March to May: in fields, woodlands, etc. from Virginia to Kansas and southward to Florida and Texas; also in California and Mexico. It closely resembles *Cardamine parviflora*, but can be distinguished by its broader, flatter pods and the hairs on the stem; and its smaller range northward may help. *Sibara* is intermediate in several respects between *Cardamine* and *Arabis*.

ROCK CRESSES AND SICKLEPODS (ARABIS)

The genus *Arabis* is widespread in northern temperate countries, and farther north. It is especially abundant in the West (fifty or more species). We have a dozen in the northeastern United States. Some species may be classed as weeds; others are grown in rock gardens. They are all plants with long narrow pods, in some species standing erect and close to the stem, in others spreading in all directions, in still others – the sicklepods – curved downward. In most of our species the leaves are unlobed and undivided; in two they are pinnately lobed or cleft. The petals are generally white, in some species pink or yellowish.

I.   *Species with pods standing erect or nearly so, close to the stem.*

TOWER-MUSTARD, A. GLABRA, grows up to 4 feet tall, the stem hairy near the base but, with the upper leaves, smooth (*glabra*, glabrous) above; the lower leaves bear branched hairs. The leaves on the stem are lanceolate with basal lobes that embrace the stem. The cream-white or yellowish petals are up to $\frac{1}{4}$ inch long. The pods are almost 4 inches long and only about $\frac{1}{25}$ inch thick.

May to July: on rock ledges and in dry soil from Quebec to Alaska and southward to North Carolina, Arkansas, New Mexico, and California.

A. HIRSUTA is similar to tower-mustard, but not so tall. The basal leaves are hairy. The leaves on the stem are narrow, the lower ones "clasping" the stem. The petals are mostly white, up to $\frac{1}{4}$ inch long. The pods are up to 2 inches long, about $\frac{1}{25}$ inch thick.

May to July: on rock ledges, on hillsides, and in woods across Canada and southward to Georgia, Louisiana, New Mexico, and California; also in Europe and Asia. American plants form varieties distinct in detail from those of the Old World.

A. DRUMMONDII reaches 3 feet in height. It is smooth, often with a whitish bloom. The basal leaves are nearly 4 inches long; those on the stem about 3 inches tapering to a point, with projecting lobes at the base which embrace or "clasp" the stem. The petals are about $\frac{1}{3}$ inch long. The pods stand nearly erect, up to 4 inches long and $\frac{1}{8}$ inch thick.

May to July: in gravel or on ledges, moist or dry, across Canada and southward to Delaware, Ohio, Illinois, Iowa, New Mexico, and California.

II. *Species whose pods extend out and upwards, or at right angles.*

A. LYRATA has several stems, a foot tall or taller, rising from a tuft of pinnately lobed leaves. There are a

PLATE 49

Arabis lyrata

Rhein

Arabis lyrata

Johnson

Cardamine hirsuta

Rickett

Cardamine bulbosa

Scribner

Cardamine pratensis

Rickett

Cardamine douglasii

D. Richards

Arabis canadensis

Johnson

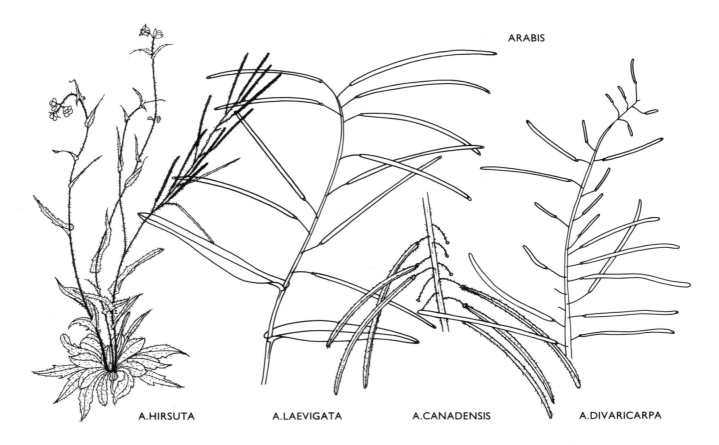

ARABIS

A.HIRSUTA   A.LAEVIGATA   A.CANADENSIS   A.DIVARICARPA

few scattered leaves on the stems, mostly narrow and not lobed. The petals are generally white, up to $\frac{1}{3}$ inch long. The pods, nearly straight, about $1\frac{1}{2}$ inches long, extend upwards.

April and May: on ledges and in dry soil, especially sand, from Vermont to Alaska and southward to Georgia, Tennessee, Missouri, Montana, and Washington; also in Asia. *Plate 49.*

A. PATENS has a 2-foot stem clothed with (mostly unbranched) hairs and bearing oblong or lanceolate leaves. These leaves have small lobes at the base which "clasp" the stem, and are toothed along the edges; like the stem they are hairy. The petals are white. The pods spread away from the stem at a slight angle.

April to June: on rocky banks and in woods from Pennsylvania to Indiana and southward to North Carolina and Tennessee.

A. DIVARICARPA has a nearly smooth stem up to 3 feet tall, bearing narrow leaves extending upward at a sharp angle and embracing or "clasping" the stem between their narrow basal lobes. The leaves at the base, also narrow, bear minute branched hairs. The pods (*-carpa*) are nearly straight, up to 4 inches long, spreading (*divari-*) nearly at right angles to the stem. The petals are pink or purplish, about $\frac{1}{4}$ inch long.

May to July: on ledges and in sand across Canada and southward to New York, Ohio, Wisconsin, Nebraska, Colorado, and California.

A. PERSTELLATA is clothed with mostly branched hairs, densely or thinly. The stem is about 2 feet tall, bearing narrow leaves, irregularly toothed, with rather small and blunt lobes at the base. The petals are white or pink. The pods are about $1\frac{1}{2}$ inches long, straight or slightly curved, extending outwards and a little upwards.

April: on wooded hillsides and ledges from New York to Minnesota and South Dakota and southward to Virginia, Tennessee, Arkansas, and Kansas. The pink-flowered, densely hairy variety (sometimes treated as a distinct species) is known only from Kentucky.

III. *The sicklepods, with curved pods pointing downwards.*

A. LAEVIGATA is conspicuously smooth and whitened with a bloom. The stem, often 3 feet tall, bears generally lanceolate and often toothed leaves, with sharp basal lobes extending around the stem. The petals are white, about $\frac{1}{5}$ inch long. The pods are up to 4 inches long and $\frac{1}{10}$ inch wide.

March to July: on wooded slopes and ledges from

Quebec to Minnesota and Colorado and southward to Georgia, Alabama, and Oklahoma. *Plate 50.*

A. VIRIDIS somewhat resembles *A. laevigata* but is smaller. The basal leaves may be pinnately lobed. The leaves on the stem have pointed lobes at the base. The whole plant is generally quite smooth (hairy in a midwestern variety) and somewhat whitened with a bloom. The petals are cream-colored, twice as long as the sepals. The curved pods reach a length of nearly 4 inches.

May and June: in woods, usually in dry rocky places, from Maine to Michigan and southward to New Jersey.

A. CANADENSIS, which reaches a height of 3 feet, is hairy on its lower parts, smooth above. The leaves are elliptic or lanceolate, often toothed, at least the lower ones hairy. The petals are cream-colored, only about $\frac{1}{5}$ inch long. The curved pods are up to 4 inches long.

April to June: in woods and on rocky slopes from Maine to Minnesota and Nebraska and southward to Georgia, Alabama, and Texas. *Plate 49.*

LEAVENWORTHIA

This genus belongs to the southeastern states, but two species reach the southern borders of the northeastern region. They are both characterized by flowers and pods borne singly on long stalks which rise above the small, pinnately divided leaves to a height of about 6 inches.

L. UNIFLORA is known from rocky woods and open, barren places in southern Ohio, southern Indiana, and Missouri, and extends southward to Alabama and Arkansas.

L. TORULOSA is distinguished by its pod; this is indented or constricted between the seeds, which form a series of bulges (*torulus* means a "small bulge"). It has been reported from wet places in Kentucky, and grows in Tennessee and Alabama. Both species flower in April and May.

PURPLE ROCKET (IODANTHUS)

One species of *Iodanthus* occurs in our range.

I. PINNATIFIDUS grows about 3 feet tall. The basal leaves have round blades on slender stalks. The leaves on the stem are ovate and toothed; the lower ones taper to a stalk-like base, having one or two pairs of short lobes at the sides near the base. The flowers vary from white to pale purple.

May and June: in wet woods from Pennsylvania to Illinois and Minnesota and southward to West Virginia, Alabama, Arkansas, and Kansas. *Plate 50.* It is shown in a field of buttercups.

ARABIDOPSIS

One European species of *Arabidopsis* has become naturalized in North America. The botanical name means "the appearance of *Arabis*" – which this species has not.

MOUSE-EAR CRESS, A. THALIANA, has a number of small, downy leaves (2 inches long) at the base of the stem, and a few very narrow leaves on the stem. The flowers are carried up to a height of about 18 inches. The petals are minute, white or purplish; the pods less than an inch long and narrow.

March to June: in dry soil from Massachusetts to Wisconsin and southward to Georgia and Arkansas. *Plate 50.*

HESPERIS

One species of this Old-World genus has made itself at home in America – a more welcome immigrant than most.

DAME'S ROCKET, also known as DAME'S-VIOLET and MOTHER-OF-THE-EVENING, H. MATRON-ALIS, is a plant often 3 feet tall or taller. The leaf-blades are lanceolate, short-stalked, toothed. The flowers make a handsome show, with petals up to an inch long varying from white through pink to purple. The pods may be 5 inches long and are quite narrow, scarcely wider than the stalks on which they stand.

May to August: on roadsides and in open woods from Newfoundland and Quebec to Michigan and Iowa and southward to Georgia, Kentucky, and Kansas. *Plate 50*. This is a well-known flower of old-fashioned gardens, English cottage-gardens and the like, and has spread as a wild flower in this country. The Latin name *Hesperis* was given to it by Pliny, famous naturalist of classical Rome, in recognition of its increased fragrance in evening (*hesperis*, Greek, means "western," hence "evening"). For the name "rocket", see under *Eruca*. "Dame's rocket" is explained by the herbalist and botanist Caspar Bauhin (who got it from Pliny) as derived from its cultivation "in gardens by [Roman] matrons." It has also been known as damask rocket ("damask" not from Damascus but a corruption of "dame's").

ALLIARIA

One European species has become naturalized in America.

GARLIC-MUSTARD, A. OFFICINALIS, is unmistakable both from the odor of garlic emitted when it is crushed and from the broadly ovate or even triangular leaf-blades. The petals are white, about $\frac{1}{4}$ inch long.

April to June: on roadsides and in moist open woods from Quebec and Ontario southward to Virginia and Kentucky and westward to Kansas. *Plate 50*. The name of the genus is from *Allium*, the onions. In England the plant is known as Jack-by-the-hedge or sauce-alone. It was used for many years as a condiment or salad, especially by the poor man who could not purchase such things and used garlic-mustard for his sauce, alone. It also had reputed medicinal powers.

DRABA

Draba is a fairly large genus of small plants chiefly of northern regions, but some species extending southward. Most of them have a tuft of small leaves at the base and a few on the stem, which seldom exceeds a foot in height and often is much less. The leaves have no teeth. At least some of the hairs are branched. The pods are short and oval or elliptic in outline.

I.   *Species with deeply cleft petals.*

WHITLOW-GRASS, D. VERNA, is interesting chiefly in being one of the earliest plants to bloom in spring. It may be only an inch tall at this time, becoming 3 or 4 inches tall in fruit. It is distinguished from the other species by having its minute petals cleft almost to the base, and by having no leaves on the flowering stems.

February to June: an Old-World species now naturalized in fields and waste places from Massachusetts and Vermont to Iowa and southward to Georgia, Tennessee, and Missouri. *Plate 50*. Whitlow was an affliction of the fingernails, which this plant was supposed to cure. *Verna* means "of spring."

II.   *Species with small tufts of basal leaves, not forming mats; more or less southern plants.*

D. REPTANS resembles whitlow-grass in general size and aspect, but the petals are at most notched, not cleft (often they are lacking), and there are usually leaves on the flowering stem, in pairs or threes. In fruit it may be a foot tall. The hairs on the lower surface of the leaves are branched.

March to June: Massachusetts to Washington and southward to Georgia, Texas, and California. *Reptans* means "creeping," which our plants mostly are not.

D. CUNEIFOLIA may be identified by its basal leaves, which are toothed and bristly with branched and unbranched hairs mixed. *Cuneifolia* means "wedge-leaved" and refers to their tapering bases. There are a few leaves on the stem. The stems are finally about a foot tall. The petals are minute or lacking.

March to May: in dry soil from Illinois to Colorado and southward to Florida and Texas; and in California and Mexico.

D. BRACHYCARPA has a much-branched stem up to 8 inches tall, with many small leaves on it, besides the basal leaves; all the leaves are elliptic, and, like the stem, downy with branched hairs. The petals are white, but are often very small or lacking. In a genus notable for its small pods, this species has very small ones, at most $\frac{1}{8}$ inch long (*brachycarpa* means "short-fruited").

March to May: in dry open soil from Virginia to Kansas and southward to Florida and Texas; also in Oregon. *Plate 50*.

III. *Mat-forming plants with crowded basal leaves; mostly northern.*

D. RAMOSISSIMA is a much-branched plant, forming mats a foot broad from which rise flowering stems

PLATE 50

Iodanthus pinnatifidus — *Rollins*

Hesperis matronalis — *Johnson*

Draba brachycarpa — *Rickett*

Draba verna — *D. Richards*

Arabis laevigata — *Scribner*

Arabidopsis thaliana — *Rickett*

Alliaria officinalis — *Scribner*

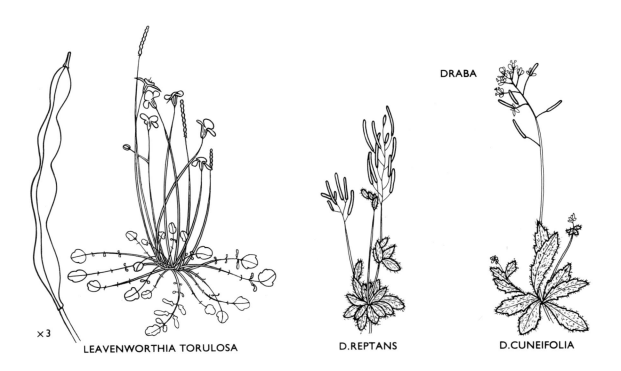

×3

LEAVENWORTHIA TORULOSA   DRABA   D.REPTANS   D.CUNEIFOLIA

more than a foot tall. The leaves in the mat are broadest near the end, tapering to the base, toothed, very finely downy. The leaves on flowering stems are lanceolate or ovate and coarsely toothed. The flowering stems are much branched (*ramosissima*), forming an inflorescence. The petals are white, $\frac{1}{4}$ inch long, the pods scarcely $\frac{1}{2}$ inch long and twisted.

April to June: on cliffs and in rocky woods from Virginia to Kentucky and southward to North Carolina and Tennessee.

D. LANCEOLATA is a northern species with dense tufts of narrow leaves at the base of the flowering stems; forming mats. The stems rise to a height of about a foot, bearing lanceolate leaves. The whole plant is ashy grey with a dense covering of branched hairs. The petals are white. The pod is often twisted.

May and June: on rocky ledges and banks from Quebec to Alaska and southward to northern New England, Michigan, Wisconsin, Colorado, and Utah.

D. ARABISANS is another species of matted plants with many basal tufts of narrow leaves which taper to their base. The stems rise a foot tall, with a few narrow leaves and a branched inflorescence. Almost the whole plant is downy with branched hairs. The minute petals are white. The pods are short, less than $\frac{1}{2}$ inch long and about $\frac{1}{4}$ as wide, generally twisted.

May to July: on rocks from Newfoundland to Ontario and Minnesota and southward to New York and Wisconsin.

Besides all these, two other Canadian or western species touch our northern borders: *D. nemorosa* in Michigan (*Plate 51*), *D. glabella* in New York; and one southern species, *D. aprica*, is reported from Missouri. The distinctive traits of these small plants must be sought in the technical books.

BERTEROA

One species of the Old-World genus *Berteroa* is now widely distributed in North America.

HOARY-ALYSSUM, B. INCANA, is like a tall *Draba* without the basal tuft of leaves. The branched stem grows up to 3 feet tall, bearing small leaves (2 inches long) without stalks and marginal teeth. The whole plant is hoary (*incana*) with branched hairs. The white petals are deeply cleft. The pod is elliptic, about twice as long as wide, with the style forming a short beak.

June to September: in fields, lawns, and waste places, a rather attractive little weed, from Nova Scotia to Montana and southward to New Jersey, West Virginia, Indiana, and Kansas; also on the Pacific coast. *Plate 51*. *B. mutabilis*, very similar but with flatter, broader pods, has appeared in Massachusetts and Kansas.

NASTURTIUM

The genus has but one species, confusingly not the "nasturtium" of our gardens, which is an exotic species in a quite different family.

WATER CRESS, N. OFFICINALE, grows partly or wholly submerged in flowing water, generally spring water. It has pinnately divided, smooth leaves and small white flowers. Roots are produced abundantly from the stem, which grows horizontally.

April to October: in cool, flowing water throughout North America; a most successful immigrant from Europe. *Plate 51*. In the Old World it is cultivated in tanks through which spring water is led, and the young sprouts are eaten in salads; they are often called in England simply "cress." The slight pungency of the leaves makes them very palatable. In this country they are more commonly gathered in the wild. The leaves have long been valued as a protection against scurvy, the "poor man's disease" of medieval Europe; they are rich in ascorbic acid (vitamin C). "Cress" is an old Anglo-Saxon word meaning any mustard-like plant. Linnaeus named water cress *Radicula nasturtium* ▽, the upside-down triangle being a sign for water; and for many years it was known to botanists as *R. nasturtium-aquaticum*. Having been transferred to a genus of its own, *Nasturtium*, the old epithet becomes illegitimate by international rules of nomenclature and is replaced by *officinale*, "of the shops."

ERUCA

We have one species of this European genus.

GARDEN ROCKET, also known as ROCKET SALAD, E. SATIVA, has long been cultivated in Europe for salads, but is little used in North America. It is a mustard-like plant, 2 feet tall, sparsely hairy, with yellowish-white petals nearly an inch long. The chief distinguishing feature is the very large, *flat* beak on the pod, half as long as the rest of the pod.

May to October: in cultivated land and waste places from Ontario to North Dakota and southward to New Jersey and Missouri; perhaps also elsewhere but nowhere abundant. The word rocket (as used for plants) is actually descended from the Latin *eruca* via the Italian *ruca*, and was originally applied to this species. Then it became applied to other, more or less similar crucifers, with qualifying words, as yellow rocket, dame's rocket, wall rocket. Now, therefore, the word is practically equivalent to crucifer.

In this genus the one American species and the one European species that has become naturalized in America seem at first sight to have nothing in common except that they are both crucifers. They are actually united by the thick pods, elliptic in outline, tipped with the styles and on long stalks, and by certain technical details of the seeds. (Even these distinctions seem questionable, since the introduced species rarely matures its pods and seeds.)

ARMORACIA

HORSE-RADISH, A. RUSTICANA, is a tall plant (up to 4 feet) with long-stalked basal leaves and a few leaves on the stem with short stalks or none. The leaf-blades are edged with blunt teeth. Some of the leaves on the stem may be pinnately cleft. The plant is topped by several racemes of small white flowers.

May to July: a plant cultivated for the well-known condiment, which is the ground-up root, and commonly found in various situations as a weed, throughout the country. Why so many plants receive the prefix "horse" to their names I do not know: we have horse-mint, horse-nettle, horse-chestnut, and others. It seems to signify something coarse and weedy or prickly, and perhaps also means "false"; for horse-mint is not a true mint, horse-nettle is not a nettle, horse-chestnut is not a chestnut; and this is not a radish. The French name for horse-radish is *raifort*, which means "strong root"; it certainly is that.

LAKE CRESS, A. AQUATICA, is a rather uncommon native American which grows in water. The submerged leaves are divided into numerous hairlike segments; those on the part of the stem above the surface are lanceolate or elliptic and toothed on the edges. The petals are white, $\frac{1}{4}$ inch long.

June to August: in quiet water from Quebec to Ontario and Minnesota and southward to Florida and Texas. *Plate 51*.

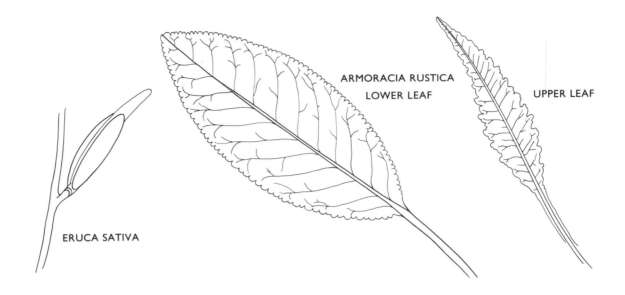

ERUCA SATIVA

ARMORACIA RUSTICA
LOWER LEAF

UPPER LEAF

CAKILE

One species of this genus inhabits the Atlantic beaches and the shores of the Great Lakes in North America.

SEA ROCKET, C. EDENTULA, has much-branched, succulent stems, bearing small leaves which are broadest near the tip and wavy-edged or toothed or scalloped or even pinnately lobed. The flowers are minute, pale purple. The most remarkable feature is the pods. Each consists of two sections, the upper one

the larger, both fleshy and as thick as they are wide. The single seed is in the upper part. In some of the plants of the Great Lakes the upper part tapers to a long beak.

July to September: along the coast from Labrador to South Carolina, and on the beaches of the Great Lakes. *Plates 51, 52. C. maritima*, with pinnately cleft leaves, is abundant in parts of the Pacific Coast, and occasionally appears near eastern ports. For the name rocket see under *Eruca*.

CAPSELLA

The Old-World genus *Capsella* has furnished a couple of all-too-familiar weeds to our lawns and roadsides.

SHEPHERD'S-PURSE or PICKPOCKET, C. BURSA-
PASTORIS, forms a rosette of pinnately cleft or divided leaves at ground level, from which arises a scrawny flowering stem up to 2 feet tall. There are a few arrowhead-shaped leaves on the stem, and several clusters of small white flowers terminate the branches. The branches elongate as the fruits develop, so that

these come to be separated. They are heart-shaped, like the medieval wallet or purse.

Shepherd's purse will grow all the year round, if weather permits, in lawns and waste places, throughout the country. *Plate 51. Bursa-pastoris* is Latin for "purse of a shepherd"; *capsella* means "little box."

C. RUBELLA is similar but less common; it inhabits the coastal states, both Atlantic and Pacific. It has minute petals ($\frac{1}{20}$ inch long) and the pod has straighter sides, or they are even curved inward.

THLASPI

This Old-World genus is represented in America by two species, both characterized by flat, circular pods notched at the end, with two or more seeds on each side of the partition. The flowers are white and very small.

PENNY-CRESS, T. ARVENSE, is a smooth plant up to nearly 3 feet tall. Most of the leaves are shaped at the base, where they meet the stem, like the head of an arrow; they have no stalk. They may or may not be toothed. The white petals are $\frac{1}{16}$ inch long or less.

PLATE 51

Nasturtium officinale *Johnson*

Draba nemorosa *Rollins*

Cakile edentula *Rollins*

Armoracia aquatica *Rickett*

Berteroa incana *Rickett*

D. Richards

Thlaspi arvense *Scribner*   Capsella bursa-pastoris   Lepidium densiflorum   *Johnson*

April to August: on roadsides and in fields and waste places from Greenland to Alaska and southward to Florida, Arkansas, and California. *Plate 51*.

T. PERFOLIATUM has more ovate leaves, with the

same arrowhead base. The petals are not more than ⅛ inch long. The pods are rather asymmetric.

March and April: in fields and waste land from Ontario to Virginia, Kentucky, and Missouri.

LEPIDIUM

These common and unattractive weeds rear their branched stems covered with small round pods along roadsides and in fields, in summer. The several species need only scant mention in this book.

PEPPER-GRASS or POOR-MAN'S-PEPPER, L. VIRGINI-CUM, is perhaps our commonest species, growing in dry places throughout our range and beyond. It is unusual in the family in having only two stamens.

L. DENSIFLORUM is a northerner and westerner which has strayed southward through our range. It has only two stamens and no petals. The basal leaves are pinnately cleft or coarsely toothed. *Plate 51*.

COW CRESS, L. CAMPESTRE, came from Europe and is now seen in fields and waste places throughout our range and westward. It is densely hairy. The leaves "clasp" the stem between their pointed lobes.

L. PERFOLIATUM, from Europe, has ovate leaves with rounded lobes at the base which "clasp" the stem; or the upper ones entirely surround the stem (which comes *per*, "through," the *folia*, "leaves").

L. RUDERALE, from Europe, is an ill-smelling plant with oval or elliptic pods. The lower leaves are pinnately cleft into lobes which are themselves pinnately cleft.

THE BLEEDING-HEART FAMILY (FUMARIACEAE)

The bleeding-hearts and their relatives have two sepals, four petals, and six stamens. The fruit is a slender pod. This basic plan is like that of some members of the poppy family, and some botanists unite the two families. In the bleeding-hearts, however, the four petals are of two different sizes and shapes, two outer enclosing two inner, the inner adhering by their tips. In some

genera both outer petals are extended backward into the hollow sacs called spurs. In others only one petal (the upper one) has a spur; this makes the flower bilaterally symmetric. The leaves are much divided.

I.   *Genera with two spurs on each flower:* Dicentra (*erect herbaceous plants*); Adlumia (*vines*).

II. *Genus with one spur on each flower:* Corydalis.

DICENTRA

These are erect, but delicate herbaceous plants with leaves divided into numerous narrow segments and white, pink, red, or purplish flowers dangling in a raceme with a usually arched central stem. *Dicentra* is from Greek words signifying "two spurs."

DUTCHMAN'S-BREECHES, D. CUCULLARIA, is a familiar and graceful plant of early spring. The two tapering spurs atop each flower make the pair of baggy breeches — upside down. The stem grows each year from a cluster of several small white corms or tubers.

April to June: in woods and on moist shady ledges from Quebec to North Dakota and southward

to Georgia, Alabama, Arkansas, and Kansas; also in Washington and Oregon. *Plate 52*. A form is known with purple and orange flowers.

SQUIRREL-CORN, D. CANADENSIS, is easily distinguished by the shape of the spurs, which are round; the flower is more nearly heart-shaped. The English name refers to the cluster of many small round, yellow corms or tubers. Both species of *Dicentra* are alike in stature (about a foot tall) and in foliage.

April and May: in woods from Quebec to Minnesota and southward to North Carolina, Tennessee, and Missouri. *Plate 52*.

PLATE 52

Dicentra canadensis   *Mayer*

Dicentra cucullaria   *Gottscho*

Dicentra eximia   *Johnson*

Cakile edentula   *Gillis*

Corydalis flavula   *Leeson*

Adlumia fungosa   *Gottscho*

Corydalis sempervirens   *Johnson*

WILD BLEEDING-HEART, D. EXIMIA, has narrow
pink flowers with short round spurs. The leaf-
segments are not so narrow as in the two commoner
species. The stem rises from a short underground
stem, a rhizome, growing to a height of nearly 2 feet.

April to September: on rock ledges in woods in
the mountains from New York southward and southwestward to Georgia, West Virginia, and Tennessee.
Plate 52. This species is often cultivated. The garden
bleeding-heart is *D. spectabilis*, from Asia.

ADLUMIA

The only other species grows in Asia.

ALLEGHANY-VINE, A. FUNGOSA, supports itself by its
leaves, which are divided and redivided into many
small, roundish, toothed segments on thin stalks; these
stalks coil around supports. The main stem may climb
to a height of 10 or 12 feet. The flowers hang in
branched clusters at the ends of branches. The petals
are white or purplish, scarcely spurred but with two

rounded lobes at the top (i.e. the part nearest the point
of attachment). After fertilization the corolla does not
fall but becomes spongy and encloses the seed-pod.

June to October: on wooded slopes, mostly in the
mountains, from Quebec to Minnesota and southward
to North Carolina and Tennessee. *Plate 52*. This is
called also wild fumitory. The true fumitory, *Fumaria
officinalis* of the Old World, gives the name to the family. It is sometimes found wild in North America.

CORYDALIS

In *Corydalis* the upper petal has a spur, so that the
flower seems not to be attached by its end. Both upper
and lower petals of the outer pair have vertical flattish
projections near the tip.

I.   *Species with pink flowers.*

PALE CORYDALIS or ROCK-HARLEQUIN, C. SEMPER-
VIRENS, is a slender plant up to 4 feet tall. The
pink petals have yellow tips, and a very short spur.

May to September: in rocky woods and openings from Newfoundland to Alaska and southward to
Georgia, Tennessee, Minnesota, Montana, and British Columbia. *Plate 52*.

II.   *Species with yellow flowers. To identify these one
must be prepared to use a hand magnifier and to make
careful measurements. Superficially and without such
study the different species are very similar. The vertical projections from the outer petals, mentioned
above, are important: in some species they bear a crest
of minute teeth; in others the ouline is smooth.*

A. Species with a toothed crest on the outer petals.

YELLOW-HARLEQUIN, C. FLAVULA, is one of the
easiest to recognize: it has the smallest flowers,
less than ½ inch long, often only ⅓ inch; and the spur
on the upper petal is very short, so that the stalk is
almost at the end of the flower.

March to May: in moist soil of wooded slopes
and bottom lands from Connecticut to southern Ontario and Nebraska and southward to North Carolina
and Oklahoma. *Plate 52*.

C. MICRANTHA has flowers about ½ inch long (*micrantha* means "small-flowered"). It is distinguished
from *C. flavula* most easily by the longer spur on the
upper petal, which brings the stalk to a position nearly
half-way from the base to the tip of the flower. The
minute sepals are often toothed.

April to June: on bluffs and banks and in rocky
woods from Minnesota to South Dakota and southward to Florida and Texas. *Plate 53*.

C. CRYSTALLINA is a southwestern species found in
Iowa and Missouri, flowering in April and May.
It is distinguished from all other species by a peculiar
mealy covering of the slender seed-pods. The flowers
are quite large, sometimes reaching nearly an inch in
length, the spur nearly half of this length.

B. Species with no toothed crest on the outer petals, the projection having a smooth outline.

GOLDEN CORYDALIS, C. AUREA, has flowers longer
than ½ inch, those of western, mountain plants
often ¾ inch. The long spur accounts for much of the
length, from one-third to one-half of the total. In eastern plants the flowering racemes are short, often not
rising above the foliage. The stouter western plants
are by many botanists considered a distinct species
under the name *C. montana*.

March to September (the later dates at high altitudes): in sandy or gravelly soil, prairies, bottomlands,
from Quebec to Alaska and southward to Pennsylvania, Illinois, Texas, and Arizona. *Plate 53*.

PLATE 53

Silene stellata   *Johnson*

Silene virginica   *V. Richard*

Silene caroliniana   *V. Richard*

Silene acaulis   *Rhein*

Silene cucubalus   *Elbert*

Corydalis micrantha   *Rickett*

Corydalis aurea   *Horne*

GROUP VII

Sepals four or five, petals four or five; petals separate and radially symmetric. Stamens as many as the petals or twice as many. Styles more than one in a flower.
Exceptions: Petals are lacking in some species of the pink family and in *Chrysosplenium*. Petals are slightly bilateral in symmetry in some species of *Heuchera*.

I. *Families with mostly undivided leaves.*

   A. Leaves paired, with teeth or lobes; styles from two to five: pink family.
   B. Leaves at the base of the stem and covered with sticky hairs; styles three: sundew family.
   C. Leaves succulent, mostly borne singly; styles four or five: live-forever family.

   D. Leaves mostly at the base of the stem; styles two or, in two genera, none: saxifrage family.
   E. Leaves borne singly, very narrow; styles five: flax family.
   F. Leaves borne singly, palmately lobed; stalks of the stamens joined to form a sheath around the pistil; styles three or four, club-shaped: passion-flower family.

II. *Families with mostly divided leaves (a few exceptions in the parsley family).*
   A. Leaf-blades divided into three heart-shaped segments; styles five: wood-sorrel family.
   B. Flowers small, white, in umbels; styles five; ovary inferior: ginseng family.
   C. Flower small, mostly white or yellow, mostly in compound umbels; styles two; ovary inferior: parsley family.

THE PINK FAMILY (CARYOPHYLLACEAE)

One marked characteristic of the pink family is the disposition of flowers in cymes; for this type of inflorescence the reader is referred to the Introduction to this volume; it is apparent also in several of the photographs and drawings presented herewith. This is a large family chiefly of northern countries, including small weeds and larger plants with handsome flowers. A number of species are valued in gardens and greenhouses: carnations, pinks, baby's-breath, and others. Some wild-growing species have proved poisonous to cattle.

The flower parts are generally in fours or five, the stamens in most species being as many as the petals or twice as many. The ovary bears several styles (from two to five). A technical feature that characterizes the family (with a few exceptions) is the attachment of the ovules in the ovary to a central stalk which is not fastened at the top.

The genera fall readily into two groups according as their sepals are joined or separate.

I. *Plants with sepals joined to form a cup, tube, or bladder.*

   A. Of these, some have more than two styles: *Silene* (styles generally three, rarely four); *Lychnis* (styles generally five, rarely four); *Agrostemma* (styles five; calyx strongly ribbed, its narrow teeth projecting between the petals).

   B. Others have two styles: *Saponaria* (blades of the petals more than $\frac{1}{4}$ inch long); *Dianthus* (calyx with several small bracts at the base); *Gypsophila* (blades of petals less than $\frac{1}{4}$ inch long).

186

II. *Plants with separate sepals; small plants with most-ly insignificant flowers.*

  A. Plants with separate sepals, and petals distinctly cleft in two: *Cerastium* (styles generally five); *Stellaria* (styles generally three).

  B. Plants with separate sepals, and petals never deeply cleft, merely notched or not even that: *Holosteum* (flowers in an umbel); *Arenaria* (stamens ten, styles three); *Sagina* (stamens and styles four or five); *Spergularia* (stamens from two to ten, styles three); *Spergula* (leaves in circles); *Paronychia* (petals minute, stamens five, styles two).

THE CAMPIONS* AND CATCHFLIES (SILENE)

The flowers of *Silene* have a calyx of five sepals which are joined, in many species forming a tube or sac narrower at the open end than in the middle; in others a tube or cup. There are five petals on narrow stalks, and ten stamens. The pistil has generally three styles (rarely four or still more rarely five). The pod (capsule) opens at the top, usually forming six teeth. The derivation of "campion" is obscure. Several species are called catchfly because of their sticky stems. These, it has been suggested, trap small crawlers, such as ants, which might otherwise steal the nectar from the flowers.

The species may be classified by the color and form of the corolla and calyx.

I. *Species with deep red petals.*

FIRE-PINK, S. VIRGINICA, has petals cleft at the end into two incurved points. It grows 2 feet tall or taller, the stems bearing some hairs and glands. The leaves on the stem are in several pairs, up to a foot long, widest between the middle and the tip, and smooth.

April to September: in open woods and on rocky slopes from western New York to southern Ontario and Minnesota and southward to Georgia and Oklahoma. *Plate 53.*

ROUND-LEAVED CATCHFLY, S. ROTUNDIFOLIA, has stems about 2 feet long that tend to lie on the ground, the tips bending upward; they may be hairy or thinly glandular. The leaves are broad, about 4 inches long, elliptic. The petals are scarlet and forked at the end.

June and July: on rocky ledges and slopes from West Virginia and southern Ohio to Georgia and Alabama.

ROYAL CATCHFLY or WILD-PINK, S. REGIA, may grow up to 5 feet tall, usually with smooth stems. The leaves are in many pairs, each ovate. The petals are scarlet, narrow, not forked or notched, their blades nearly an inch long.

June to August: on prairies and in dry woodlands from Ohio to Missouri and southward to Georgia and Oklahoma.

*Some species of *Lychnis* are also called campion.

II. *Species with white, pink, or lavender petals. Among these some have a calyx which, especially in the fruiting stage, is larger in the middle than at the ends, as if "inflated." Others have a tubular or cup-shaped calyx which fits tightly around the pod.*

  A. Species with inflated calyx.

BLADDER CAMPION, S. CUCUBALUS, is now a familiar roadside weed in most parts of North America. It grows up to 3 feet tall with smooth lanceolate or ovate leaves. The petals are white, forked. The flowers often furnish a perfect example of the inflorescence called a cyme.

April to September: on roadsides and in waste places from Newfoundland to British Columbia and southward to Virginia, Tennessee, Kansas, Colorado, and Oregon; a native of Europe. *Plate 53.*

S. CSEREI resembles *S. cucubalus* but the leaves are thicker and the inflorescence narrower. It is found from New York to Montana and southward to New Jersey and Missouri, flowering from May to September.

SNOWY CAMPION, S. NIVEA, is a smaller plant than the preceding, about a foot tall, with lanceolate leaves and few flowers. The petals are white, only slightly notched.

June to August: in woods in moist soil from Pennsylvania to Minnesota and North Dakota and southward to Maryland, Tennessee, Missouri, and Nebraska.

STARRY CAMPION, S. STELLATA, is at once recognized by its petals which are cut at the outer edge into several fine lobes. The leaves are in circles of four. They are very finely downy on the lower surface.

July to September: in woods and thickets from Massachusetts, to North Dakota and southward to Georgia, Arkansas, and Texas. *Plate 53.*

STICKY COCKLE or NIGHT-FLOWERING CATCH-FLY, S. NOCTIFLORA, has sticky-hairy stems up to 3 feet tall. The flowers open at night. The petals are cream-white, pinkish at the base, forked, fragrant.

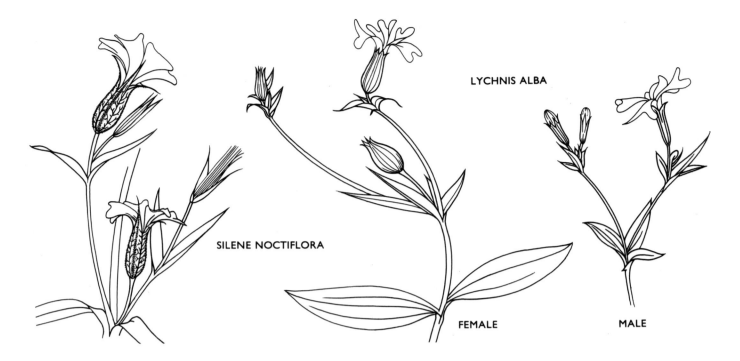

The calyx has conspicuous green veins which usually branch and form a network.

May to September: an immigrant from Europe now widely distributed in waste places and along road-sides through most of North America. *Plate 54*. Often confused with *Lychnis alba*. In *S. noctiflora* the green veins in the calyx are usually connected by conspicuous green branches; these are not seen in *Lychnis alba*. Also the leaves (or bracts) just below the flowers are long and narrow in the *Silene*, short and elliptic in the *Lychnis*. There is no separation of stamens and pistils in the *Silene* as there is in the *Lychnis*.

 B. Species with tubular or cup-shaped calyx, not inflated around the pod.

MOSS CAMPION, S. ACAULIS, is welcomed by moun-taineers, for it frequents high altitudes. Like many other arctic and alpine species, it forms dense clumps of much-branched small stems clothed with needle-like leaves. The petals are pink or lilac or occa-sionally white, about ½ inch long, sometimes forked, sometimes merely notched, sometimes not even that. The flowers are numerous on the small tussocks.

June to August: around the world in the arctic and boreal zones, and extending south down the moun-tain chains of New Hampshire, Colorado, Montana, and Washington, above tree line. *Plate 53*.

S. CAROLINIANA, like the preceding species, makes clumps of stems; but they are taller — up to 8 inches — with oblong leaves, well separated, up to 2 inches long, a bit broader in the end half. The flowers are usually closely clustered at the tip. The petals vary from white to pink; they are about ½ inch long, and may be notched at the end.

April to June: in dry sandy or rocky woods and openings from New Hampshire to Ohio and Mis-souri and southward to South Carolina and Alabama. *Plate 53*.

S. DICHOTOMA has hairy stems, growing up to 3 feet tall. The leaves are narrow, lanceolate. The upper part of the stem forks (it is "dichotomous"), the flow-ers being borne on one side of each branch. The petals are white (occasionally pink), and deeply cleft.

June to September: in fields and waste places, an immigrant from Europe, now naturalized from Que-bec to California and southward.

SLEEPY CATCHFLY, S. ANTIRRHINA, may usually be identified by the dark sticky zones on the stem midway between the nodes at which the leaves are borne. Small insects are usually to be found trapped in these zones. The stem may be nearly 3 feet tall, with pairs of narrow leaves at rather wide intervals. The petals are pink or white, less than ½ inch long, more or less cleft; or they may be lacking altogether.

May to September: in dry sandy or rocky places from Quebec to British Columbia and throughout the United States; also in Mexico and South America. This wandering American species has turned the tables on our many visitors from the Old World: it has invaded Europe.

SWEET-WILLIAM-CATCHFLY or NONE-SO-PRETTY, S. ARMERIA, is very smooth, about a foot tall, with ovate leaves whitened with a bloom. The flowers are at the summit of the stem in a cyme whose branches are so short it approaches a head or umbel. The petals are pink (or sometimes white), about ¼ inch long.

June to October: introduced as a garden plant, now established as a wild flower on roadsides and in waste places from Quebec to Minnesota and southward to Virginia, Ohio, Illinois, and Iowa.

Besides the above, several other Old-World species appear in scattered places in North America. *S. conica* has small white or rose petals less than ¼ inch long, and narrow tapering leaves. *S. conoidea* has an inflated calyx and white, pink, or purple petals up to ½ inch long. *S. gallica* has lower leaves that widen towards the tip, and pink or white flowers along one side of the stem; the petals are about ⅓ inch long. *S. nutans* has small pink or white flowers that hang down (*nutans*) from their stalks; the petals are ¼ inch long or a little longer.

CAMPIONS (LYCHNIS)

The campions* are plants of the north, chiefly in Europe and Asia but a few species extending all around the world and reaching down in North America and at least one penetrating the southern United States. The botanical name is derived from the Greek word for "lamp" and refers to the brilliant flowers of some species. They somewhat resemble *Silene* but are distinguished by generally having five styles (though there are exceptions). The fruit opens at the tip generally into five or ten teeth. As in *Silene*, the calyx of some species is "inflated," forming a sort of bladder with a narrow mouth.

I.   *Species with inflated calyx.*

RED CAMPION, L. DIOICA, is a very common wild
     flower of English roadsides. It grows (in this country) some 3 feet tall, with forked, hairy stems. The petals are rose-red, forked at the end, about ½ inch long. Each flower has stamens or pistil, not both; *dioica* means "in two households."

     May to September: in waste places and on roadsides from Newfoundland to Ontario and southward to Virginia and Missouri. *Plate 54*. Grigson, surveying the English names of this plant, characterizes it as "a plant of snake, of devil, goblin, and of death, if it is picked."

WHITE CAMPION, L. ALBA, resembles red campion
     save in the color of its flowers. It is somewhat taller (up to 4 feet), downy and somewhat glandular. The fragrant flowers open at night, their white petals attracting the moths which carry the pollen. The petals are forked. Like *L. dioica*, it has "two households," stamens and pistils being in separate flowers and on separate plants. The calyx of pistillate flowers is distended, especially in the fruiting stage; that of staminate flowers is tubular, cylindric, or nearly so.

     May to September: in waste places, in fields, and on roadsides from Quebec across Canada and southward to North Carolina, Missouri, Utah, and Califor-

nia. *Plate 54*. This, like *L. dioica*, is a sinister plant. Whereas picking red campion brings death to your father, picking this one kills your mother; one English name is mother-die, and a German name signifies "death plant." Another superstition is that if you pick it you will be struck by lightning. This species is so similar to *Silene noctiflora* that the two are often confused. See under *Silene* for the distinction.

II. *Species with tubular or bell-shaped calyx, not infla-
     ted.*

RAGGED-ROBIN, L. FLOS-CUCULI, is quickly known
     by its pink petals deeply cleft into usually four narrow and unequal lobes. The plant grows some 4 feet tall. It is mostly smooth but somewhat sticky.

     May to July: in waste places and fields (where it often forms large colonies) from Quebec to New England, New York, and Pennsylvania. *Plate 54*.

MULLEIN-PINK or DUSTY-MILLER, L. CORONARIA,
     is distinguished from all other species of *Lychnis* by the white wool with which its stem and leaves are covered. It is a slender plant, generally unbranched and with few flowers, about 3 feet tall. The petals are bright purplish-crimson, an inch long, and not forked (they may be slightly notched).

     June to August: in waste places and woodlands and on roadsides from Maine to Ontario and southward to Delaware, Ohio, and Indiana. *Plate 54*. This is a European plant escaped from cultivation. Curiously, it has been confused with corn cockle, because it was originally placed by Linnaeus in *Agrostemma*, and so some gardeners have saddled it with the botanical name of corn cockle, *Agrostemma githago*.

L. CHALCEDONICA, an Asian plant, has escaped from
     cultivation and is established in some places. It has hairy stems and many ovate leaves. The flowers are in a dense head, the petals scarlet and forked. *Plate 54*. *L. drummondii*, a western species, is found in Minnesota and Michigan. It has a sticky stem and a tall, slender inflorescence.

*Species of *Silene* are also known as campions.

AGROSTEMMA

There is but one species.

CORN COCKLE, A. GITHAGO, a slender plant up to 3
feet tall or taller, has a silky-downy stem and very
narrow leaves. The distinguishing feature of the flower is the calyx, which bears ten strong ribs and ends in
five long, narrow teeth which project beyond the petals. The petals are red, with black spots near the base.

June to September: a native of Europe and established as a weed in fields and sometimes on roadsides
throughout our range and beyond. *Plate 54*. In Europe
it has been a troublesome weed in the corn (wheat),
though now apparently becoming rare. The seeds, if
harvested with the grain, can make the flour unwhole-
some or dangerous; they contain a saponin (see under
Saponaria).

SAPONARIA

These plants are weeds introduced from the Old
World. The calyx is shaped like a narrow flask. The
petals (white or pink) are shallowly notched, not forked. There are two styles, and the pod (capsule) opens
to make four teeth. An extract from either species
forms a lather with water (the Latin for "soap" is *sapo*;
hence the botanical name). The action is due to a group
of substances called saponins, which are poisonous.

BOUNCING-BET or SOAPWORT, S. OFFICINALIS, is
the better known of the two in this country, both
for its abundance and for the presence of the soaplike
material in its stem and leaves. It is a smooth plant,
up to 3 feet tall, with ovate or lanceolate leaves which
have three veins branching from the base. The fragrant flowers are in close clusters ("congested cymes")
in the axils of leaves and at the tip of the stem. The
calyx has five teeth but they are often arranged to make
two lobes. The petals are white or pale pink, often
"double" – i.e. extra petals present. They tend to bend
downwards.

June to October: once a cultivated plant, now a
weed in waste places and along roads and railroads
practically throughout the country. *Plate 55*.

COWHERB or COW COCKLE, S. VACCARIA (*vacca* is
Latin for "cow"), is a more slender plant than *S.
officinalis*, 2 feet tall, with lanceolate leaves and smaller
flowers on longer stalks. The calyx has five sharp
angles. The petals are pink.

June to September: in waste places and fields
throughout the country but less common than bouncing-Bet. Some botanists place this species and some
of its relatives in a separate genus.

PINKS (DIANTHUS)

The carnations and sweet-Williams of our gardens and hothouses are species of *Dianthus*; as are also
a number of species grown in rock gardens. We have
no native species in the eastern United States, but
several from the Old World are found in dry fields and
on roadsides; the two listed below are the only ones at
all common, but the garden pink, *D. plumarius* (tufts
of whitish leaves at base) and sweet-William, *D. bar-
batus* (flowers very crowded), are occasionally found.

DEPTFORD PINK, D. ARMERIA, may reach 3 feet in
height. The leaves are very narrow and stand up
close to the stem. At the tip are one or more close clusters of small flowers (often only one open at a time),
with a pair of narrow bracts beneath each cluster, and
a similar bract beneath each flower. The bracts are
longer than the flower-stalk. The petals are rose with
minute white spots, slightly toothed at the edge, the
visible part only about $\frac{1}{5}$ inch long.

May to July: in dry fields and waste places from
Quebec and Ontario to Georgia, Kentucky, and Missouri; also on the West Coast; *Plate 55*. The English
name commemorates the fields near Deptford, where
the plants grew in abundance. There are no fields
there now, Deptford being a part of industrial Lon-
don.

MAIDEN PINK, D. DELTOIDES, has a slender creeping stem (rhizome) from which the erect stems
grow. The leaves on the erect stems are very narrow,
almost threadlike. The flowers are less crowded than
those of *D. armeria*, being on longer stalks. The bract
at the base of each flower is short and broad with a narrow point. The blades of the petals are up to $\frac{2}{5}$ inch
long, rose-purple, toothed at the edge.

May to August: in sandy fields from New England to Michigan and southward to New Jersey and
Illinois. *Plate 55*.

PLATE 54

Silene noctiflora

Gottscho

Lychnis alba

Johnson

Agrostemma githago

Elbert

Lychnis dioica

Gottscho

Lychnis flos-cuculi

Rickett

Lychnis coronaria

Roche

Lychnis chalcedonica

Houseknecht

BABY'S-BREATH (GYPSOPHILA)

The species of *Gypsophila* are low branching plants with numerous small flowers. *G. muralis* is a native of Europe now established as a weed from Maine to Minnesota and southward to New Jersey and Indiana, flowering all summer. The leaves are very narrow and about $\frac{1}{3}$ inch long. The flowers are on threadlike stalks from the axils of leaves. The petals are pink or purplish, their blades about $\frac{1}{4}$ inch long. *G. paniculata* is the cultivated baby's-breath, with very numerous white flowers, the blades of the petals only about $\frac{1}{8}$ inch long. This grows wild in sandy or rocky places from New England to Manitoba and southward to Indiana and Nebraska. *G. perfoliata*, with broad-based leaves, and *G. elegans*, slender and up to 2 feet tall, are reported in scattered places, flowering from June or July to October.

CHICKWEEDS (CERASTIUM AND STELLARIA)

The distinction between the two genera here considered is curiously like that between *Silene* and *Lychnis*, depending on the number of styles and the manner in which the seed-pod (capsule) opens. But the chickweeds are so small that it is much more difficult to determine such points. *Cerastium* usually has five styles, and the pod opens at the tip so as to make ten teeth. *Stellaria* usually has three styles, and the pod releases the seeds by splitting to the base into three or six parts. But the number of styles in both genera is variable, as is the number of petals and stamens in *Stellaria*. Chickweeds found in wet places are likely to be *Stellaria*. Hairy or sticky-downy plants of dry places may be *Cerastium*. Both genera have forked petals, usually five. Perhaps the commonest chickweed of lawns is *S. media*, which is smooth or nearly so. *C. vulgatum* is also common in lawns; it is downy and is called mouse-ear chickweed.

The name *Stellaria* refers to the starlike small flowers of many species (*stella* is Latin for "star"); some are called starworts. *Cerastium* is from a Greek word meaning "horned"; the small, curved seed-pod of some species suggests a horn. The English name refers to the use of the plants by small birds; they pick the seeds in lawns; and entire plants are accepted by canaries and other cage-birds.

MOUSE-EAR CHICKWEED, C. VULGATUM, is a spreading, branching plant which forms mats. It is hairy and usually somewhat sticky. The leaves are an inch long or longer.

April to October, or sometimes throughout the year: in lawns and fields and on roadsides throughout the country; a native of the Old World. *Plate 55.*

C. VISCOSUM tends to grow erect, with stems up to a foot long. It is hairy or downy and sticky. The leaves are about an inch long.

March to July: in fields and waste places practically throughout the country. *C. semidecandrum* closely resembles *C. viscosum*, the principal difference being in the small leaves (bracts) under the flowers and in the sepals: in *C. semidecandrum* these are partly white and translucent. In sandy places in the Atlantic states from Massachusetts to North Carolina.

C. NUTANS is another sticky-hairy species, but a North American native, not an immigrant. It has rather weak, sprawling stems (to which habit the Latin *nutans*, "nodding," refers) up to 2 feet long. The leaves are rather narrow, up to 3 inches long.

March to June: in varied situations in woodlands practically throughout the country.

C. ARVENSE is a matted plant, with creeping leafy stems from which rise flowering branches up to 2 feet tall. The leaves are typically very narrow, but are very variable. Numerous races exist, some hairy, some smooth, some sticky. These have been given names as varieties or even as separate species.

April to August: in gravelly or sandy soil almost throughout North America. *Plate 55.*

CHICKWEED, S. MEDIA, is the common smoothish, spreading small weed of lawns with ovate leaf-blades on short stalks. The five petals are so deeply cleft that they may be taken for ten; they do vary in number and are sometimes lacking. The stamens also vary in number.

Often growing and even flowering throughout the year and found everywhere, especially in lawns. *Plate 55.*

STAR CHICKWEED, S. PUBERA, is in marked contrast to the preceding species: an erect woodland plant up to a foot tall. The leaves are mainly elliptic and up to about 3 inches long. The petals are about $\frac{1}{4}$ inch long, deeply cleft.

March to May: in woods from New York and New Jersey to Illinois and southward to Florida and Alabama. *Plate 55.*

PLATE 55

Stellaria graminea — *Rickett*

Dianthus deltoides — *Johnson*

Stellaria media — *Rickett*

Dianthus armeria — *Gottscho*

Saponaria officinalis — *Johnson*

Cerastium vulgatum — *Scribner*

Cerastium arvense — *Scribner*

Stellaria pubera — *Allen*

STITCHWORTS, S. LONGIFOLIA and S. GRAMINEA,
(for the English name see under *S. holostea*), are
very similar (although native on opposite sides of the
Atlantic). They are slender plants with weak, four-
angled stems about 18 inches tall, bearing very narrow
leaves up to 2 inches long. The flowers of *S. graminea*
are all at the tip of the stem in a widely branched inflorescence. Those of *S. longifolia* are in smaller, long-
stalked clusters from the axils of leaves. The petals of
both are only about ⅕ inch long.

S. *longifolia* grows in meadows and woodlands
from Newfoundland and Labrador to Alaska and
southward to South Carolina, Louisiana, New Mexico, and California, flowering from May to July. *S. graminea* is from Europe, now naturalized in grasslands
and waste places from Newfoundland and Quebec to
Minnesota and southward to South Carolina, Indiana,
and Missouri (if all identifications are correct), flowering from May to October. *Plate 55. S. longipes* is a
similar but very variable species, shorter by about a
foot and stiffer, in the open often in tufts, with clusters
of a few flowers, or single flowers, both from the upper
axils and from the tip of the stem. It grows in varied
situations, mostly moist, practically throughout Canada and southward to New York, Indiana, Minnesota,
Arizona, and California.

S. HOLOSTEA is the greater stitchwort of England,
with four-angled stems up to 18 inches tall and
narrowly lanceolate leaves. The flowers are in a branched inflorescence at the summit. The petals spread to
nearly an inch across, each cleft to about the middle.

May and June: cultivated and escaped to roadsides and woodlands locally from New England to
North Carolina and West Virginia. The name stitchwort is not directly connected with needle and thread,
but with the sudden sharp pains known as stitches, for
the relief of which these plants were supposed to be
effective. But perhaps this belief was due to the needle-
like leaves — stitches being such sharp pains as might
be made by a sharp point — and may hark back to the
doctrine of signatures (for which see under *Hepatica*).

S. AQUATICA, a weed from Europe, is naturalized in
wet places from Quebec to Minnesota and southward to North Carolina and Louisiana, and in British
Columbia. It differs from other species of *Stellaria* in
having five styles, and for this reason is by some botanists placed in a separate genus, *Myosoton* (Greek for
"mouse-ear"). The leaves are ovate, often indented at
the base, without stalks. The spreading stems, which
may lie on the ground, reach a length of nearly 3 feet.
The flowers grow singly on long stalks from the axils
of leaves, with petals over ¼ inch long. They appear
from May to November.

S. FONTINALIS is a curious little species without petals
and with inch-long leaves that broaden towards
their tip. It is known only from wet rocky places and
springs in Kentucky and Tennessee.

HOLOSTEUM

Only one species of this Old-World genus has
become established in North America.

JAGGED-CHICKWEED, H. UMBELLATUM, somewhat
resembles both *Stellaria* and *Cerastium*, but is at
once distinguished by having its flowers in an umbel.

It is a pale little plant, about a foot tall, with leaves,
about an inch long, mostly near the base. The flowers
are tiny, the petals white, not cleft.

March to May: in fields and on roadsides from
Massachusetts to Ohio and southward to Georgia and
Kentucky.

THE SANDWORTS (ARENARIA)

The sandworts are small, generally bushy plants,
mostly with tiny leaves and small white flowers. The
petals are not cleft as in *Stellaria* and *Cerastium*. There
are generally ten stamens and three styles (with some
variation). They are mostly plants of stony arctic and
alpine regions or of sandy situations in the West and
Southwest (*arena* is Latin for "sand"). Some are cultivated in rock gardens. Besides those here described, a
few others may just touch our northern borders.

GROVE SANDWORT, A. LATERIFLORA, has a threadlike creeping stem (rhizome) from which arise
leafy branches about a foot tall bearing elliptic leaves
about an inch long or somewhat longer. The flowers
are in small, long-stemmed clusters at and near the
ends of the branches. The petals vary from ⅙ to ⅓ inch
in length, being longer than the sepals.

May to August: in gravelly or grassy places all
around the world in the north, extending south in
America to Maryland, Ohio, Missouri, South Dakota, New Mexico, and California. *Plate 56.*

A. MACROPHYLLA resembles *A. lateriflora*, but the
flowering stems are only 6 inches tall and bear

PLATE 56

Sagina procumbens *Scribner*

Arenaria lateriflora *Johnson*

Arenaria caroliniana *Uttal*

Arenaria groenlandica *Gottscho*

Paronychia virginica *Lenhart*

Paronychia argyricoma *Core*

Sagina nodosa *Elbert*

Arenaria stricta *Johnson*

ARENARIA

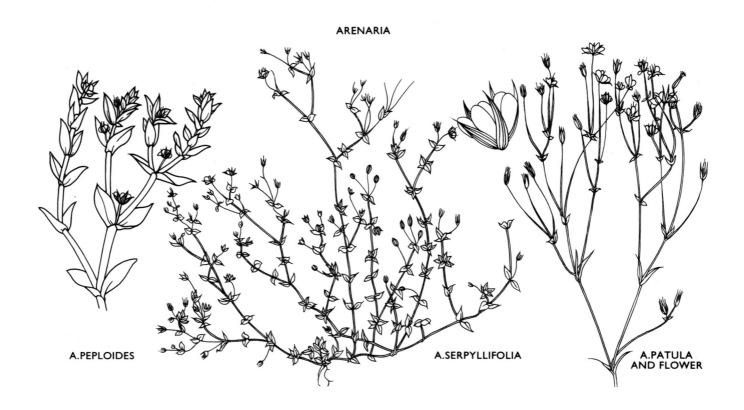

A.PEPLOIDES   A.SERPYLLIFOLIA   A.PATULA AND FLOWER

narrower leaves up to nearly 3 inches long. The petals are barely as long as the sepals.

May to August: in sandy and stony places from Labrador to Wisconsin and southward to Massachusetts; also in the West.

ROCK SANDWORT, A. STRICTA, has branching, wiry stems up to a foot tall bearing many crowded needle-like leaves. The flowers rise above the leaves in a branched cluster. The petals may reach $\frac{1}{3}$ inch in length, twice as long as the sepals. The species varies greatly in dimensions in different parts of its range and is sometimes divided into several varieties and species.

May to July: on limestone ledges, stony soil, etc. from Labrador and Quebec to Alaska and southward to South Carolina, Kentucky, Arkansas, Texas, and British Columbia. *Plate 56.*

A. PATULA is a more southern sandwort, very bushy, with stems up to 8 inches tall, and relatively few needle-like leaves. The petals are commonly heart-shaped.

April to June: in stony barrens and open woods and on limestone ledges from Ohio to Minnesota and southward to Virginia, Alabama, and Texas.

THYME-LEAVED SANDWORT, A. SERPYLLIFOLIA grows about 8 inches tall, with very slender, usually much-branched stems bearing tiny ovate leaves

only about $\frac{1}{5}$ inch long. The flowers are in clusters at the tips of the branches. The sepals are only $\frac{1}{8}$ inch long, the petals even shorter.

April to August: a native of Europe and Asia now naturalized in dry sandy places practically throughout North America. *Serpyllum* is an old name for thyme, now named *Thymus*.

MOUNTAIN SANDWORT, A. GROENLANDICA, greets the hiker on our mountain-tops, with indented petals commonly $\frac{2}{5}$ inch long crowning low mounds of leafy stems not more than 6 inches high. The leaves are crowded, needle-like, less than an inch long.

June to August: on granite ledges from Greenland and Labrador southward to the high mountains of New England. *Plate 56.* A variety with taller, less bunched stems and leaves and smaller petals extends south at lower altitudes into Connecticut, Georgia, and Tennessee.

PINE-BARREN SANDWORT, A. CAROLINIANA, forms dense tufts with forking stems that lie on the ground. The flowering stems may reach a height of 8 inches. Most of their leaves are near the base; their upper parts are glandular. The flowers are on long stalks in branched clusters. Their narrow petals are about $\frac{2}{5}$ inch long.

May to July: in sandy and barren soils on the coastal plain locally from Rhode Island to Florida; uncommon in our range. *Plate 56.*

SEA-CHICKWEED, A. PEPLOIDES, differs from all the other species in having thick, succulent stem and leaves. It grows to a height of nearly 2 feet. The flowers grow either in clusters at the summit or singly in the axils of leaves. There are five or six very small petals and eight or ten stamens.

May to September: on sea beaches around the northern hemisphere, extending south in the United States to Virginia and California. The difference between this species and the others is so marked that it is often placed in a separate genus, *Honkenya* (named after G. A. Honckeny, an European botanist of the eighteenth century).

PEARLWORTS (SAGINA)

The pearlworts are low plants, some species forming mats, with threadlike leaves and tiny flowers on rather long stalks. A magnifier reveals that the sepals, petals, stamens, and styles usually number four or five (the petals may be lacking).

S. DECUMBENS has a more or less erect, threadlike stem up to 6 inches tall; flower-parts in fives. It grows in sandy fields from Massachusetts to Kansas and southward to Florida and Texas, flowering (somewhere) from March to August.

BIRDSEYE, S. PROCUMBENS, is a more northern plant, smaller, more matted; flower-parts in fours. It is found in damp soil in Canada, reaching southward to Maryland, West Virginia, and Michigan, and flowering from April to November; also in Europe and Asia. *Plate 56.* In Europe it was believed to have a special power to keep fairies away; and, on a girl's lips, to attract lovers.

S. NODOSA grows in tufts with stems up to 8 inches long, with small bulb-like masses of leaves that make the stem look like a string of beads (*nodosa* means "knotty"). There are five petals. It grows in rocky or sandy places in far northern countries around the world, reaching our range in Maine, Massachusetts, Michigan, and Minnesota. *Plate 56.*

SAND-SPURREYS (SPERGULARIA)

Sand-spurreys are small plants somewhat suggesting an *Arenaria*, with threadlike leaves. There are from two to ten stamens and three styles. Several species occur in Canada, growing usually in tidal mud; some of these enter the United States, the two described below being the commonest.

S. RUBRA is about a foot tall, much branched. The petals are pink, shorter than the sepals — which are not $\frac{1}{4}$ inch long. There are usually ten stamens. This Old-World plant grows in sandy or gravelly soil from Newfoundland to Minnesota and southward to Virginia and (rarely) Alabama; also in New Mexico, California, and South America; flowering from May to October.

S. MARINA has a stature and form similar to those of *S. rubra*, but is fleshy, the leaves thicker and more succulent. The petals are white or rose. There are not more than five stamens. This is a plant chiefly of the seashore, from Quebec to Florida, but is also found across the continent in salt or brackish marshes and wet soil, extending southward to New York, Illinois, Texas, New Mexico, and Mexico, flowering (somewhere in this vast range) from June to October.

SPURREY (SPERGULA)

Spurrey is at once distinguished from the sand-spurreys and all the other small-flowered and thin-leaved genera of the pink family by having its leaves in circles instead of in pairs. It has five or ten stamens and five styles.

S. ARVENSIS, known in England as corn-spurrey because it grows in cornfields ("corn" in England is wheat), is naturalized almost throughout North America. Its stems may exceed a foot in height, bearing circles of leaves about 2 inches long at intervals of 2 or 3 inches. The petals are white, about $\frac{1}{8}$ inch long. The seeds were grown to make an edible meal.

March to October: in cultivated land and waste places from Newfoundland to Alaska and southward to Virginia, Missouri, and California.

THE WHITLOW-WORTS (PARONYCHIA)

An affliction of the finger-nails was known as whitlow, and these little plants were supposed to provide a cure because of their scaly surface (compare *Draba verna*). They are matted, spreading plants with narrow leaves and minute flowers. Where the leaves are attached to the stem a magnifier will reveal small, almost transparent stipules.

SILVERLING, P. ARGYROCOMA, has leaves and stems silvery with silky hair. It grows about a foot tall, with leaves about an inch long. It is found in rocky places in the mountains from Maine and New Hampshire to Georgia and Tennessee, flowering from June to September. *Plate 56.*

P. virginica, smooth, with narrower leaves, is found from Maryland to Tennessee and North Carolina. *Plate 56. P. canadensis*, with elliptic leaves, grows in sandy soil from New Hampshire to Minnesota and southward to Georgia, Alabama, Arkansas, and Kansas. *P. fastigiata*, with leaves narrowly elliptic or lanceolate but broadest near the tip, may grow 10 inches tall. The inflorescence is commonly quite leafy. It occurs in dry woods and rocky places from Massachusetts to Minnesota and southward to Florida and Texas. All these species flower in summer.

THE SUNDEW FAMILY (DROSERACEAE)

There are two American genera in this family, but only one in the northeastern states.

THE SUNDEWS (DROSERA)

These plants are remarkable for their leaves, which bear numerous hairs tipped with sticky glands. Small insects alighting on the leaves are caught by these sticky tips; and the hairs around bend towards the captive, completing its entanglement. A digestive material is exuded by the glands, and enables the plant to actually absorb foods from the insect's body. Such "insectivorous" or "carnivorous" plants are thus to a certain extent independent of the soil for certain elements in their nutrition.

For other "insectivorous" or "carnivorous" plants, see the pitcher-plants, *Sarracenia*. Perhaps it is worth mentioning that the "man-eating plant of Madagascar" and all other such monsters exist only in the imagination of journalists and other humorists.

The flowers of sundews are in a false raceme on a leafless stem curved at the end. Each has five sepals, five white, pink, or purple petals, about five stamens, and a pistil with usually three styles cleft so that they seem to be six. Our species flower from June to August. They grow typically in bogs and other wet places.

The botanical name is derived from the Greek word for "dew" and refers to the glistening drops at the ends of the hairs.

ROUND-LEAVED SUNDEW, D. ROTUNDIFOLIA, is the most widespread species. It is easily distinguished by its leaf-blades, which are circular or broader than long, on distinct stalks. It grows practically throughout North America. *Plate 57.*

D. INTERMEDIA has leaf-blades up to an inch long, broader towards the end, on stalks up to 2 inches long. The flowers are white. It is found from Newfoundland to Ontario and Minnesota, southward on the coastal plain to Florida and thence to Texas; also inland to South Carolina and Tennessee. *Plate 57.*

D. ANGLICA resembles *D. intermedia* in the form of the leaves, but their blades are twice as long, up to 2 inches, on shorter stalks. The petals are slightly longer, $\frac{1}{4}$ inch as against $\frac{1}{6}$ inch. The range separates the two species to some extent: *D. anglica* grows from Labrador and Newfoundland to Alaska and southward to Quebec, Ontario, Wisconsin, Idaho, and California. *Plate 57.*

DEW-THREAD, D. FILIFORMIS, has leaves shaped like pieces of string, without any distinction between stalk and blade; the purple glandular hairs are borne over their whole surface. They may be 10 inches long. Some stand erect; others assume various curves. The flowers are purple, on a stem up to 9 inches tall. These plants are found on the coastal plain from Massachusetts to Delaware; a variety extends from North Carolina and Florida to Louisiana. *Plate 57.*

D. LINEARIS has narrow leaves, but they broaden gradually and slightly towards the tip to form a distinct blade. They are up to 2 inches long. The species occurs in scattered places from Newfoundland to Alberta and southward to Maine, Michigan, and Wisconsin. *Plate 57.*

Two other species are found from Virginia southward: Pink sundew, *D. capillaris*, only 8 inches tall, with short leaf-stalks; and *D. brevifolia*, only 4 inches tall, likewise with short leaf-stalks (this occurs also in Missouri).

PLATE 57

Sedum pulchellum   *Elbert*

Sedum rosea   *Johnson*

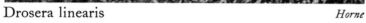

Drosera linearis   *Horne*

Drosera filformis   *Ryker*

Drosera anglica   *Scribner*

Drosea intermedia   *Horne*

Drosera rotundifolia   *Justice*

THE LIVE-FOREVER FAMILY (CRASSULACEAE)

The *Crassulaceae* are almost all succulent plants with undivided and unlobed leaves. The flower-parts are in fours or fives. The stamens may be twice as many as the other parts. Even the pistils are four or five, forming a group of pods (follicles).

Several species are called live-forever. Their leaves contain so much water (which is protected from evaporation) that they will remain alive for a considerable time even after being detached. Species of various genera are cultivated, especially in rock gardens: *Crassula, Sedum, Sempervivum* (hen-and-chickens).

THE STONECROPS AND LIVE-FOREVER (SEDUM)

The genus *Sedum* is a large one, the species difficult to identify. They are largely plants of rocky places, often cultivated in rock gardens and on walls and stone steps. The petals are white, yellow, or purple. The stamens are twice as many as the petals, which may number four or five. The fruits are follicles.

I.   *One species has flower-parts in fours, only stamens or pistils in any one flower, petals pink or yellow.*

ROSEROOT, S. ROSEA, has a tuft of stems arising from the thick, short, main stem; a foot tall or taller. The leaves are crowded, mostly in circles. The staminate flowers are yellowish, the pistillate purplish.

May to August: in the arctic and subarctic regions of North America and northern Europe and Asia, and southward in the mountains to Maine, Vermont, New York, and Pennsylvania, North Carolina, Colorado, and British Columbia. If the stem is cut it emits the odor of roses. *Plate 57.*

II. *Species with perfect flowers — containing both stamens and pistils — and thick, cylindric leaves.*

ROCK-MOSS, S. PULCHELLUM, has a group of stems up to 18 inches tall, bearing numerous leaves about an inch long, singly. The flowers are borne on several spreading branches. The petals are white, pink, or purple.

May to July: on rocks and cliffs from West Virginia to Illinois and Kansas and southward to Georgia, Alabama, Arkansas, and Texas. *Plate 57.*

WALLPEPPER or LOVE-ENTANGLE, S. ACRE, is a common and troublesome weed. The stems creep. They bear short, thick leaves, mostly singly. The flowering stems rise to a height of 4 inches, bearing spreading branches covered with small yellow flowers.

June and July: in dry, sandy soil, rocky places, etc. from Quebec to Washington and southward to North Carolina and Illinois. *Plate 58.* The English name wallpepper is reflected in the Latin *S. acre;* both refer to the sharp taste of the leaves. It is also called poor-man's-pepper and — among other things — welcome-home-husband-though-never-so-drunk.

III. *Species with perfect flowers (containing both stamens and pistils) and flat leaves.*

LIVE-FOREVER or ORPINE, S. TELEPHIUM, is a widespread and variable species from the Old World, escaped from cultivation in North America. The stem, scarcely 2 feet tall, bears ovate, toothed leaves mostly in pairs. The flowers are crowded in a dense, broad inflorescence, usually purplish-red but sometimes yellowish.

August and September: on roadsides and in edges of fields from Newfoundland to Minnesota and southward to New Jersey and Indiana. *Plate 58.* The red-flowered form, with leaves borne singly or in circles of three, is sometimes considered a separate species, *S. purpureum.* Another form is separated as *S. telephioides,* with few or no teeth on the leaves and pink petals. *Plate 58.* This is evidently a complex group of plants, the relationships and status of which are in need of study.

S. telephium has long been valued in Europe for its powerful magic and medicinal powers. Many superstitions are connected with the resistance of its leaves to drying — they confer freedom from all ailments on the household. It was supposed to be potent against cancer, fevers, sterility, and various other ills. The leaves were also eaten in salads.

A number of other species of *Sedum* have escaped from cultivation in scattered places. And *S. nuttalianum* of the Southwest, with narrow leaves borne singly and flowers scattered on the branches, occurs in Missouri.

S. TERNATUM has a creeping stem from which rise erect flowering branches. In spite of its name the leaves are not generally in threes: there is a cluster of about six at the base of each erect branch. The leaves

PLATE 58

Sedum ternatum   *D. Richards*

Sedum acre   *Rickett*

Penthorum sedoides   *Rickett*

Sedum telephioides   *Elbert*

Saxifraga aizoön   *Voss*

Sedum purpureum   *Elbert*

Sedum glaucophyllum   *Elbert*

Sedum telephium   *Horne*

on the erect branches are variously arranged. The petals are white.

April to June: on damp rocks and moss from New York to Michigan and southward to Georgia and Tennessee; farther north escaped from cultivation. *Plate 58*.

CLIFF STONEWORT, S. GLAUCOPHYLLUM, somewhat resembles *S. ternatum*, but its leaves are whitish (*glauco-*, "glaucous") and arranged spirally around the flowering stem. The petals are white.

May to August: on damp rocks in Virginia and West Virginia. *Plate 58*.

PENTHORUM

Our one species of this genus is described below.

DITCH-STONECROP, P. SEDOIDES, differs from other *Crassulaceae* in not being succulent. The stem grows 2 or 3 feet tall, bearing lanceolate, toothed leaves singly. The flowers generally lack petals; there are five sepals, ten stamens, and five pistils united in their lower parts. The pistils develop into a five-horned pod which opens by the falling off of the horns.

July to October: in moist soil, on river-banks, etc. from Maine to Minnesota and Nebraska and southward to Florida and Texas. *Plate 58*. Because of the union of the pistils and lack of succulence this genus is by some botanists placed in the saxifrage family.

THE SAXIFRAGE FAMILY (SAXIFRAGACEAE)

The saxifrage family is composed of mostly small herbaceous species, many of them with most of their leaves at the base. The flowers of our species, except one, have five sepals and five petals and five or ten stamens. The distinctive feature is the pistil, which is generally composed of two simple pistils joined by their basal parts only, the two styles projecting as two beaks.

Some botanists place hydrangeas, mock orange, currants, and gooseberries in this family. These are all shrubs with which we are not concerned in this book. The following herbaceous genera are here considered to compose the family.

I. *Flowers with five petals and ten stamens:* Astilbe (*leaves divided; flowers very numerous in a branched inflorescence*); Saxifraga (*leaves on flowering stem few and small*); Mitella (*usually one or two leaves on flowering stem; petals pinnately cleft*); Tiarella (*no leaves on flowering stem*).

II. *Flowers with five petals and five stamens:* Heuchera (*usually no leaves on flowering stem; flowers small in a tall, branched inflorescence*); Boykinia (*several stalked leaves on flowering stem, similar to long-stalked basal leaves*); Sullivantia (*one leaf on flowering stem, near base; base of flower cup-shaped with sepals, petals, and stamens on the margin*); Parnassia (*single green-veined flowers on tall stems, usually with a single leaf on the flowering stem*).

III. *Flowers with four or five sepals, no petals, and from four to ten stamens; growing in water:* Chrysosplenium.

ASTILBE

Most of the species of *Astilbe* are Asiatic; several are cultivated. One is a native American.

FALSE GOAT'S-BEARD, A. BITERNATA, closely resembles *Aruncus* in the rose family, which is the "true goat's-beard" (if a plant can be said to wear truly the beard of a goat!). The flowers are very many, very small, white or yellowish, in a large branched raceme on a stem which may be 6 feet tall or taller. Some plants have perfect flowers; those of other plants have no stamens (and often no petals either). The leaves are large, the blade divided into three segments which are again similarly divided (biternate); the ultimate segments variously toothed, lobed, or perhaps again divided.

May to July: in mountain woods from Virginia to Kentucky and southward to Georgia and Tennessee. *Aruncus* has numerous stamens, no pistils in the flowers of some plants, no stamens in the flowers of other plants. There are usually three pistils. *Astilbe* generally has ten stamens, two pistils.

THE SAXIFRAGES (SAXIFRAGA)

The saxifrages are mostly plants of northern regions; many species extend around the world in arctic zones — a pretty and interesting group. They grow often on rock ledges, and the name may be thought to refer to this (from two Latin words meaning "rock" and "break"); but another, authentic derivation is from the reputed power of certain European species to cure "the stone"; such species bear small round tubers on the roots, and the doctrine of signatures (see under *Hepatica*) was applied. The flowers of saxifrages have five sepals, five petals, ten stamens, and two pistils joined at their base and forming two seed pods (follicles) similarly joined. The base of the flower is cuplike and joined to the lower part of the ovary. The leaves are mostly at the base, but some species have also leaves on the flowering stem (besides the bracts of the inflorescence).

I. *Species with leaves on the flowering stem, below the inflorescence.*

S. AIZOON has small leaves on the stem, much larger ones at the base; the stem is up to a foot tall. The basal leaves are rather leathery, narrow but broadest near the tip, toothed on the margins. The flowers are white.

June to September: on rocks throughout Canada and southward to New York, Michigan, and Minnesota; and in Europe and Asia. *Plate 58.*

YELLOW MOUNTAIN SAXIFRAGE, S. AIZOIDES, grows up to 8 inches tall. Branches at the base form loose mats, covered with very narrow, toothless leaves about an inch long. The leaves on the flowering stem are similar. The flowers are yellow, often dotted with red or orange.

June to September: across Canada and southward to New York, Vermont, and Michigan. *Plate 59.*

II. *Species with no leaves on the flowering stem (except the bracts of the inflorescence).*

A. Species with white petals spotted with yellow.

S. CAROLINIANA has a much-branched inflorescence reaching a height of 18 inches or more. The leaves are broad, not more than twice as long as they are broad, sharply toothed, with a definite stalk. A southeastern species.

May and June: on cliffs and slopes in the mountains of Virginia, North Carolina, and Tennessee.

MOUNTAIN-LETTUCE, S. MICRANTHIDIFOLIA, resembles *S. caroliniana* in its widely branched inflorescence, but the basal leaves are much narrower and sometimes a foot long, tapering to the base. It grows to about 3 feet tall.

May and June: on wet rocks and banks from Pennsylvania to West Virginia and southward to Georgia and Tennessee. *Plate 59.*

S. MICHAUXII is similar to *S. micranthidifolia*, but only half as tall. The flowers are not perfectly radially symmetric, having three petals larger than the other two.

June to October: on rock ledges in the woods of Virginia, West Virginia, and Kentucky and southward to Georgia and Tennessee.

B. Species with no leaves on the flowering stem and petals not spotted with yellow.

EARLY SAXIFRAGE, S. VIRGINIENSIS, is the most widespread of our saxifrages. Its stem rises from a basal rosette, about a foot or 18 inches tall. The leaves are ovate or elliptic, toothed. The whole plant is more or less downy. The petals are white (but forms are known with green petals or none).

April to June: on rock ledges and slopes from Quebec to Manitoba and southward to Georgia and Oklahoma. *Plate 59.*

S. PENSYLVANICA has flowering stems sometimes 4 or 5 feet tall. The basal leaves are up to a foot long, lanceolate, toothed, standing more or less erect. The sepals of the flowers are bent sharply downwards. The petals are greenish-yellow, whitish, or even purple.

April to June: in swamps, wet meadows, and bogs from Maine to Ontario and Minnesota and southward to Virginia, Indiana, and Missouri. *Plate 59.* Associated with this species is *S. forbesii*, differing only in certain details, such as in forming two almost separate seed-pods. It is reported from sandstone cliffs in Illinois, Wisconsin, Minnesota, and Missouri. Often considered a form of *S. pensylvanica*.

Besides the species described above, a number of northern species barely enter our northern borders, on the high mountains of Maine and New Hampshire, or northern Michigan or Minnesota. *S. texana* of the Southwest is found in southwestern Missouri.

MITELLA

The plants of the genus *Mitella* are apparently scrawny, unattractive little plants with minute flowers — but a hand magnifier reveals unexpected delights. The white or yellowish petals are deeply cleft pinnately so that the flower resembles a bit of lace. The two halves of the pistil form a two-beaked pod — the bishop's cap or miter. It splits open between the beaks, revealing the black seeds held in a sort of basket.

BISHOP'S-CAP or MITERWORT, M. DIPHYLLA, has a
group of long-stalked leaves at the base, their pointed blades indented at the base and slightly lobed; and a pair (occasionally three) of similar blades with no stalks half-way up the stem. The stem grows up to 18 inches tall. The flowers are scattered in a spike-like

raceme. Each is only ¼ inch across, with white petals.
April to June: in woods from Quebec to Minnesota and southward to South Carolina, Tennessee, and Missouri. *Plate 59.*

M. NUDA is only half as tall as *M. diphylla.* The blades
of the basal leaves are roundish, indented where the long stalk is attached, slightly pointed and lobed. There may be a single, stalkless blade on the stem, or there may be none. The flowers are greenish-yellow. The segments of the petals are longer and curved.
May to August: in cool woods and swamps from Labrador to Mackenzie and southward to Pennsylvania, Michigan, Wisconsin, North Dakota, and Montana. *Plate 59.*

TIARELLA

Only one species of *Tiarella* is at all common in the northeastern states, though a southern species extends north to Virginia and Kentucky. Several others are found in the West. The name means "little tiara," from the odd form of the fruit. A tiara was the headdress of the classical Persians — a kind of turban.

FOAMFLOWER, T. CORDIFOLIA, is a delicate plant
rarely more than a foot tall. From the under-

ground stem (rhizome) at the base of the flowering stem spring long-stalked leaves with ovate blades deeply indented at the base. The two halves of the pistil are curiously different in size, and the resulting fruit has a large lobe and a small one. The flowers are about ⅔ inch across, with narrow white petals.
April to July: in moist woods from Nova Scotia to Michigan and southward to Georgia and Alabama. *Plate 60.*

THE ALUMROOTS (HEUCHERA)

The alumroots have long-stalked, round-bladed leaves growing from an underground stem (rhizome) and, from the same point, a tall flowering stem bearing many small flowers. The flowering stem is generally leafless but may bear a few small leaves. The flowers have five sepals, five petals, five stamens, a pistil with two styles. The fruit is a two-beaked pod, opening between the beaks.
The familiar garden flower called coral-bells is a southwestern species of *Heuchera.*
The English name of the genus refers to the astringent quality of the rhizome (rather than the root).
Our native species are not easy to distinguish. Such characteristics as hairiness or smoothness are unreliable; the species vary in this respect, and also hybridize, forming groups intermediate in character. The small flowers are our best guide, and the distinguishing features mentioned below must be studied with the hand magnifier.
We first form two groups by the general form of

the flower. In some species it is radial in symmetry, the same on all sides. In others the upper side of the flower is longer than the lower, so that the symmetry is bilateral (see the drawings).

I.   *Species with radially symmetric flowers (all sides the
same length or very nearly so). The stamens in this group project noticeably beyond the perianth.*

A. Among the species of group I the following
have long hairs on the outside of the flower. The petals are much longer than the sepals.

H. VILLOSA is distinguished by its leaf-blades, which
are typically deeply lobed, with sharp pointed lobes. The leaf-stalks are often (not always) clothed with reddish hairs (they are "villous"). The flowers, when they open, are about ⅛ inch long at most. The petals are white or pink, twice as long as the sepals.

PLATE 59

Saxifraga aizoides *Scribner*

Saxifraga virginiensis *Rickett*

Mitella nuda *Rhein*

Mitella diphylla *Johnson*

Mitella diphylla *Rickett*

Saxifraga micranthidifolia *Elbert*

Saxifraga pensylvanica *Scribner*

Mitella diphylla *Rickett*

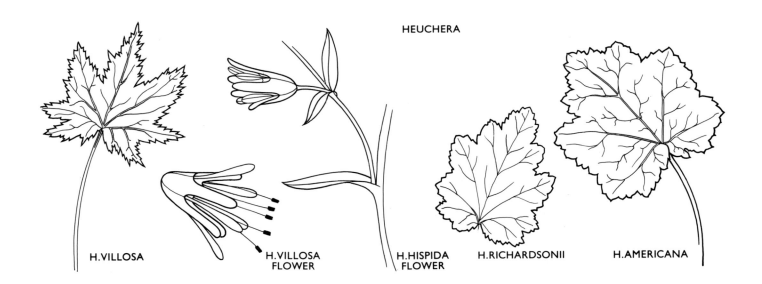

HEUCHERA

H.VILLOSA   H.VILLOSA FLOWER   H.HISPIDA FLOWER   H.RICHARDSONII   H.AMERICANA

June to August: on wooded slopes and rock ledges from Virginia to Missouri and southward to Georgia, Alabama, and Arkansas. *Plate 60.*

H. PARVIFLORA has leaf-blades shallowly lobed with round lobes, the lobes notched and the part between notches bearing a very small point. Leaf-stalks, lower surface of leaf-blades, and stem may all bear white hairs. The flowers are much like those of *H. villosa*, perhaps a bit smaller.

July to September: on moist shady ledges from Virginia to Missouri and southward to North Carolina, Alabama, and Arkansas. Some plants found from Kentucky to Missouri and Arkansas differ in having minute glands instead of hairs; they have been named *H. puberula*, but are perhaps only a variety of *H. parviflora. Parviflora* means "with small flowers."

   B. The remaining species with radially symmetric flowers (group I) have flowers not covered with hairs on the outside (they may bear a few hairs). The petals are about the same length as the sepals or slightly longer.

H. AMERICANA is our most widespread species, and like many species that range over a wide territory, it varies greatly. The leaf-blades are lobed with broad, sometimes almost triangular lobes, and toothed with broad, rounded teeth. The leaf-stalks and stem are mostly smooth; there may or may not be hairs on the under surface of the blades. The flowers are about $\frac{1}{4}$ inch in length when they open. (They may be very slightly oblique in profile, as in group II.) The petals

are generally reddish. The inflorescence is tall and nearly cylindric.

April to June: in woods and on shaded rocks from Connecticut to Ontario and Michigan and southward to Georgia, Alabama, and Arkansas.

H. hispida, a species of the mountains of Virginia and West Virginia, is distinguished by the hairy upper surface of the leaf-blades. The flowers are somewhat larger, and slightly oblique as in group II.

II.   *Species with bilaterally symmetric flowers, with oblique profile as seen from the side, the upper side longer than the lower. The petals are as long as the sepals or slightly longer, and the stamens also of about the same length.*

H. RICHARDSONII has leaves lobed with broad, round lobes, generally sharply toothed. The stem and leaf-stalks bear shaggy white hairs, often dense, rarely sparse; and similar hairs adorn the veins on the lower surface of the blades. The flowers are in a tall cylindric inflorescence. They are among the largest in the genus — up to $\frac{2}{5}$ inch when they open. The petals are greenish.

May to July: on prairies and in dry, rocky woods from Michigan to Alberta and southward to Indiana, Missouri, South Dakota, and Colorado. *Plate 60.* Named for Sir John Richardson who explored North America in the nineteenth century.

The very variable group that has been named *H. hirsuticaulis* is perhaps the result of natural hybridization between *H. richardsonii* and *H. americana.* Characteristics intermediate between these species in various degrees are seen in the plants, and the very variability suggests a hybrid origin. The flowers may be radially or bilaterally symmetric. *Hirsuticaulis* means "with hirsute [stiff-hairy] stem."

PLATE 60

Parnassia glauca   *Johnson*

Parnassia palustris   *Johnson*

Heuchera villosa   *Uttal*

Tiarella cordifolia   *Johnson*

Parnassia glauca   *Gottscho*

Heuchera richardsonii   *Johnson*

Sullivantia sullivantii   *D. Richards*

H. PUBESCENS has minutely downy leaf-stalks, leaf-
blades, and stems. The leaf-blades are rather
deeply lobed. The flowers are in a conical inflorescence
(wider at the base, tapering to the tip). They are nearly
as large as those of *H. richardsonii*. The petals are
slightly longer than the sepals.

May to August: in woods from Pennsylvania to
Kentucky and southward to North Carolina. *H. longi-
flora* resembles *H. pubescens*. The flowers are a bit
smaller, the petals yellowish, about the same length as
the sepals. This is a species of upland woods in West
Virginia and Kentucky and southward to Alabama.

BOYKINIA

The other species of *Boykinia* are in the southern
and western states. Only one is found in the northeastern region, and that along its southern borders.

BROOK-SAXIFRAGE, B. ACONITIFOLIA, has a stem up
to 2 feet tall bearing a few stalked leaves singly.
These leaves and the long-stalked basal leaves have
round blades deeply lobed and sharply toothed. The
flowers are small and white. The plants are much like
a saxifrage except for the number of stamens, which
are as many as the petals.

June and July: along streams and in wet woods
from Virginia to Kentucky and southward to Georgia
and Alabama.

SULLIVANTIA

The two species of *Sullivantia* that grow in the
northeastern states are low plants often lying on the
ground, with a tuft of stalked, round-bladed basal
leaves and an almost leafless flowering stem. The flowers have a cup-shaped base, on the rim of which stand
the sepals, petals, and stamens. The flowers are small,
white. The fruit is a two-beaked pod, splitting open
between the beaks. The differences between our two
species are very small.

S. RENIFOLIA is our more widespread species. The
leaves are lobed, the sides of the lobes nearly
parallel. The sepals are short and blunt.

June to August: on wet cliffs from Wisconsin to
Minnesota and Iowa and southward to Illinois and
Missouri.

S. SULLIVANTII grows to the southeast of *S. renifolia*.
It differs in the shape of the leaf-lobes, which are
rounded; and in the longer, sharper sepals.

June to August: on wet cliffs from Ohio to Indiana and southward to Kentucky. *Plate 60*. The somewhat redundant name commemorates William Star-
ling Sullivant, an accomplished amateur botanist of
Cleveland, Ohio, best known for his studies of mosses
during the nineteenth century.

GRASS-OF-PARNASSUS (PARNASSIA)

The species of *Parnassia* are not only not grasses,
they bear no resemblance to grasses. The name de-
rives from the first century, having then been given to
a plant of Mount Parnassus now thought to belong to
this genus. The leaves have unbranched veins extending from the base of the blade to the apex. There is a
tuft of leaves at the base, and a flowering stem, mostly
a foot tall or taller, which may bear one leaf or none
and a single flower. The petals are white, $\frac{1}{2}$ inch long
or longer, with green or yellowish veins. Besides the
five stamens, five bodies are present as substitutes for a
second circle of stamens. They are generally cleft and
bear glands, adding greatly to the interest and beauty
of the flower.

P. GLAUCA has ovate leaf-blades. There is usually one
stalkless blade on the stem, about half-way up
or lower. The stamen-substitutes are cleft into three
prongs.

July to October: in wet meadows, bogs, etc. from
Newfoundland to Saskatchewan and southward to
New Jersey, Ohio, Iowa, and South Dakota. *Plate 60*.

P. PALUSTRIS has leaves with round blades indented
at the base. The single leaf on the flowering stem
envelops the stem between its two basal lobes. The
stamen-substitutes in the flower are cleft into many
slender hairlike parts.

July and August: in wet soils from Labrador to
Alaska and southward to New York, Michigan, Minnesota, North Dakota, and Oregon; also in Europe
and Asia. *Plate 60*.

Besides these two species, several others enter our southern
states: *P. asarifolia*, with leaf-blades broader than they are long; *P.
grandifolia*, with three-pronged stamen-substitutes longer than the
true stamens, and petals nearly an inch long; *P. parviflora*, with petals
not $\frac{1}{2}$ inch long and stamen-substitutes cleft into from five to seven
narrow parts.

PLATE 61

Chrysosplenium americanum   *Rickett*

Chrysosplenium americanum   *Rickett*

Schrankia nuttallii   *Rickett*

Cassia hebecarpa   *Horne*

Cassia marilandica   *Taylor*

Cassia fasciculata   *Johnson*

THE GOLDEN-SAXIFRAGES (CHRYSOSPLENIUM)

The golden saxifrages have four or five green or yellowish sepals, no petals, and from four to ten very short stamens. They are plants of wet places, with creeping stems and small round leaves. The botanical name, referring to the spleen, probably alludes to some reputed medicinal uses.

WATER-MAT, C. AMERICANUM, grows in running brooks or springs or on wet mud. The creeping stem sends up erect branches with a single flower at the tip of each. The leaves are mostly in pairs.

March to June: in springs, brooks, and wet places from Quebec to Saskatchewan and southward to Georgia, Ohio, Indiana, and Iowa. *Plate 61*.

C. IOWENSE is an Arctic species which has been found in Iowa. It bears its leaves singly. Their blades are broader than they are long. The flowers have yellowish sepals.

THE FLAX FAMILY (LINACEAE)

We are concerned here with only one genus in this family, the flax genus.

FLAX (LINUM)

Flax has been cultivated since before history began for the fibers in its stems and the oil in its seeds. The botanical name reflects this antiquity, being the classical Latin name for the fiber; almost the same name existed in Greek and in Old Teutonic. We see it in the words line (still used in parts of England for the fiber), linen, linseed, and even lingerie. With this plant, which is often seen in this country growing wild, are associated a number of native species, with no English names unless we call them all wild flax. They are all slender plants (often with a single unbranched stem), with small, narrow leaves. The flowers have five sepals, five petals, five stamens, and a pistil with five styles. The petals may be blue, white, or yellow (or red in a cultivated species). The fruit is a roundish capsule.

I.   *Species with blue flowers.*

FLAX, L. USITATISSIMUM, sends its single stem up to 3 feet tall. The leaves are narrowly lanceolate, with three veins lengthwise. The petals are about $\frac{1}{2}$ inch long.

June to September: escaped from cultivation in waste places, fields, etc. throughout. *Plate 62*.

L. LEWISII is a western plant, named for Meriwether Lewis, who, with William Clark, led a famous expedition across North America. It has usually several stems from the same crown, and the leaves are less evidently three-veined. It is a plant of the western prairies and banks, reaching eastward into our range in Minnesota and Wisconsin. It may be the same as the European *L. perenne*.

II.   *Species with yellow petals.*

L. VIRGINIANUM grows up to 3 feet tall, with a spreading inflorescence of thin, wiry flower-stems. The yellow petals are about $\frac{1}{2}$ inch long, the sepals about $\frac{1}{8}$ inch.

June to August: in dry, open woods from Maine to Ontario and Iowa and southward to Georgia and Alabama.

L. RIGIDUM is seen along our western borders. It is stiff, bushy, with angled branches bearing very narrow leaves. The flowers are relatively large, the petals about $\frac{1}{2}$ inch long.

June and July: in dry soil from Minnesota to Alberta and southward to Missouri, Texas, and Mexico. *Plate 62*.

L. STRIATUM, up to 3 feet tall, is distinguished by the narrow flanges ("wings") which extend down the stem from the base of each leaf. The yellow petals are about $\frac{1}{4}$ inch long, the sepals about $\frac{1}{16}$ inch.

June to August: in damp woods, swamps, and bogs from Massachusetts to Ontario, Michigan, and Missouri and southward to Florida and Texas.

L. MEDIUM is rarely more than 2 feet tall and often shorter, with a single main stem topped by a stiff, branching inflorescence. The leaves are very narrow, less than an inch long, with no visible veins. The yellow petals may be $\frac{1}{3}$ inch long, or less.

June to August: in dry woodlands from Maine to Missouri and southward to Florida and Texas.

PLATE 62

Linum usitatissimum *Rickett*

Passiflora incarnata *Johnson*

Oxalis violacea *Johnson*

Passiflora lutea *D. Richards*

Oxalis stricta *Johnson*

Linum rigidum *Johnson*

L. SULCATUM reaches 30 inches in height. It may be
distinguished from the preceding species by careful examination of the sepals, which will reveal a fringe of glandular hairs or teeth on all their margins. The stem is grooved (sulcate) lengthwise.

June to September: in dry prairies and sandy places from Michigan to Manitoba and southward to Georgia, Alabama, and Texas; also rarely in New England.

L. INTERCURSUM is distinguished from *L. medium*
only by certain characteristics of the fruit. This, the capsule, is narrower (the width less than half the length), and splits into sharp-pointed segments.

June to August: in sandy soil or peaty barrens on the coastal plain from Massachusetts to Georgia and Alabama; inland in Indiana.

THE PASSION-FLOWER FAMILY (PASSIFLORACEAE)

In this mainly tropical family only one genus inhabits the northeastern United States.

PASSION-FLOWERS (PASSIFLORA)

The names – English and Latin – come from the extraordinary flower, which made a great impression upon the early explorers of America. There are five sepals and five petals, much alike in color, seated upon the cup-shaped base of the flower. Just within this perianth rise two or three circles of narrow objects, making a very decorative fringe. The explorers, among whom were priests, saw in this the crown of thorns of the crucifixion. (Even today, botanists call this the crown or *corona*.) Within this is a complex apparatus consisting of a stalked pistil whose three styles, ending in knob-like stigmas, project sideways from the summit; they suggested the nails. The five stamens, joined around the pistil, were taken to represent the five wounds. And the ten parts of the perianth were the apostles, Peter and Judas being excluded.

The plants are vines, with palmately three-lobed or three-cleft leaves borne singly, and climb by coiling tendrils. The tendrils were, of course, the scourges.

The fruit is a round berry.

MAYPOPS, P. INCARNATA, may climb or trail with a
stem up to 25 feet long. The leaves are cleft into three lobes which taper to sharp points. The perianth is white, about 2 inches across. The fringe, the outer part nearly an inch long, is purple and pink. The yellow berry, about 2 inches thick, is edible.

June to September: in thickets, along hedges, and trailing on open ground from Maryland to Missouri and Oklahoma and southward to Florida and Texas. *Plate 62*.

P. LUTEA is smaller, the stem up to 10 feet long. The
leaves are three-lobed, the lobes with blunt ends. The perianth is greenish-yellow, about an inch across; the outer part of the fringe is yellow. The fruit, about $\frac{2}{5}$ inch across, is purple.

June to September: in thickets and edges of woods from Pennsylvania to Kansas and southward to Florida and Texas. *Plate 62*.

THE WOOD-SORREL FAMILY (OXALIDACEAE)

In some ways the wood-sorrel family resembles the geranium family: particularly in having its parts in fives. It differs in having five distinct styles on the ovary. In our species, which all belong to the genus *Oxalis*, the leaf-blades are divided palmately into three segments, each notched, heart-shaped.

THE WOOD-SORRELS (OXALIS)

All our species of *Oxalis* are small plants with yellow, white, purple, or violet flowers. They are easily recognized by the leaf-blades mentioned above. They have ten stamens. The narrow seed-pods often split open explosively, scattering the seeds.

The name *Oxalis* is derived from a Greek word

for "sharp," referring to the sharp taste of the leaves. "Sorrel" is connected with "sour" and has the same connotation. The botanical name has given a word to chemistry: *oxalic* acid. This is the substance responsible for the sour taste of the foliage. It is poisonous in any large quantity, but the leaves of the European *O. acetosella* have always been eaten in salads and soups, and the species has even been cultivated for the purpose.

I. *Species with white, violet, or purple flowers.*

COMMON WOOD-SORREL, O. MONTANA, is a plant of northern forests and mountains. The flowers are borne singly on stalks about 6 inches long. The petals are white veined with pink or purple, or entirely pink or purple; they are notched, often quite deeply.

May to August: in damp woods from Quebec to Saskatchewan and southward in the mountains to North Carolina and Tennessee. *Plate 177.* This is the American counterpart of the European *O. acetosella*, and has often gone by that name.

VIOLET WOOD-SORREL, O. VIOLACEA, has leaves colored on the under surface; a breath of wind across a field of these plants turns it suddenly from green to crimson or violet. There are several flowers to a stem, the petals purple or violet.

April to July: in open woods and prairies and fields from Massachusetts to Minnesota and Colorado and southward to Florida and Texas. *Plate 62.*

II. *Species with yellow flowers.*

O. GRANDIS is the largest of these, with stems up to 4 feet tall and leaves often 2 inches broad. The flowers are borne in clusters which may stand just above the leaves. The flowers are from $\frac{1}{2}$ to $\frac{3}{4}$ inch across.

June to September: in woods from Pennsylvania to Illinois and southward to Georgia and Alabama.

YELLOW WOOD-SORREL, O. DILLENII, has leaning stems up to 2 feet long. There are usually not more than three flowers on a stem. In fruit the stalks that bear the pods are bent down, the pods standing erect.

May to October: in dry soil throughout the United States.

YELLOW WOOD-SORREL, O. STRICTA, is an extremely variable species difficult to characterize. There are usually more than five and less than ten flowers in each cluster. The flower-stalks are not bent down in fruiting but extend outwards and upwards.

May to October: the most abundant and variable species, in fields, lawns, waste places, etc. from Quebec to North Dakota and Colorado and southward to Georgia, Oklahoma, and Arizona. *Plate 62.*

CREEPING LADY'S-SORREL, O. REPENS, has a creeping (*repens*) stem, rooting at the nodes. The flowers are only $\frac{1}{4}$ inch across or slightly more. The flower-stalks are bent down in fruiting like those of *O. dillenii*.

April to November: in waste places, gardens, greenhouses, etc. practically throughout the country; a southern species, also European and Asian. *O. recurva*, another southern species, is found in Kentucky. The petals are more than $\frac{1}{2}$ inch long. The seed-pod is hairy.

THE GINSENG FAMILY (ARALIACEAE)

The herbaceous plants of the ginseng family resemble those of the parsley family in having flowers in umbels and in having divided leaves. But the leaf-stalks do not sheathe the stem, and the fruit is a berry or berry-like stone-fruit. There are five petals, five stamens, and an inferior ovary from which rise two or more styles. As in many genera of the parsley family, there are no distinct sepals, merely a sort of rim for a calyx.

ARALIA

The genus *Aralia* is characterized by large leaves divided into three segments and these again mostly pinnately divided, each leaf giving the impression of a leafy branch. The small white or greenish flowers are in many umbels, a number of which are grouped in a complex inflorescence.

WILD SARSAPARILLA, A. NUDICAULIS, has a single leaf and flowering stem growing from a rhizome. The much-divided leaf is from 8 to 16 inches tall. The flowering stem, which has no leaves (it is "nude"), is not so tall. It bears from two to seven umbels. There are usually five styles, which are still present on the young fruits. The berries are nearly black. The roots are aromatic, yielding a substitute for sarsaparilla.

May to July: in woods from Newfoundland to British Columbia and southward to Georgia (in the mountains), Tennessee, Missouri, Colorado, and Idaho. *Plate 63.*

AMERICAN SPIKENARD, A. RACEMOSA, has a branching stem from 2 to 10 feet tall, bearing several leaves. The leaf-segments are heart-shaped (indented at the base) and taper to sharp points. The umbels are numerous, arranged in clusters along a central stem. The fruits are purple.

June to August: in woods and thickets from Quebec to Manitoba and southward to Georgia and northern Mexico. *Plate 63.* The roots are aromatic. Spike-

nard or nard is an ointment prepared from a tropical Indian plant; and the name is given to the plant itself. Why the name is applied to two very dissimilar American plants I do not know.

BRISTLY SARSAPARILLA, A. HISPIDA, is easily distinguished by the bristles, at least on the lower part of the stem (which is "hispid"). The stem bears several leaves, like that of *A. racemosa*, but the leaf-segments are not indented at the base, nor do they taper to the tip; they are ovate. The umbels are less numerous.

June to August: in dry woods, especially in rocky or sandy places, from Newfoundland to Manitoba and southward to New Jersey, North Carolina, Ohio, Illinois, and Minnesota. *Plate 63.*

THE GINSENGS (PANAX)

The ginsengs are easily distinguished from the species of *Aralia* by the disposition of their leaves, which are in one circle, usually of three, on the stem. Each leaf is palmately divided into from three to seven segments. The white or greenish flowers are in a single simple umbel at the summit of the stem. There are two or three styles.

GINSENG, P. QUINQUEFOLIUS, has long been known to the Chinese as extremely valuable in their medicine (not, apparently, in ours); and since they pay high prices for the root-tuber, the plants have been much sought and the species has become rare. It is known by its usually five leaf-segments, which are

stalked. It stands from 8 inches to 2 feet tall. There are usually two styles. The berry is red.

June and July: in deep, cool woods from Quebec to Manitoba and southward to Florida, Louisiana, and Oklahoma. *Plate 63.*

DWARF GINSENG or GROUND-NUT, P. TRIFOLIUS, is not more than 8 inches tall. The leaves, near the top of the stem, are divided into three or five segments, these being without stalks. There are usually three styles. The berry is yellow.

April to June: in moist woods and openings from Quebec to Minnesota and southward to Georgia (in the mountains), Indiana, and Nebraska. *Plate 63.*

THE PARSLEY FAMILY (UMBELLIFERAE)

The *Umbelliferae* have their name from their characteristic inflorescence, which is an umbel (*umbella*, "umbrella"). In an umbel the flowers are on stalks (called rays) that radiate from the tip of a stem as the ribs of an umbrella radiate from the end of the stick. The umbels of the parsley family are mostly compound; that is, the rays bear not single flowers but smaller umbels. In many species of *Umbelliferae*, as in many other families, the stalks of the flowers are associated with the special leaves called bracts, here much smaller than the foliage leaves; since the stalks radiate from one point, their bracts are in a circle just below them. This is what the botanist terms an involucre; it is sometimes useful in identifying

these plants. The smaller umbels at the ends of the main rays may in turn have smaller involucres.

The flowers of *Umbelliferae* are small, individually not conspicuous, but often very numerous. There may be five sepals; but these may be minute or even lacking.* There are five petals and five stamens. The pistil has an inferior ovary embedded in the stem below the sepals, and two styles rising in the center of the flower. Each style has a sort of bulb at its base which may be mistaken for an ovary.

---

*To be absolutely consistent, the botanist should then call the rest of the perianth, what we generally call petals, sepals; but this would be confusing within a family. Botanists are not always consistent any more than plants are.

PLATE 63

Panax trifolius   *Horne*

Aralia hispida   *Johnson*

Panax quinquefolius   *Gottscho*

Aralia racemosa   *Rickett*

Aralia nudicaulis   *Johnson*

The fruit is a small dry thing in two halves attached to a central stalk. Each half bears lengthwise ribs or the projecting flanges called wings. These small objects are often useful in identification, since characteristics of the flowers do not vary greatly, and leaves are often too complex for non-technical description. It is suggested that the reader consult the drawings of the fruit to be sure of what he has.

The leaves are generally divided and the divisions are often again divided until a feathery effect results. One characteristic that identifies the family is the sheath at the base of the leaf-stalks which embraces the stem where the leaf is attached.

It is important to be able to recognize the family, for, although many species are used as vegetables or as condiments, some others are highly poisonous. There are many records of deaths, especially of children, from chewing the leaves of one common umbellifer; and another species has actually been used in the execution of criminals. Among the economically valuable species are parsley, celery, carrot, parsnip, dill, caraway, and fennel.

More than fifty genera are known in the northeastern United States, ranging from tiny aquatics a few inches tall to plants with enormous leaves and standing 8 feet. Many of the species are weedy and lack attractive flowers; these are given scant attention in the following pages.

I.   *A few genera have yellow flowers.*

A. Two of these have leaves that lack teeth on the margins of all their segments: *Taenidia* and *Pseudotaenidia* (distinguished by their fruits).

B. The remaining yellow-flowered species have toothed leaves: *Thaspium* (leaves divided into three, the divisions again into three); *Zizia* (like *Thaspium* but one flower in the center of each cluster without a stalk: and see drawings of fruits); *Polytaenia* (leaves divided pinnately into narrow segments); *Pastinaca* (leaves divided pinnately into large, coarsely toothed segments).

II. *The remaining genera in our range have white or sometimes pink or purplish flowers.* These may be conveniently separated into four groups by the characteristics of their leaves.*

A. Four genera have undivided, unlobed leaves: *Eryngium* (flowers in close masses, not in umbels; leaves long and narrow); *Hydrocotyle* (tiny plants growing in water; umbels of some in several storeys, or minute flowers in clusters in axils of leaves; leaf-blades round); *Centella* (tiny plants of wet places; only two to five flowers in an umbel, close to the ground; leaf-blades ovate); *Lilaeopsis* (small plants of wet places: leaves rodlike with no blades).

B. Three genera have leaves palmately divided, mostly into three segments: *Sanicula* (stalked flowers have stamens only; flowers without stalks or with shorter stalks have pistils; involucre quite conspicuous); *Cryptotaenia* (involucre small or lacking); *Heracleum* (very tall plant; sheathing part of leaf-stalk very broad; segments of leaf-blade stalked; outer petals of umbel forked). (See also *Osmorhiza*.)

C. Three genera have leaves pinnately divided, *the segments not themselves divided* (they may be toothed or lobed): *Sium* (a small involucre present); *Berula* (involucre fairly large; segments of leaves often lobed); *Oxypolis* (practically no involucre).

D. The remaining genera of white-flowered plants have leaves divided and the segments again divided or deeply cleft (in this group especially fruits are necessary for identification; see the drawings); *Osmorhiza* (the lower parts when crushed emit the odor of licorice; plants softly hairy); *Daucus* (involucre composed of bracts divided pinnately into narrow segments); *Erigenia* (red-brown heads on stamens; leaves not expanded at flowering time); *Scandix* (leaves cut into very numerous, very narrow divisions; only from one to three main rays in an umbel); *Ptilimnium* (leaves cut into numerous hairlike divisions; involucre present, of hairlike parts); *Spermolepis* (leaves cut into numerous hairlike parts; no involucre); *Angelica* (upper leaf-stalks all sheath; tall plants; no involucre); *Conium* (numerous leaf-segments with blunt teeth; involucre present; fruit flat with prominent ribs); *Conioselinum* (numerous leaf-segments; no involucre); *Cicuta* (segments of leaves long, narrow, mostly sharply toothed, rather widely separated; growing in wet places); *Chaerophyllum* (numerous leaf-segments; fruit long and narrow); *Torilis* (fewer leaf-segments, with sharp teeth).

**A species of *Thaspium* has a variety with purple flowers; see above, under I.*

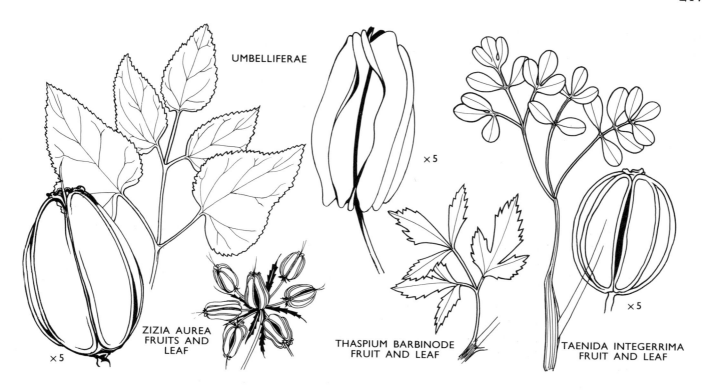

UMBELLIFERAE

ZIZIA AUREA
FRUITS AND
LEAF

×5

THASPIUM BARBINODE
FRUIT AND LEAF

×5

×5

TAENIDA INTEGERRIMA
FRUIT AND LEAF

TAENIDIA

The genus contains but one species.

YELLOW PIMPERNEL, T. INTEGERRIMA, is easily recognized by the lack of teeth around the margins of the leaf-segments. It is a graceful plant usually between 2 and 3 feet tall. The flowers are in an open umbel, with no bracts. The petals are yellow. The fruit bears four narrow lengthwise ribs on each side.

May to July: in dry, open woodlands, and on rocky hillsides from Quebec to Minnesota and southward to Georgia and Texas. The botanical name refers to the narrow ribs on the fruit.

PSEUDOTAENIDIA

The name, of course, means "false Taenidia." It somewhat resembles that genus, though it is not really closely related. There is only one species.

FALSE YELLOW PIMPERNEL, P. MONTANA, is commonly 2 or 3 feet tall. The leaves are divided into three, and the long-stalked segments again into three, and these again similarly divided into the ultimate segments, which are small elliptic blades without teeth. There are no bracts around the umbels. The fruit immediately distinguishes this genus from *Taenidia*, for it is flat and the edges pass into thin "wings," two on each edge. Without the fruit the two genera can scarcely be distinguished.

April to July: on rocky slopes from Maryland to Pennsylvania, Virginia, and West Virginia.

THE MEADOW-PARSNIPS (THASPIUM)

The species of *Thaspium* have leaves divided with three or five; the leaves at the base have undivided blades in some species. All the segments and the undivided blades have toothed edges. The petals are yellow, or brown-purple in a form of one species. It is important to notice that all the flowers (and fruits) are stalked; this at once distinguishes *Thaspium* from *Zizia*, which otherwise resembles it closely. The fruit of *Thaspium* also is distinctive, having the thin blades known as wings in place of ribs.

T. TRIFOLIATUM is a widespread species. The basal leaves have ovate blades, usually indented at the base, on long stalks. The leaves on the stem are divided. There are two varieties, one with yellow flowers, the other with brown-purple flowers. The yellow-flowered variety is the only one in most of the Midwest; it is often mistaken for golden Alexanders, *Zizia aptera*.

May to July: in woodlands from Rhode Island to Minnesota and South Dakota and southward to Florida, Louisiana, and Oklahoma. *Plate 64*.

T. BARBINODE is named for the tufts of white hairs ("beards," *barbi-*) at each node. The stem grows up to 4 feet tall. The basal leaves are divided. The flowers are pale yellow, almost cream-colored.

April to June: in woodlands from New York and Ontario to Minnesota and southward to Florida and Oklahoma. *T. pinnatifidum*, with leaf-segments cleft into many narrow lobes, is known from Kentucky.

ZIZIA

The plants in this genus closely resemble those of *Thaspium*, having leaves on the stem divided and re-divided by threes, and the basal leaves either divided or not. The flowers are yellow, in umbels which lack bracts. In fact one species, *Z. aptera*, is more like *Thaspium trifoliatum* than is any other species of *Thaspium*. There are two points of difference, easily seen with a hand magnifier. In *Zizia* the central flower of each cluster is without a stalk. And the fruits of *Zizia* have ribs but no "wings." All the species of *Zizia* are commonly 2 or 3 feet tall.

GOLDEN ALEXANDERS, Z. AUREA, has basal leaves divided like those on the stem. The rays of the umbel are mostly of the same length, and there may be up to twenty of them.

April to June: in meadows and damp woods and on roadsides from Quebec to Saskatchewan and southward to Florida and Texas. *Plate 64*. This is the common golden Alexanders of the Atlantic states.

The English name belongs properly to an European plant associated with Alexandria.

Z. TRIFOLIATA has basal leaves divided like those on the stem. It may be distinguished from *Z. aurea* by the teeth on the leaf-segments, which are large. The rays of the umbel are of several lengths, and generally not more than ten.

May and June: in woods mostly in the mountains from Virginia to Kentucky and southward to Georgia and Tennessee.

Z. APTERA is the species that has basal leaves with undivided blades on long stalks; the blades are ovate, usually indented at the base, rather bluntly toothed at the edge.

April to June: in fields, prairies, woods from Quebec to British Columbia and southward to Georgia, Missouri, Utah, and Oregon. This is the common *Zizia* in the Midwest.

POLYTAENIA

Only one species of this western genus reaches the northeastern states. (Another inhabits Texas.)

PRAIRIE-PARSLEY, P. NUTTALLII, has leaves pinnately divided into segments of which some are again divided or deeply cleft, the ultimate small blades being wider at the tip than farther down. The stem may be

3 feet tall. The flowers are yellow, in umbels without bracts. The fruit is flat with thick, corky wings at each side.

April to June: in prairies and open woodlands from Michigan to North Dakota and southward to Alabama and Texas.

PASTINACA

Only one species of the genus occurs in the United States.

PARSNIP, P. SATIVA, was early brought from Europe and cultivated in this country, and has escaped to become a common weed. It grows up to 5 or 6 feet tall. The leaves are pinnately divided into coarsely toothed and lobed segments. The flowers are yellow, in large

umbels usually without bracts. The fruit is flat, with the margins extended into thin "wings."

May to October: a weed in waste places, on roadsides, and in fields throughout the United States. *Plate 64*. *Pastinare* in Latin means "to dig"; a parsnip is something dug. The English name is derived from the Latin by way of Old French.

PLATE 64

Thaspium trifoliatum   *Elbert*

Zizia aurea   *Scribner*

Hydrocotyle americana   *Rickett*

Thaspium trifoliatum   *Elbert*   Hydrocotyle umbellata   *Uttal*

Eryngium aquaticum   *Allen*

Pastinaca sativa   *Rhein*   Eryngium yuccifolium   *D. Richards*

ERYNGOES (ERYNGIUM)

The genus *Eryngium* differs from other umbellifers in having its flowers in dense heads instead of umbels; that is, the flowers have practically no individual stalks. In spite of this, they are placed in the family *Umbelliferae* because of their flowers, which are on the umbelliferous plan. The petals are white or blue. The plants mostly have stiff, narrow leaves, saw-toothed or pinnately lobed or prickly.

The prickly European sea-holly, *E. maritimum*, is mentioned in Shakespeare's *Merry Wives of Windsor*. Candied roots of these plants were supposed to have several virtues and were grown in the garden.

RATTLESNAKE-MASTER or BUTTON-SNAKEROOT, E. YUCCIFOLIUM, grows from 2 to 6 feet tall or more, with stiff, narrow leaves (the lower ones often 3

feet long) which have prickles along the margin. The veins run lengthwise, unbranched.

July and August: on prairies and in open woodlands from New Jersey to Minnesota and southward to Florida and Texas. *Plate 64.* The English names refer to a supposed ability to cure snake-bite, or perhaps to drive away rattlesnakes. The names are shared by other plants, notably the equally stiff, narrow-leaved blazing-stars of the *Compositae;* there seems to be no justification for any such mastery.

E. AQUATICUM is found in marshes, ponds, and bogs from New Jersey to Florida. It is easily distinguished by its leaves, which have narrowly elliptic blades on definite stalks, and many veins running from the single central vein to the margin. *Plate 64.*

WATER-PENNYWORTS (HYDROCOTYLE)

The flowers of *Hydrocotyle* are minute, scarcely qualifying, to many persons, as wild flowers. But the round leaf-blades are odd enough to attract attention; they are the "pennies," on stalks which often rise from water. The genus is therefore worthy of passing mention. The plants grow mostly in mud or in shallow water. The petals are white or greenish.

H. UMBELLATA, as its name suggests, has flowers in a definite umbel. *Plate 64. H. verticillata* has an inflorescence of several storeys. Both these species have leaf-blades attached in the middle to the stalks which run from creeping stems to a height of about 6 inches. Both are widespread in North America, flowering in summer.

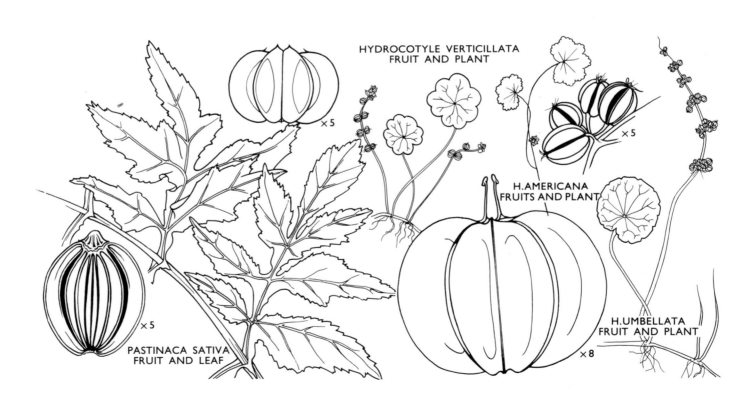

H. AMERICANA has tiny flowers, with almost no stalks, clustered in the axils of its leaves. *Plate 64.* The similar European species, *H. vulgaris*, was thought by old writers to have no flowers. It was believed to cause the disease of the liver in sheep which is really due to the liver fluke.

Other species have leaf-blades attached to the stalks at a deep indentation which extends to the center. Two of these, *H. sibthorpioides* and *H. ranunculoides*, are found from Pennsylvania southward. The former has leaves less than $\frac{1}{2}$ inch across. In the latter species they are more than 2 inches.

CENTELLA

Our only species is *C. erecta*, a small plant with ovate leaf-blades indented at the base on stalks 2 to 12 inches tall. The umbels grow from the creeping stem at the same point as the leaves, each on a stalk only 4 inches tall at most. Plants are found in marshes and other wet places from Delaware southward.

LILAEOPSIS

Only one species of *Lilaeopsis* forms a part of the northeastern flora (a second just reaches southeastern Virginia from the south).

L. CHINENSIS is among the most curious of flowering plants, having no real leaves, only leaf-stalks. These are hollow cylinders with cross partitions at intervals, only 1 or 2 inches long or a little longer. The umbels are carried to about the same height, and bear a few minute flowers.

June to September: in mud along the coast from Nova Scotia to Florida and Mississippi. Linnaeus named this under the impression it grew in China. (Compare *Asclepias syriaca*.)

THE SANICLES OR BLACK SNAKEROOTS (SANICULA)

The species of *Sanicula* have leaves that distinguish them from most other umbellifers, being palmately divided into three or five more or less elliptic, sharply toothed segments. The flowers are inconspicuous, greenish, in umbels whose main stems (rays) are of different lengths. Some flowers are staminate only, some perfect (with both stamens and pistil); the staminate flowers generally have longer stalks. The fruit

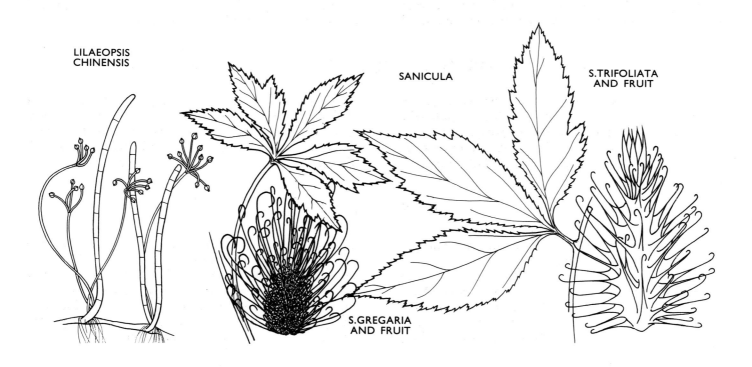

LILAEOPSIS CHINENSIS

SANICULA

S.TRIFOLIATA AND FRUIT

S.GREGARIA AND FRUIT

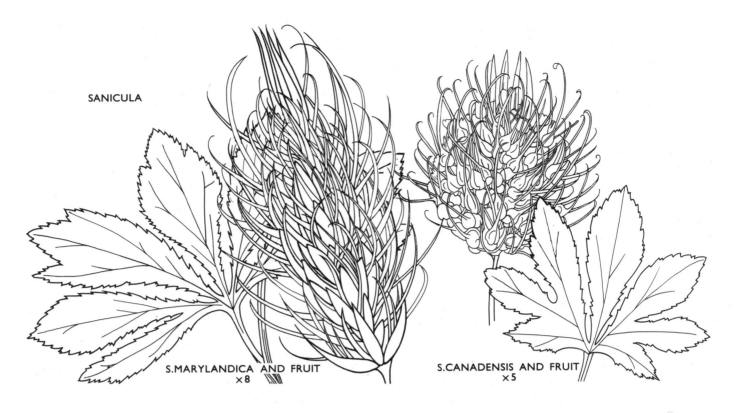

SANICULA

S.MARYLANDICA AND FRUIT
×8

S.CANADENSIS AND FRUIT
×5

is covered with hooked bristles. In general all our species flower from May to July, in woods, and are widely distributed throughout our range and southward and westward. The differences between species are minute details. In *S. gregaria* (*Plate 65*) and *S. marilandica* the two styles, curving outward, may be seen on the fruit. In the former the leaves are divided into three or five segments. In the latter there are five segments but the two outer ones are generally so deeply cleft that there appear to be seven. In *S. trifoliata* the fruits have a distinct beak formed by the five erect, pointed sepals. In *S. canadensis* neither sepals nor styles appear above the bristles.

The name *Sanicula* is connected with the Latin *sanus*, "healthy." The English species was supposed to have the power of healing wounds.

HONEWORT OR WILD-CHERVIL (CRYPTOTAENIA)

Only because it is common does *C. canadensis* merit inclusion among wild flowers. The minute white flowers are on stalks of different lengths, the small umbels on only a few main stalks (rays sometimes only two or three) which form the compound umbel. The fruit, as usual in these genera, is quite distinctive. The leaf-blades are divided palmately into three ovate, toothed segments. This plant, like the sanicles, grows in woods throughout our range and beyond. *Plate 178.* The name refers to the hidden (*crypto-*) ribs.

HERACLEUM

We have one native species, and an European species is occasionally found.

COW-PARSNIP or MASTERWORT, H. LANATUM, is a
tall weed, up to 10 feet, with enormous leaves. Each leaf is divided, above the broad stalk which embraces the stem, into three broad, irregularly lobed and toothed segments. The principal umbel is from 4 to 8 inches wide. The outermost petals of the outermost flowers are larger than the others and cleft into two lobes. The fruit is heart-shaped, the edges flat and thin, the central part with five ribs on each side, and, between these, four dark lines extending from the notch at the top about half-way down.

PLATE 65

Sanicula gregaria

Johnson

Osmorhiza longistylis

Gottscho

Erigenia bulbosa

Horne

Heracleum lanatum

Rickett

Osmorhiza longistylis

Rickett

Oxypolis rigidior

Rickett

Heracleum lanatum

Rickett

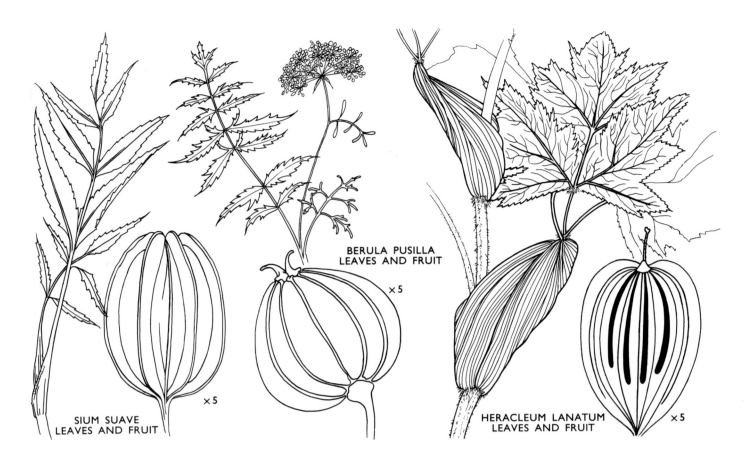

SIUM SUAVE
LEAVES AND FRUIT ×5

BERULA PUSILLA
LEAVES AND FRUIT
×5

HERACLEUM LANATUM
LEAVES AND FRUIT ×5

June to August: in moist places from Labrador to Alaska and southward to Georgia, Indiana, Kansas, New Mexico, and California. *Plate 65*. The genus was dedicated by the Roman naturalist Pliny to Hercules (Heracles).

The European cow-parsnip, *H. sphondylium*, is similar but has leaves pinnately divided into from three to seven segments. It is found in waste places in New England and New York, flowering from June to August. In England it has long been used as pig food, or, in Cornish speech, lisamoo. The prefix "cow-" (like "horse-") signifies something rough or coarse.

WATER-PARSNIPS AND HOG-FENNEL (SIUM, BERULA, AND OXYPOLIS)

These three genera are alike in growing in swamps, bogs, or shallow water, and in having leaves that are pinnately divided into usually toothed segments which are not themselves divided. The first two have similar fruits, with narrow ribs; the fruits of *Oxypolis* have thin marginal extensions or "wings," with ribs on the central part.

WATER-PARSNIP, S. SUAVE, grows up to 6 feet tall.

The leaf-segments are narrow, sharply toothed. Plants that grow in water may have submerged leaves cut into very fine segments.

July to September: in wet meadows, swamps, etc. from Newfoundland to British Columbia and southward to Florida, Louisiana, Utah, and California.

WATER-PARSNIP, B. PUSILLA, is smaller, up to 3 feet tall. The leaf-segments are lanceolate or ovate, with long sharp teeth or even lobes.

June to September: in swamps and streams from New York to British Columbia and southward to Illinois, Iowa, Texas, and California.

HOG-FENNEL, O. RIGIDIOR, is extremely variable in the character of its leaves, the segments ranging from $\frac{1}{5}$ inch to $1\frac{1}{2}$ inches wide and without teeth to sharply and coarsely toothed. The stem grows up to 6 feet tall.

July to September: in bogs and swamps and wet woods from New York to Minnesota and southward to Florida and Texas. *Plate 65*.

OSMORHIZA CLAYTONI

OXYPOLIS RIGIDIOR ×10

×10

SWEET-CICELY (OSMORHIZA)

Osmorhiza owes its names, English and Greek, to the sweet, licorice-like odor of stems and roots when they are crushed. (True licorice is obtained from a plant of the bean family.) The leaves are divided pinnately into mostly softly hairy segments which are broad and rather bluntly toothed. The umbels are small, with few main stalks which bear only a few small flowers. The fruits are characteristic, long and narrow and beset (as seen through a magnifier) with sharp hairs lying along the ribs. The girl's name of these plants is really a corruption of *seseli*, an old Greek name for some sweet-scented plant; and sweet-Cicely in England is a different species of *Umbelliferae*.

We have two common species, which differ only in details. Both flower in May and June; both grow in woodlands and moist roadsides.

O. CLAYTONI has short styles, shorter than the petals at flowering time, and only about $\frac{1}{16}$ inch long on the fruit. It ranges from Quebec to Saskatchewan and southward to North Carolina, Alabama, Arkansas, and Kansas. It is the less sweet-scented of the two, and the more common in the northern states.

O. LONGISTYLIS has styles longer than the petals, and up to $\frac{1}{6}$ inch long on the fruit. It occurs from Quebec to Alberta and southward to Georgia, Kentucky, Texas, and northern New Mexico. *Plate 65*.

The two species seem never to occur together.

Two other northern and western species may be found in northern New England, Michigan, and Minnesota. They are distinguished by the lack of bracts under the individual flower-stalks.

CARROTS (DAUCUS)

The genus *Daucus* contributes one of our most familiar — and often troublesome — weeds, and a valuable vegetable. It is easily identified by the bracts under the umbels: they are pinnately divided into sharp, narrow segments. The fruit also is distinctive, the ribs bearing curved, sharp spines. The whole umbel of fruits forms a "bird's-nest" by the curving inward of the stalks (rays).

WILD CARROT or QUEEN-ANNE'S-LACE, D. CAROTA, is the weed that everyone knows. It grows about

5 feet tall, forming many handsome umbels of white flowers. A curious feature is the single flower colored dark brownish-red in the center of many umbels. Races are known with pink flowers.

The edible carrot is the root of an Asiatic form of this species.

May to October: in roadsides and waste places throughout North America; an immigrant from the Old World. *Plate 66*. A species with smaller umbels and not exceeding 2 feet in height, *D. pusillus*, grows in the South and extends to southern Missouri.

ERIGENIA

There is only one species of *Erigenia*.

HARBINGER-OF-SPRING, E. BULBOSA, sends its leaves and stem up not from a bulb but from a corm. At flowering time the leaves are undeveloped, and the umbels of small flowers crown the plant, about 6 inches above the ground. Because of the red-brown stamen-tips and the white petals the plant is also called pepper-and-salt. Later, when the flat, nearly circular fruits develop, the leaves expand. Each has three main segments, these variously divided into narrow, toothless segments.

February to May: in woods and roadsides thickets from western New York and Ontario to Minnesota and southward to the District of Columbia, Alabama, and Arkansas. *Plate 65*. One of the earliest of spring flowers in many places.

SCANDIX

One species of this Old-World genus has become established in the United States.

VENUS'-COMB, S. PECTEN-VENERIS (the English name is a translation of the Latin), is a rather rough plant a foot or more tall. The leaves are pinnately divided, the segments pinnately divided, and so on, the ultimate segments being very narrow. The umbel has few main stalks, sometimes only one. The distinctive feature is the fruit, which is a rodlike structure about 1½ inches long; only the basal one-fourth has seeds. The cluster of these long, straight objects forms the "comb of Venus." It is also called, in England, shepherd's-needle.

This is a native of the Mediterranean lands, established as a weed from New Jersey to South Dakota and southward to Alabama and Texas, flowering from May to July.

PTILIMNIUM

The leaf-blades of *Ptilimnium* are divided into hairlike segments, mostly arranged pinnately; or they may be lacking, only the leaf-stalk remaining. The species tend to be southern and southwestern. Besides the one described below, *P. costatum*, with leaf-segments in circles, occurs in Illinois and Missouri; *P. nuttallii*, with leaf-segments 2 inches long or more, grows from Kentucky to Missouri; and *P. fluviatile*, with leaf-stalks which bear no blades, is found from Maryland to West Virginia. The fruit of all species is marked by a broad smooth band between the ribs.

MOCK BISHOP'S-WEED, P. CAPILLACEUM, grows from 4 inches to 6 feet tall. The leaves are divided pinnately into hairlike ("capillaceous") segments. The small white flowers are in umbels a couple of inches across which rise above the leaves.

June to October: in swamps and marshes, fresh or brackish, along the coast from Massachusetts to Florida and Texas, and inland in Illinois, Missouri, and Oklahoma. *Plate 66*.

SPERMOLEPIS

Three species form this genus which seems never to have acquired an English name; they are all chiefly southern and southwestern. The fruit is distinctive: roundish and covered with warts or short prickles. The flowers are few and inconspicuous. The leaves are divided into hairlike segments. They grow about 2 feet tall. They flower from April to June. *S. divaricata* has warty fruits on approximately equal branches. It grows in sandy places mostly on the coastal plain from Virginia southward and westward, and to Missouri and Kansas. *S. inermis* is similar, with umbels composed of very unequal branches. It is found in sandy soil from Indiana to Nebraska and southwestward to Mexico. *S. echinata* is marked by short hooked prickles on the fruit. It occurs in prairies and rocky places from Missouri to Louisiana and California.

PLATE 66

Ptilimnium capillaceum   *Uttal*

Cicuta maculata   *Gottscho*

Daucus carota   *Rickett*

Daucus carota   *Mayer*

Daucus carota   *Rickett*

Torilis japonica   *Rickett*

Angelica atropurpurea   *Elbert*

Conium maculatum   *Rickett*

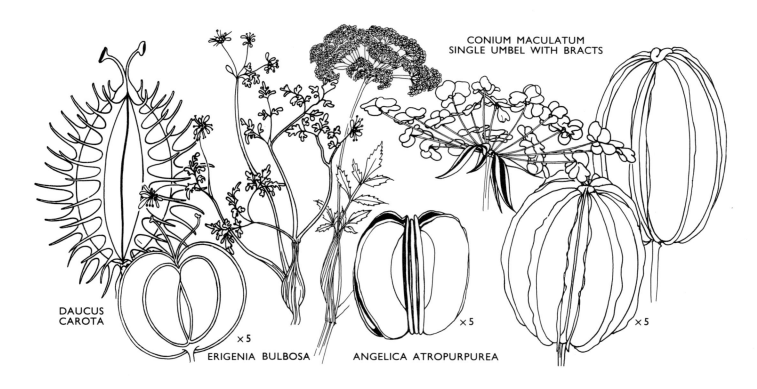

CONIUM MACULATUM
SINGLE UMBEL WITH BRACTS

DAUCUS
CAROTA

ERIGENIA BULBOSA   ANGELICA ATROPURPUREA   × 5

× 5   × 5

ANGELICA

The name of this genus indicates something of the esteem in which certain species were held by the ancients; an European species is connected with many superstitions and much folklore. It was – and still is – also used as an ingredient of cakes or as a candy, certain parts being boiled in sugar for this purpose; and leaf-stalks were eaten as celery is eaten and have something of the same flavor. The American *A. atropurpurea* was used in the same way in colonial days.

The plants unfortunately resemble the deadly poisonous *Cicuta maculata*; no plant of this appearance should be eaten without careful identification. A distinction that may be useful is that in *Angelica* the veins run to the tips of the teeth of the leaf-segments; in *Cicuta* they end in the notches between teeth.

These are mostly tall, stout plants with large, divided leaves and broad umbels of white or greenish flowers. The leaves of some common species are attached by very broad sheaths which are sometimes larger than the blades. The fruits are distinctive, having broad thin extensions to either side and three narrow ribs in the middle of each face.

ALEXANDERS, A. ATROPURPUREA, grows from 3 to
10 feet tall. The lower leaves are very large, pinnately divided and the segments pinnately divided into ovate or lanceolate, toothed, sharp-pointed seg-

ments. The uppermost leaves often consist mainly of sheath. The name Alexanders refers to the ancient city of Alexandria and has been given to a succession of various herbs.

May to September: in bottomlands, swamps, thickets, from Labrador to Minnesota and southward to Maryland, West Virginia, and Illinois. *Plate 66*.

A. TRIQUINATA is similar, with smaller leaf-sheaths.
It grows in the mountains from Pennsylvania and West Virginia southward to North Carolina.

A. VENENOSA may be distinguished by a fine down on
the stem. The leaf-segments are blunter than those of the other species. The name means "poisonous," but I find no record of actual poisoning.

July to September: in dry woods and open places from Massachusetts to Minnesota and southward to Florida, Mississippi and Arkansas.

A. LUCIDA is by some placed in a separate genus,
Coelopleurum, because the marginal extensions of the fruits are thick and corky. The leaf-segments are often irregularly lobed or cleft.

June to September: on the rocky coasts of Greenland and Labrador and southward to New York; also on the West Coast and in Asia.

CONIUM

The one species of *Conium* that has migrated from the Old World to the New is another good argument for knowing and not nibbling the plants of this family; it is deadly poisonous.

POISON-HEMLOCK, C. MACULATUM, is supposedly the plant used for the execution of criminals in ancient Greece, much as some American states use poisonous gas. The philosopher Socrates was thus executed. It is a plant which may reach 10 feet in height. The leaves are pinnately divided and the segments again pinnately divided, the ultimate segments being ovate or oblong and pinnately cleft or lobed. The small white flowers are in umbels about 2 inches across. Around each umbel is a circle of bracts each with a green stripe down the center. The fruit is round and marked by prominent thick ribs which at first are distinctly wavy, apparently becoming straight later.

June to August: in waste places practically throughout the United States. *Plate 66*. All parts are dangerous; children have been poisoned by blowing into whistles made from the hollow stems. (That I escaped such a fate was due not to teaching but to providence!) The name hemlock is of uncertain origin. This plant has nothing to do with the forest tree of that name.

CONIOSELINUM

Of this genus one species is native in the northeastern United States.

HEMLOCK-PARSLEY, C. CHINENSE, is one of the most misnamed species in the plant kingdom. It is neither hemlock nor parsley, and it does not come from China. The name of the genus is compounded of two other names. The plant grows from 4 inches to 5 feet tall. The leaves are pinnately divided into segments which are pinnately divided, the ultimate segments being mostly ovate and deeply pinnately cleft. The leaf-stalk forms a wide sheath with translucent margins. There is practically no involucre around the umbel. The fruit is elliptic, with prominent ribs.

July to September: in thickets, meadows, and woods from Labrador to Minnesota and southward to Pennsylvania, the mountains of North Carolina, Indiana, and Missouri.

WATER-HEMLOCKS (CICUTA)

These are among the most poisonous plants of this country. They may be known by the pinnately divided leaves with the segments widely spaced, narrow, and mostly toothed. *The veins run to the notches between the teeth.* The fruits are round and flat with thick ribs on each face.

SPOTTED COWBANE, C. MACULATA, is a stout, branching plant which may reach 8 feet in height. The leaf-segments are narrow, widely separated, with a few distinct, sharp marginal teeth. The flowers are in numerous umbels about 4 inches across. The plant grows from a cluster of small root-tubers.

June to September: in meadows and prairies, ditches and swamps from Quebec to Manitoba and southward to Florida, Texas, and northern Mexico. *Plate 66*.

C. BULBIFERA is distinguished by the small bulbs in the axils of the leaves.

July to September: in swamps and wet places throughout the northern United States.

CHAEROPHYLLUM

This name is given to a group of small weeds with delicate, rather feathery foliage, the leaves divided and redivided pinnately into small, pinnately lobed segments. The flowers are small and relatively few, the umbels being simple — not compound — in our commonest species. The genus is fairly easy to recognize by its fruits. These are much longer than wide, lanceolate in outline, with prominent ribs. The species are not easy to distinguish. They all flower in spring and early summer.

The name is interesting as being the word from which the English name chervil was derived; it comes from two Greek words meaning, together, "delightful leaf." Chervil, however, is the name of a species of

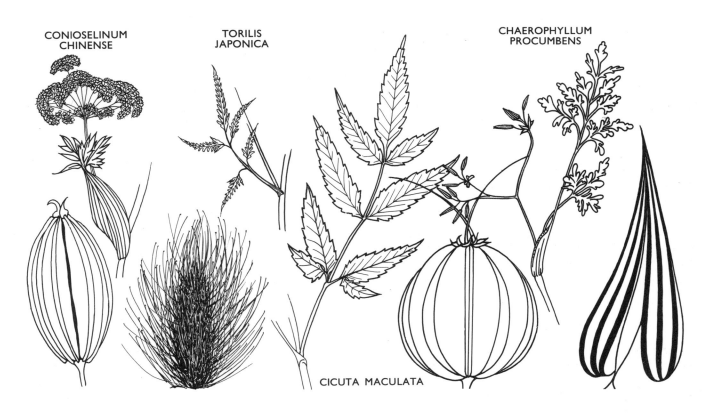

CONIOSELINUM CHINENSE — TORILIS JAPONICA — CHAEROPHYLLUM PROCUMBENS — CICUTA MACULATA

Anthriscus, *A. cerefolium*, an Old-World herb cultivated for the pleasant odor and taste of its leaves. ("*Cerefolium*" is obviously a Latinized *Chaerophyllum*.) *Chaerophyllum temulum*, an European weed, is called in England rough-chervil; so we may perhaps coin the name wild-chervil for our common species.

WILD-CHERVIL, C. PROCUMBENS, has a weak, branched stem. The leaf-segments are more or less ovate. There are usually not more than six flowers in an umbel; at the base of the umbel is a circle of bracts. It grows in low, shady places from New York to Michigan and Kansas and southward to Georgia, Mississippi, and Arkansas.

C. TEXANUM differs in having very narrow leaf-segments and downy branches. It is found on prairies and in dry, open woods from Missouri and Kansas to Louisiana and Texas.

C. TAINTURIERI resembles *C. procumbens*, but has hairy stems and often hairy leaves. It occurs in open woodlands and waste places from Virginia to Kansas and southward to Florida and Texas. *Plate 67*.

TORILIS

We have a single species of this genus, a native of the Old World, well established here. Two others occasionally stray into our range.

HEDGE-PARSLEY, T. JAPONICA, grows from 1 to 3 feet tall, the stem much branched, the leaves mostly pinnately divided, the segments sharply toothed. The fruit is nearly egg-shaped and is covered with hooked bristles.

June to August: in fields, waste places, and open woods from New York to Iowa and Kansas and southward to Florida and Texas. *Plate 66*.

C A N A N

PACIFIC

Mt Olympus △ WASHINGTON

Mt Rainier △

△ Mt Adams

Mt Hood △ Columbia R.

ROCKY MOUNTAINS

MONTANA

NORTH DAKOTA

OREGON

Cascade Range

Coast Ranges

Siskiyou Mts

△ Mt Shasta

IDAHO

Big Horn Mts

SOUTH DAKOTA

Black Hills

Bad Lands

Sacramento

△ Mt Lassen

Great Basin

WYOMING

NEBRASKA

North

L. Tahoe

Great Salt Lake

Wasatch Mts

Sierra Nevada

UNITED

CALIFORNIA

NEVADA

Uinta Mts

△ Long's Peak

San Joaquin

UTAH

I T E D

Mt Whitney △

COLORADO

KANSAS

Colorado R.

Arkansas R.

OCEAN

South Coast Ranges

Mojave Desert

Grand Canyon

Colorado Desert

ARIZONA

NEW MEXICO

OKLA.

TEXA

Edwards Plateau

M E X I C O

Rio Grande